Test Bank

for

Whitney and Rolfes's

Understanding Nutrition

Tenth Edition

Harry Sitren
University of Florida

THOMSON

WADSWORTH

Australia • Canada • Mexico • Singapore • Spain • United Kingdom • United States

Printed in the United States of America
2 3 4 5 6 7 08 07 06 05 04

Printer: Thomson/West

ISBN: 0-534-62232-1

For more information about our products, contact us at:
Thomson Learning Academic Resource Center
1-800-423-0563

For permission to use material from this text or product, submit a request online at
http://www.thomsonrights.com.
Any additional questions about permissions can be submitted by email to **thomsonrights@thomson.com.**

Thomson Wadsworth
10 Davis Drive
Belmont, CA 94002-3098
USA

Asia
Thomson Learning
5 Shenton Way #01-01
UIC Building
Singapore 068808

Australia/New Zealand
Thomson Learning
102 Dodds Street
Southbank, Victoria 3006
Australia

Canada
Nelson
1120 Birchmount Road
Toronto, Ontario M1K 5G4
Canada

Europe/Middle East/South Africa
Thomson Learning
High Holborn House
50/51 Bedford Row
London WC1R 4LR
United Kingdom

Latin America
Thomson Learning
Seneca, 53
Colonia Polanco
11560 Mexico D.F.
Mexico

Spain/Portugal
Paraninfo
Calle/Magallanes, 25
28015 Madrid, Spain

TABLE OF CONTENTS

A Note on Test Bank Style and Use...v

Part 1 – Test Bank for *Understanding Nutrition* 1

Chapter 1 – An Overview of Nutrition 1
Chapter 2 – Planning a Healthy Diet..16
Chapter 3 – Digestion, Absorption, and Transport...25
Chapter 4 – The Carbohydrates: Sugars, Starches, and Fibers 39
Chapter 5 – The Lipids: Triglycerides, Phospholipids, and Sterols...54
Chapter 6 – Protein: Amino Acids 72
Chapter 7 – Metabolism: Transformations and Interactions...90
Chapter 8 – Energy Balance and Body Composition..103
Chapter 9 – Weight Management: Overweight and Underweight...114
Chapter 10 – The Water-Soluble Vitamins: B Vitamins and Vitamin C 125
Chapter 11 – The Fat-Soluble Vitamins: A, D, E, and K 145
Chapter 12 – Water and the Major Minerals..161
Chapter 13 – The Trace Minerals 178
Chapter 14 – Fitness: Physical Activity, Nutrients, and Body Adaptations 199
Chapter 15 – Life Cycle Nutrition: Pregnancy and Lactation...214
Chapter 16 – Life Cycle Nutrition: Infancy, Childhood, and Adolescence...................................229
Chapter 17 – Life Cycle Nutrition: Adulthood and the Later Years 246
Chapter 18 – Diet and Health..255
Chapter 19 – Consumer Concerns about Foods and Water 271
Chapter 20 – Hunger and the Global Environment..289

Part 2 – Test Bank for *Nutrition Pathways* Telecourse Videos...**295**
        (Provided by Dallas County Community College District)

Lesson 1: Nutrition Basics..295
Lesson 2: The Digestive System 297
Lesson 3: Carbohydrates: Simple and Complex 299
Lesson 4: Carbohydrates: Fiber...301
Lesson 5: Fats: The Lipid Family 304
Lesson 6: Fats: Health Effects 306
Lesson 7: Protein: Form and Function 309
Lesson 8: The Protein Continuum 311
Lesson 9: Metabolism..313
Lesson 10: Weight Control: Energy Regulation...315
Lesson 11: Weight Control: Health Effects 317
Lesson 12: Vitamins: Water-Soluble..320
Lesson 13: Vitamins: Fat-Soluble...322
Lesson 14: Major Minerals and Water...324
Lesson 15: Trace Minerals...327
Lesson 16: Physical Activity: Fitness Basics 331
Lesson 17: Physical Activity: Beyond Fitness 334

Lesson 18: Life Cycle: Pregnancy 337
Lesson 19: Life Cycle: Lactation and Infancy 339
Lesson 20: Life Cycle: Childhood and Adolescence 342
Lesson 21: Life Cycle: Adulthood and Aging 345
Lesson 22: Diet and Health: Cardiovascular Disease 347
Lesson 23: Diet and Health: Cancer, Immunology, and AIDS 350
Lesson 24: Diet and Health: Diabetes 354
Lesson 25: Consumer Concerns and Food Safety 357
Lesson 26: Applied Nutrition 360

A NOTE ON TEST BANK STYLE AND USE

The test bank consists of the two major types of test questions, namely objective and essay. Essay questions require students to generate their own thoughts (creativity) and organize a response to reveal their level of recall knowledge, comprehension, evaluation, application, and/or reasoning. In this test bank, two types of essay questions are offered: restricted response (e.g., Compare and contrast...) and extended response (e.g., Describe...; Discuss...).

Among the various types of objective tests, measurement professionals overwhelmingly prefer multiple-choice over completion, true-false, and matching items. Multiple-choice items are the most flexible and adaptable. When properly written, they are capable of assessing not only recall knowledge but also application of knowledge. In turn, the application of knowledge may require certain levels of comprehension and analytical reasoning. In this test bank the majority of the objective questions are the multiple choice format. At the end of this section in each chapter, there are 20 matching items.

The instructor may select among the different types of questions to construct an examination. However, studies show that combining different types of questions in the same test may result in distractions that affect efficient use of available test time. Since assessment of student learning from objective tests is more reliable as the number of questions increases, the elimination of as many distractions as possible will promote better use of time, thus allowing more items to be included in the same time period.

While reading through these questions, you will notice the consistency of style and format. With few exceptions, each multiple-choice question is composed of a stem followed by four options - one and only one correct option and three distractors. The stem is presented in either question form or as an incomplete statement. In keeping with recommendations of measurement professionals, there are no options with "All of the above" or "None of the above" as responses. Where appropriate, two or more correct answers are combined into a compound response within the same option. In the matching section, there are 20 stems and 20 options. Each option can be used only once.

For your convenience, several features are included in the format. The column to the far left of each multiple-choice question presents the correct option (a,b,c, or d). The next column reveals the page number(s) in the text Understanding Nutrition (9th ed.) where information relates to the question. Finally, the symbol (K) refers to questions that require simple recall of knowledge whereas the symbol (A) refers to questions that require application of knowledge. The matching items also indicate the page number(s) corresponding to the text information.

About the Test Bank Preparer –
Dr. Sitren teaches a large, undergraduate, introductory nutrition course to nutrition majors and non-majors at the University of Florida. He has also been active on education committees of national nutrition societies and has participated as a member and chair of several committees for the preparation of nutrition assessment examinations for health professionals. During this time, he worked closely with test measurement specialists on the craftsmanship of challenging, critical, and disseminating objective test questions.

CHAPTER 1
AN OVERVIEW OF NUTRITION

AN PAGE(S)

c   3(K)   01.   Features of a chronic disease include all of the following **except**
                        a.   it develops slowly.
                        b.   it lasts a long time.
                        c.   it produces sharp pains.
                        d.   it progresses with little change.

b   3(K)   02.   Characteristics of an acute disease include all of the following **except**
                        a.   it develops quickly.
                        b.   it progresses slowly.
                        c.   it runs a short course.
                        d.   it causes sharp symptoms.

c   4(A)   03.   A parent who offers a child a favorite snack as a reward for good behavior is
                        displaying a food behavior known as
                        a.   social interaction.
                        b.   reverse psychology.
                        c.   positive association.
                        d.   habitual reinforcement.

a   4(A)   04.   A person who eats a bowl of oatmeal for breakfast every day would be displaying a
                        food choice most likely based on
                        a.   habit.
                        b.   availability.
                        c.   body image.
                        d.   environmental concerns.

b   4(K)   05.   What is the chief reason people choose the foods they eat?
                        a.   Cost
                        b.   Taste
                        c.   Convenience
                        d.   Nutritional value

d   4(A)   06.   Which of the following represents a food choice based on negative association?
                        a.   A tourist from China who rejects a hamburger due to unfamiliarity
                        b.   A child who spits out his mashed potatoes because they taste too salty
                        c.   A teenager who grudgingly accepts an offer for an ice cream cone to avoid
                              offending a close friend
                        d.   An elderly gentleman who refuses a peanut butter and jelly sandwich
                              because he deems it a child's food

a   5(A)   07.   The motive for a person who alters his diet due to religious convictions is most
                        likely his
                        a.   values.
                        b.   body image.
                        c.   ethnic heritage.
                        d.   functional association.

c 5(A)   08.   A person viewing an exciting sports match of her favorite team and eating because of nervousness would be displaying a food choice behavior most likely based on
   a.   habit.
   b.   availability.
   c.   emotional comfort.
   d.   positive association.

d 4(K)   09.   Excluding fast-food establishments, approximately what percentage of restaurants in the United States show an ethnic emphasis?
   a.   15
   b.   30
   c.   45
   d.   60

c 5(K)   10.   What is the term that defines foods that contain nonnutrient substances whose known action in the body is to promote well-being to a greater extent than that contributed by the food's nutrients?
   a.   Fortified foods
   b.   Enriched foods
   c.   Functional foods
   d.   Health enhancing foods

c 6(K)   11.   Nonnutrient substances found in plant foods that show biological activity in the body are commonly known as
   a.   folionutrients.
   b.   inorganic fibers.
   c.   phytochemicals.
   d.   phyllochemicals.

c 7(A)   12.   All of the following are classified as macronutrients **except**
   a.   fat.
   b.   protein.
   c.   calcium.
   d.   carbohydrate.

a 7(A)   13.   Which of the following is an example of a macronutrient?
   a.   Protein
   b.   Calcium
   c.   Vitamin C
   d.   Vitamin D

a 7(A)   14.   Which of the following is classified as a micronutrient?
   a.   Iron
   b.   Protein
   c.   Alcohol
   d.   Carbohydrate

c 7(A)   15.   Which of the following is an example of a micronutrient?
   a.   Fat
   b.   Protein
   c.   Vitamin C
   d.   Carbohydrate

b   9(K)   16.   In the body, the chemical energy in food can be converted to any of the following **except**

        a.   heat energy.
        b.   light energy.
        c.   electrical energy.
        d.   mechanical energy.

b   6,7(K)   17.   By chemical analysis, what nutrient is present in highest amounts in most foods?

        a.   Fats
        b.   Water
        c.   Proteins
        d.   Carbohydrates

a   7(K)   18.   Which of the following is **not** one of the six classes of nutrients?

        a.   Fiber
        b.   Protein
        c.   Minerals
        d.   Vitamins

c   9(A)   19.   Which of the following statements most accurately describes the composition of most foods?

        a.   Contain only one of the three energy nutrients, although a few contain all of them
        b.   Contain equal amounts of the three energy nutrients, except for high fat foods
        c.   Contain mixtures of the three energy nutrients, although only one or two may predominate
        d.   Contain only two of the three energy nutrients, although there are numerous other foods that contain only one

d   6(K)   20.   Which of the following is an organic compound?

        a.   Salt
        b.   Water
        c.   Calcium
        d.   Vitamin C

c   7(A)   21.   Which of the following is characteristic of an essential nutrient?

        a.   Cannot be found in food
        b.   Cannot be degraded by the body
        c.   Cannot be made in sufficient quantities by the body
        d.   Cannot be used to synthesize other compounds in the body

d   6(A)   22.   Which of the following most accurately describes the term organic?

        a.   Products sold at health food stores
        b.   Products grown without use of pesticides
        c.   Foods having superior nutrient qualities
        d.   Substances with carbon-carbon or carbon-hydrogen bonds

a   6(A)   23.   Which of the following is an organic nutrient?

        a.   Fat
        b.   Water
        c.   Oxygen
        d.   Calcium

c   7(K)   24.   Approximately how many nutrients are considered indispensable in the diet?
- a.   15
- b.   25
- c.   40
- d.   55

d   7(A)   25.   Which of the following **cannot** add fat to the body?
- a.   Alcohol
- b.   Proteins
- c.   Carbohydrates
- d.   Inorganic nutrients

d   9(K)   26.   When consumed in excess, all of the following can be converted to body fat and stored **except**
- a.   sugar.
- b.   corn oil.
- c.   alcohol.
- d.   vitamin C.

c   8,9(K)   27.   Which of the following nutrients does **not** yield energy during its metabolism?
- a.   Fat
- b.   Proteins
- c.   Vitamins
- d.   Carbohydrates

c   8(K)   28.   International units of energy are expressed in
- a.   newtons.
- b.   calories.
- c.   kilojoules.
- d.   kilocalories.

c   8(K)   29.   Approximately how many milliliters are contained in a half-cup of milk?
- a.   50
- b.   85
- c.   125
- d.   200

c   8(K)   30.   A normal half-cup vegetable serving weighs approximately how many grams?
- a.   5
- b.   50
- c.   100
- d.   200

b   8(A)   31.   How much energy is required to raise the temperature of one **liter** of water 1°C?
- a.   10 calories
- b.   1 kilocalorie
- c.   10,000 calories
- d.   1000 kilocalories

a   9(K)   32.   Gram for gram, which of the following provides the most energy?
- a.   Fats
- b.   Alcohol
- c.   Proteins
- d.   Carbohydrates

a 9(A) 33. Which of the following nutrient sources yields **more** than 4 kcalories per gram?
   a. Plant fats
   b. Plant proteins
   c. Animal proteins
   d. Plant carbohydrates

a 9(A) 34. Which of the following results from the metabolism of energy nutrients?
   a. Energy is released.
   b. Body fat increases.
   c. Energy is destroyed.
   d. Body water decreases.

c 9(A) 35. A weight reduction regimen calls for a daily intake of 1400 kcal which includes 30 g of fat. Approximately what percentage of the total energy is contributed by fat?
   a. 8.5
   b. 15
   c. 19
   d. 25.5

a 9(A) 36. A diet provides a total of 2200 kcalories of which 40% of the **energy** is from fat and 20% from protein. How many **grams** of carbohydrate are contained in the diet?
   a. 220
   b. 285
   c. 440
   d. 880

d 9(A) 37. What is the kcalorie value of a meal supplying 110 g of carbohydrates, 25 g of protein, 20 g of fat, and 5 g of alcohol?
   a. 160
   b. 345
   c. 560
   d. 755

c 11(K) 38. Which of the following is a feature of the minerals as nutrients?
   a. They are organic in form.
   b. They yield 4 kcal per gram.
   c. Some become dissolved in body fluids.
   d. Some may be destroyed during cooking.

b 6;11(A) 39. Which of the following is **not** a characteristic shared by minerals?
   a. Yield no energy
   b. Unstable to light
   c. Stable in cooked foods
   d. Structurally smaller than vitamins

c 11(K) 40. How many minerals are known to be required in the diet of human beings?
   a. 6
   b. 12
   c. 16
   d. 24

b   6-11(A)   41.   Overcooking a food is **least** likely to affect which of the following groups of nutrients?
   a.   Vitamins
   b.   Minerals
   c.   Proteins
   d.   Carbohydrates

b   10(K)   42.   Which of the following is **not** a characteristic of the vitamins?
   a.   Essential
   b.   Inorganic
   c.   Destructible
   d.   kCalorie-free

d   10(K)   43.   Which of the following is/are **not** fat-soluble?
   a.   Vitamin A
   b.   Vitamin K
   c.   Vitamin D
   d.   B vitamins

d   10(K)   44.   How many vitamins are known for human beings?
   a.   5
   b.   8
   c.   10
   d.   13

b   13(K)   45.   In nutrition research, observations of the quantities and types of foods eaten by groups of people and the health status of those groups are known as
   a.   case-control studies.
   b.   epidemiological studies.
   c.   human intervention trials.
   d.   correlation-control studies.

d   12(A)   46.   What is the benefit of using controls in an experiment?
   a.   The size of the groups can be very large
   b.   The subjects do not know anything about the experiment
   c.   The subjects who are treated are balanced against the placebos
   d.   The subjects are similar in all respects except for the treatment being tested

b   12(A)   47.   The study of how a person's genes interact with nutrients is termed
   a.   genetic counseling.
   b.   nutritional genomics.
   c.   genetic metabolomics.
   d.   nutritional nucleic acid pool.

b   14(A)   48.   What is the benefit of using placebos in an experiment?
   a.   All subjects are similar
   b.   All subjects receive a treatment
   c.   Neither subjects nor researchers know who is receiving treatment
   d.   One group of subjects receives a treatment and the other group receives nothing

b   14,15(K)   49.   What is the meaning of a double-blind experiment?
      a.   Both subject groups take turns getting each treatment.
      b.   Neither subjects nor researchers know which subjects are in the control or
            experimental group.
      c.   Neither group of subjects knows whether they are in the control or
            experimental group, but the researchers do know.
      d.   Both subject groups know whether they are in the control or experimental
            group, but the researchers do not know.

a   13(A)   50.   What is the benefit of using a large sample size in an experiment?
      a.   Chance variation is ruled out
      b.   There will be no placebo effect
      c.   The experiment will be double-blind
      d.   The control group will be similar to the experimental group

b   15(A)   51.   Overeating and gaining body weight is an example of a
      a.   variable effect.
      b.   positive correlation.
      c.   negative correlation.
      d.   randomization effect.

b   16(K)   52.   The lowest amount of a nutrient that is consumed over a prolonged period and that
            maintains a specific function is called the nutrient
      a.   allowance.
      b.   requirement.
      c.   tolerable limit.
      d.   adequate intake.

c   16,17(A)   53.   If a group of people consumed an amount of protein equal to the average
            requirement for their population group, what percentage would receive
            insufficient amounts?
      a.   2
      b.   33
      c.   50
      d.   98

b   19(A)   54.   Recommended Dietary Allowances may be used to
      a.   measure nutrient balance of population groups.
      b.   assess dietary nutrient adequacy for individuals.
      c.   treat persons with diet-related illnesses.
      d.   calculate exact food requirements for most individuals.

d   19(K)   55.   Recommended Dietary Allowances are based on the
      a.   Lower Tolerable Limit.
      b.   Upper Tolerable Limit.
      c.   Subclinical Deficiency Value.
      d.   Estimated Average Requirement.

d   17(K)   56.   The amount of a nutrient that meets the needs of about 98% of a population is
            termed the
      a.   Adequate Intake.
      b.   Daily Recommended Value.
      c.   Tolerable Upper Intake Level.
      d.   Recommended Dietary Allowance.

c   17(K)   57.   The RDA (Recommended Dietary Allowances) for nutrients are generally
a.   more than twice as high as anyone needs.
b.   the minimum amounts that average people need.
c.   designed to meet the needs of almost all healthy people.
d.   designed to prevent deficiency disease in half the population.

b   16,17(K)   58.   How are the RDA for almost all vitamin and mineral intakes set?
a.   Low, to reduce the risk of toxicity
b.   High, to cover virtually all healthy individuals
c.   Extremely high, to cover every single person
d.   At the mean, to cover most healthy individuals

d   18(A)   59.   Which of the following represents a rationale for setting the RDA for energy?
a.   Because protein is an energy nutrient, the figures for energy intake are set in proportion to protein intake.
b.   Because a large number of people are overweight, the figures are set to induce a gradual weight loss in most individuals.
c.   Because the energy needs within each population group show little variation, the figures are set to meet the needs of almost all individuals.
d.   Because a margin of safety would result in excess energy intake for a large number of people, the figures are set at the average energy intake.

c   17(K)   60.   Which of the following is **not** a feature of the Adequate Intake (AI) and the Recommended Dietary Allowance (RDA)?
a.   Both values exceed the average requirements
b.   AI values are more tentative than RDA values
c.   The percentage of people covered is known for both values
d.   Both values may serve as nutrient intake goals for individuals

a   16,17(K)   61.   Which of the following is a purpose of both the RDA and Adequate Intake?
a.   Setting nutrient goals for individuals
b.   Identifying toxic intakes of nutrients
c.   Restoring health of malnourished individuals
d.   Developing nutrition programs for schoolchildren

b   16(K)   62.   Which of the following is **not** a set of values within the Dietary Reference Intakes?
a.   Adequate Intakes
b.   Estimated Average Intakes
c.   Tolerable Upper Intake Levels
d.   Recommended Dietary Allowances

c   19(K)   63.   The Dietary Reference Intakes may be used to
a.   treat people with diet-related disorders.
b.   assess adequacy of all required nutrients.
c.   plan and evaluate diets for healthy people.
d.   assess adequacy of only vitamins and minerals.

d   17,18(K)   64.   What does the Tolerable Upper Intake Level of a nutrient represent?
a.   The maximum amount allowed for fortifying a food
b.   A number calculated by taking twice the RDA or three times the AI
c.   The maximum allowable amount available in supplement form
d.   The maximum amount from all sources that appears safe for most healthy people

a   18(K)   65.   What set of values is used to recommend the average kcalorie intake that maintains population groups in energy balance?
- a.   Estimated Energy Requirement
- b.   Adequate Average Requirement
- c.   Recommended Dietary Allowance
- d.   Acceptable Energy Distribution Range

d   18(K)   66.   The percentage range of intakes for protein, fat, and carbohydrate that are thought to reduce the risk of chronic diseases is termed the
- a.   Estimated Energy Requirements.
- b.   Tolerable Range of Kilocalorie Intakes.
- c.   Estimated Energy Nutrient Recommendations.
- d.   Acceptable Macronutrient Distribution Ranges.

d   18(K)   67.   What is the AMDR for carbohydrate?
- a.   5-10%
- b.   15-25%
- c.   30-40%
- d.   45-65%

b   18(A)   68.   Which of the following figures falls within the carbohydrate range of the AMDR?
- a.   35
- b.   50
- c.   70
- d.   90

a   18(K)   69.   What is the AMDR for protein?
- a.   10-35%
- b.   40-45%
- c.   50-65%
- d.   70-85%

c   18(A)   70.   What is the upper range of fat intake in the AMDR?
- a.   20
- b.   25
- c.   35
- d.   50

b   18(K)   71.   What is the AMDR for fat?
- a.   10-30%
- b.   20-35%
- c.   40-55%
- d.   60-75%

d   18(A)   72.   If a person consumed the upper AMDR limit for protein as part of a diet containing 2,500 kcal, approximately how many grams of protein would be ingested?
- a.   41
- b.   63
- c.   135
- d.   219

a   18(K)   73.   What is the weight (lbs) of the "reference" adult male?
                     a.   154
                     b.   165
                     c.   172
                     d.   179

b   18(K)   74.   What is the weight (lbs) of the "reference" adult female?
                     a.   110
                     b.   126
                     c.   132
                     d.   139

a   20(K)   75.   Which of the following is used to detect nutrient deficiencies?
                     a.   Assessment techniques
                     b.   Nutrient stages identification
                     c.   Overt symptoms identification
                     d.   Outward manifestations assessment

b   21(K)   76.   Which of the following is used to determine the presence of abnormal functions
                     inside the body due to a nutrient deficiency?
                     a.   Diet history
                     b.   Laboratory tests
                     c.   Body weight loss
                     d.   Physical examination

d   21(K)   77.   Inspection of hair, eyes, skin, and posture is part of the nutrition assessment
                     component known as
                     a.   diet history.
                     b.   anthropometrics.
                     c.   biochemical testing.
                     d.   physical examination.

a   21(K)   78.   Which of the following is an anthropometric measure?
                     a.   Body weight
                     b.   Blood pressure
                     c.   Blood iron level
                     d.   Food intake information

a   22(A)   79.   Which of the following would most likely lead to a primary nutrient deficiency?
                     a.   Inadequate nutrient intake
                     b.   Reduced nutrient absorption
                     c.   Increased nutrient excretion
                     d.   Increased nutrient destruction

c   22(K)   80.   What type of deficiency is caused by inadequate absorption of a nutrient?
                     a.   Primary
                     b.   Clinical
                     c.   Secondary
                     d.   Subclinical

a   21,22(K)   81.   Which of the following represents the usual sequence of stages in the development of a nutrient deficiency resulting from inadequate intake?
   a.   Declining nutrient stores, abnormal functions within the body, and overt signs
   b.   Abnormal functions within the body, declining nutrient stores, and overt signs
   c.   Abnormal functions within the body, overt signs, and declining nutrient stores
   d.   Declining nutrient stores, overt signs, and abnormal functions within the body

b   22(A)   82.   A subclinical nutrient deficiency is defined as one that
   a.   shows overt signs.
   b.   is in the early stages.
   c.   shows resistance to treatment.
   d.   is similar to a secondary deficiency.

b   22(K)   83.   Which of the following is an **overt** symptom of iron deficiency?
   a.   Anemia
   b.   Headaches
   c.   Skin dryness
   d.   Decreased red blood cell count

d   22(K)   84.   What entity coordinates nutrition-related activities of federal agencies?
   a.   U.S. Public Health Service
   b.   Food and Drug Administration
   c.   Dietary Reference Intakes committee
   d.   The National Nutrition Monitoring program

b   23(K)   85.   What is the program that outlines the health priorities of the United States and promotes policies on health and disease prevention?
   a.   NHANES
   b.   Healthy People
   c.   Surgeon General's Recommendations Group
   d.   American Dietetics Association Practice Group

a   24(K)   86.   Factors known to be related to a disease but not proven to be causal are called
   a.   risk factors.
   b.   genetic factors.
   c.   degenerative factors.
   d.   environmental factors.

c   24,25(K)   87.   Which of the following statements defines the association between a risk factor and the development of a disease?
   a.   All people with the risk factor will develop the disease.
   b.   The absence of a risk factor guarantees freedom from the disease.
   c.   The more risk factors for a disease, the greater the chance of developing that disease.
   d.   The presence of a factor such as heredity can be modified to lower the risk of degenerative diseases.

c   24(K)   88.   The diseases most common today in the United States include all of the following **except**
    a.   cancer.
    b.   diabetes.
    c.   tuberculosis.
    d.   diseases of the heart and blood vessels.

b   24(K)   89.   Of the ten leading causes of illness and death, how many are associated directly with nutrition?
    a.   1
    b.   4
    c.   7
    d.   10

d   24(K)   90.   Which of the following leading causes of death in the U.S. does **not** bear a relationship to diet?
    a.   Cancer
    b.   Heart disease
    c.   Diabetes mellitus
    d.   Pneumonia and influenza

b   25,25(K)   91.   What behavior is the major cause of death in the United States?
    a.   Poor diet
    b.   Tobacco use
    c.   Alcohol intake
    d.   Sexual behavior

c   25(K)   92.   Which of the following factors makes the greatest contribution to deaths in the United States?
    a.   Guns
    b.   Alcohol
    c.   Tobacco
    d.   Automobiles

a   31-33(K)   93.   Which of the following best describes a college-educated nutrition and food specialist who is qualified to make evaluations of the nutritional health of people?
    a.   Registered dietitian
    b.   Licensed nutritionist
    c.   Master of nutrient utilization
    d.   Doctor of food and nutritional sciences

b   31-33(K)   94.   All of the following are minimum requirements for becoming a Registered Dietitian **except**
    a.   earning an undergraduate degree.
    b.   completing a three-week clinical internship or the equivalent.
    c.   completing approximately 60 semester hours in nutrition and food science.
    d.   passing a national examination administered by the American Dietetic Association.

c   32(A)   95.   Who would be the most appropriate person to consult regarding nutrition information?
    a.   Chiropractor
    b.   Medical doctor
    c.   Registered dietitian
    d.   Health food store manager

a   34(K)   96.   What section of a research article contains a detailed description of the study's findings, including any tables and figures?
    a.   Results
    b.   Abstract
    c.   Conclusions
    d.   Methodology

c   31-33(K)   97.   Which of the following describes the limitations, if any, for a person who disseminates dietary advice to the public?
    a.   The title "dietitian" can be used by anyone in all states.
    b.   The title "nutritionist" can be used by anyone in all states.
    c.   A license to practice as a nutritionist or dietitian is required by some states.
    d.   A license to practice as a nutritionist or dietitian is mandatory in all states.

c   33(A)   98.   A person who assists registered dietitians has the formal title of
    a.   dietetic assistant.
    b.   nutrition assistant.
    c.   dietetic technician.
    d.   nutrition technician.

c   34(K)   99.   What section of a research article describes the procedures used in performing the study?
    a.   Results
    b.   Introduction
    c.   Methodology
    d.   Review of literature

a   34(K)   100.   All of the following are recognized, credible sources of nutrition information **except**
    a.   Who's Who in Nutrition.
    b.   Food and Drug Administration.
    c.   American Dietetic Association.
    d.   United States Department of Agriculture.

MATCHING (Answers can be used only once.)

G	6	01.	Substance containing no carbon, hydrogen or oxygen
D	7	02.	Number of indispensable nutrients for human beings
K	6	03.	Most substances containing carbon-hydrogen bonds
J	7	04.	Substance containing nitrogen
E	8	05.	Energy (kcal) required to increase temperature of 1 liter of water from 0°C to 100°C
H	7	06.	Nutrient with the highest body concentration
F	9	07.	Nutrient with the highest energy density
C	9	08.	Energy (kcal) yield of five grams of sugar
A	9	09.	Energy (kcal) yield of one gram of alcohol
N	10	10.	A water-soluble vitamin
B	11	11.	Number of indispensable minerals for human beings
L	14	12.	An inert medication
M	16	13.	The RDA for this fat-soluble nutrient exceeds the population mean
I	18	14.	The RDA for this nutrient is set at the population mean
P	20	15.	Excess nutrient intake leads to this
O	20	16.	Deficient nutrient intake leads to this
Q	21	17.	Measurement of physical characteristics
S	21	18.	Inspection of skin, tongue, eyes, hair, and fingernails
R	21	19.	A nutrient deficiency showing outward signs
T	22	20.	A nutrient deficiency in the early stages

A.	7		K.	Organic
B.	16		L.	Placebo
C.	20		M.	Vitamin A
D.	40		N.	Vitamin C
E.	100		O.	Undernutrition
F.	Fat		P.	Overnutrition
G.	Iron		Q.	Anthropometrics
H.	Water		R.	Overt deficiency
I.	Energy		S.	Physical examination
J.	Protein		T.	Subclinical deficiency

ESSAY QUESTIONS

PAGE(S)

4,5 01. Describe six behavioral or social motives governing people's food choices.

4,5 02. Explain how food choices are influenced by habits, emotions, physical appearance, and ethnic background.

5 03. Discuss some of the consequences of eating in response to emotions.

6,7 04. What is the meaning and significance of the popular phrase "You are what you eat"?

6;10,11 05. Define the term organic. How do the properties of vitamins relate to their organic nature? Contrast these points with the properties of inorganic compounds such as minerals.

14,15 06. Explain the importance of the placebo and the double-blind technique in carrying out research studies.

14 07. List the strengths and weaknesses of epidemiological studies, laboratory-based studies, and clinical trials.

16-19 08. What approach is taken in setting recommendations for energy intakes? Why is this approach taken? How does this approach differ from that taken for other nutrients?

16-18 09. Describe the steps involved in establishing nutrient values that make up the Dietary Reference Intakes.

16-18 10. Compare and contrast the meaning of Adequate Intakes, Recommended Dietary Allowances, Estimated Average Requirements, and Tolerable Upper Intakes Levels for nutrients.

20,21 11. List and discuss four methods commonly used to assess nutritional status of individuals.

16-19 12. Compare and contrast the rationales underlying dietary recommendations for individuals versus those for the population.

22,23 13. Discuss how the results from national nutrition surveys are used by private and government agencies and groups.

23 14. List 10 goals of the Healthy People 2010 program.

24,25 15. Discuss the meaning and significance of the relationships between risk factors and chronic diseases.

30;33,34 16. List ways in which to identify a reliable nutrition information website.

32,33 17. A. Explain the education and training requirements associated with obtaining registration as a dietitian.
        B. List several career areas in which registered dietitians are often employed.

33-36 18. A. List techniques that help identify nutrition quackery.
        B. Where can you find reliable sources of nutrition information?

CHAPTER 2
PLANNING A HEALTHY DIET

AN PAGE(S)

d   40(K)   01.   What are the "ABCDMV" principles of diet planning?
a.   Abundance, B vitamins, kcalories, diet control, minerals, and variety
b.   Abundance, balance, conservative, diversity, moderation, and vitamins
c.   Adequacy, bone development, correction, vitamin density, master, and variety
d.   Adequacy, balance, kcalorie control, nutrient density, moderation, and variety

b   40,41(A)   02.   Which of the following is the most nutrient dense food relative to calcium content?
a.   Whole milk
b.   Nonfat milk
c.   Low-fat milk
d.   Cheddar cheese

c   40(K)   03.   Nutrient density refers to foods that
a.   carry the USDA nutrition labeling.
b.   are higher in weight relative to volume.
c.   provide more nutrients relative to kcalories.
d.   contain a mixture of carbohydrate, fat, and protein.

d   40(K)   04.   The concept of nutrient density is most helpful in achieving what principle of diet planning?
a.   Variety
b.   Balance
c.   Moderation
d.   kCalorie control

a   40,41(A)   05.   Which of the following is an expression of the nutrient density of a food?
a.   0.01 mg iron per kcal
b.   110 kcal per cup
c.   0.5 mg iron per serving
d.   110 kcal per serving

a   41(A)   06.   Applying the principle of variety in food planning also ensures the benefits of
a.   dilution.
b.   moderation.
c.   vegetarianism.
d.   nutrient density.

c   42,43(K)   07.   Which of the following is **not** a feature of a food group plan?
a.   Excludes some foods
b.   Considered a tool for diet-planning
c.   Sorts foods of similar water content
d.   Specifies the number of servings from each group

a   43(A)   08.   Which of the following foods would be placed in the "miscellaneous" category of food group plans?
- a.   Jam
- b.   Watermelon
- c.   Raw carrots
- d.   Brussels sprouts

d   42,43(A)   09.   Which of the following is **not** characteristic of the Daily Food Guide?
- a.   Most foods can be placed into one of the five groups in the Guide.
- b.   The Guide can be used with great flexibility once its intent is understood.
- c.   The Guide specifies that a certain quantity of food be consumed from each group.
- d.   Following all of the Guide's rules ensures that the day's needs for all nutrients are met.

a   44(A)   10.   Which of the following is an alternative choice for meats in the Daily Food Guide?
- a.   Nuts
- b.   Bacon
- c.   Baked potatoes
- d.   Sweet potatoes

b   44(K)   11.   What are two major nutrients supplied by the fruit and vegetable group?
- a.   Vitamins D and E
- b.   Vitamins A and C
- c.   Protein and calcium
- d.   B vitamins and iron

b   44(A)   12.   Consider the following menu from the point of view of the Daily Food Guide.

Breakfast	Lunch	Supper

2 eggs
1 tsp margarine
2 slices enriched white
    bread
coffee
	2 oz tuna fish
	lettuce
	1 tbsp mayonnaise
	1 c whole milk
	1 apple
		3 oz hamburger meat
		1 oz cheese
		2 slices enriched white
		    bread
		½ c cooked rice
		½ c carrots
		coffee

Which of the following describes the nutritional value of the fruits and vegetables in this menu?
- a.   A source of vitamin A source is missing.
- b.   A source of vitamin C source is missing.
- c.   The Five Food Group recommendations are met.
- d.   The Five Food Group recommendations are exceeded.

b   46(A)   13.   Which of the following foods could help meet the iron needs of vegetarians who consume dairy?
- a.   Coconut
- b.   Legumes
- c.   Skim milk
- d.   Potato salad

b   46(K)   14.   According to the principles of the Daily Food Guide, the foundation of a healthful diet should consist of
                          a.   dairy.
                          b.   grains.
                          c.   vegetables.
                          d.   meats and alternatives.

d   43(K)   15.   In the Daily Food Guide, consuming the lowest number of servings from each food group would provide the energy needs for
                          a.   teenage girls.
                          b.   most children.
                          c.   sedentary men.
                          d.   sedentary women.

d   45,46(A)   16.   Which of the following is a feature of the Food Guide Pyramid?
                          a.   Alcoholic beverages are not included.
                          b.   The group representing complex carbohydrates includes legumes.
                          c.   The recommended number of milk and milk products servings is 4 to 6.
                          d.   A standard serving size is generally smaller than what people typically eat.

d   46(K)   17   Which of the following is descriptive of the USDA Food Guide Pyramid?
                          a.   An education tool for teaching nutrition to children which consists of food blocks that require stacking in a specific order
                          b.   A three-dimensional structure designed to assist the average consumer in the use of the Food Exchange System
                          c.   A system of specialized containers of several different sizes which allows for better storage and preservation of perishable food items
                          d.   A graphic representation of the Dietary Guidelines that displays complex carbohydrates at the base and fats and sweets at the very top

a   46(K)   18.   In the Food Guide Pyramid, the small dots and triangles scattered in the background represent
                          a.   fats and sugars.
                          b.   salt and pepper.
                          c.   calcium and iron.
                          d.   vitamins and minerals.

c   46(K)   19.   According to the Food Guide Pyramid, approximately what percentage of the day's food servings should be derived from plant foods?
                          a.   20
                          b.   50
                          c.   75
                          d.   95

d   47(K)   20.   A diet survey of thousands of people has shown that adequate intake(s) from among the food groups occurred only for
                          a.   bread.
                          b.   milk/dairy.
                          c.   fruit and dairy.
                          d.   meat and vegetable.

a   47(K)   21.   In a survey of the eating habits of over 8,000 people, what percentage made food
                    selections consistent with the recommendations of the Food Guide Pyramid?
                    a.   1
                    b.   5
                    c.   15
                    d.   40

b   48(K)   22.   A measure of how well the diet of Americans meets the recommendations of the
                    Food Guide Pyramid and the *Dietary Guidelines* is known as the
                    a.   Market Basket.
                    b.   Healthy Eating Index.
                    c.   ABC's of Good Health.
                    d.   National Assessment Survey.

c   46(K)   23.   All of the following are examples of legumes **except**
                    a.   lentils.
                    b.   peanuts.
                    c.   potatoes.
                    d.   garbanzo beans.

a   48(K)   24.   Food exchange systems were originally developed for people with
                    a.   diabetes.
                    b.   terminal diseases.
                    c.   cardiovascular disease.
                    d.   life-threatening obesity.

a   50(K)   25.   In food exchange lists, to what group are olives assigned?
                    a.   Fat
                    b.   Meat
                    c.   Carbohydrate
                    d.   Meat substitute

d   48,49(A)   26.   Which of the following is a feature of the Food Exchange System?
                    a.   Foods are grouped according to their source.
                    b.   Adequate intakes of minerals and vitamins are virtually guaranteed.
                    c.   A fat portion provides about twice the energy level as a carbohydrate
                            portion.
                    d.   All foods are grouped according to their content of carbohydrate, protein,
                            and fats.

a   52.53(K)   27.   Which of the following is a characteristic of enriched grain products?
                    a.   They have all of the added nutrients listed on the label.
                    b.   They have the fiber restored from the refining procedure.
                    c.   They have virtually all the nutrients restored from refining procedure.
                    d.   They have only 4 vitamins and 4 minerals added by the food processor.

c   52(K)   28.   What nutrient makes up most of the endosperm section of grains such as wheat
                    and rice?
                    a.   Fat
                    b.   Fiber
                    c.   Starch
                    d.   Protein

d   52,53(A)   29.   Which of the following breads has the highest fiber content?
    a.   White
    b.   Refined
    c.   Enriched
    d.   Whole-grain

d   52(K)   30.   The part of the grain that remains after being subjected to refining is the
    a.   bran.
    b.   germ.
    c.   husk.
    d.   endosperm.

b   52-54(K)   31.   All of the following are features of the process of nutrient enrichment of flours **except**
    a.   it includes products such as pastas.
    b.   fiber levels are similar to those in the whole grains.
    c.   it is required of all refined grain products that cross state lines.
    d.   thiamin and riboflavin are added in amounts exceeding their levels in the whole grain.

a   53(K)   32.   What mineral is added in the enrichment process of refined flours?
    a.   Iron
    b.   Iodine
    c.   Calcium
    d.   Magnesium

b   53(K)   33.   The latest addition to the enrichment process of grains is
    a.   iron.
    b.   folate.
    c.   protein.
    d.   calcium.

c   52(A)   34.   The addition of liberal amounts of calcium to some commercially available orange juice products by juice processors is most properly termed nutrient
    a.   enrichment.
    b.   restoration.
    c.   fortification.
    d.   mineralization.

d   53(K)   35.   The most highly fortified foods on the market are
    a.   TV dinners.
    b.   imitation foods.
    c.   enriched breads.
    d.   breakfast cereals.

a   54;56(K)   36.   General features of the legumes include all of the following **except**
    a.   they are high in fat.
    b.   they are low in cost.
    c.   they are rich in fiber.
    d.   they include peanuts.

a   55(A)   37.   Textured vegetable protein is usually made from
                        a.   soybeans.
                        b.   corn stalks.
                        c.   a mixture of legumes.
                        d.   cruciferous vegetables.

b   55(A)   38.   Which of the following terms is used to describe a cut of meat having a low fat
                        content?
                        a.   End
                        b.   Round
                        c.   Prime
                        d.   Choice

d   55(A)   39.   A meat described as "prime cut" means that it
                        a.   has an extended shelf life.
                        b.   usually carries a high price.
                        c.   is served only in restaurants.
                        d.   is higher in fat than other cuts of meat.

d   55,56(A)   40.   Which of the following is a feature of U.S. laws governing information on food
                        labels?
                        a.   The term "fresh" can be used **only** for raw and moderately processed food.
                        b.   Nutrition labeling **must** appear on virtually all processed as well as fresh
                                foods.
                        c.   Restaurant foods **must** provide nutrient content information on the menu.
                        d.   Nutrition labeling is **not** required on foods produced by small businesses
                                or products produced and sold in the same establishment.

d   55(K)   41.   According to food labeling laws, acceptable synonyms for nonfat milk include all
                        of the following **except**
                        a.   skim milk.
                        b.   no fat milk.
                        c.   zero-fat milk.
                        d.   reduced-fat milk.

a   56,57(K)   42.   Information that must be lawfully provided on food labels includes all of the
                        following **except**
                        a.   the amount recommended for ingestion each day.
                        b.   the amounts of specified nutrients and food components.
                        c.   the net contents expressed by weight, measure, or count.
                        d.   the name and address of the manufacturer, packer, or distributor.

c   56(A)   43.   A food label ingredient list reads: Wheat flour, vegetable shortening, sugar, salt,
                        and cornstarch. What item would be found in the lowest amount in the food?
                        a.   Salt
                        b.   Sugar
                        c.   Cornstarch
                        d.   Wheat flour

b   57(K)   44.   According to nutrition labeling laws, the amounts of what two vitamins **must** be listed on the package label?
    a.   Vitamins D and E
    b.   Vitamins A and C
    c.   Thiamin and riboflavin
    d.   Vitamins B6 and niacin

a   57(K)   45.   Food labels express the nutrient content in relation to a set of standard values known as the
    a.   Daily Values.
    b.   FDA Standards.
    c.   Reference Dietary Intakes.
    d.   Recommended Dietary Intakes.

b   57(A)   46.   By law, a serving size on beverage food labels is
    a.   4-6 fluid ounces.
    b.   8 fluid ounces.
    c.   10-12 fluid ounces.
    d.   16 fluid ounces.

c   57(K)   47.   Approximately how many milliliters constitute a fluid ounce?
    a.   10
    b.   20
    c.   30
    d.   40

c   57(K)   48.   Approximately how many grams are in an ounce?
    a.   10
    b.   20
    c.   30
    d.   40

b   57(K)   49.   All of the following are features of serving size information on food labels **except**
    a.   serving sizes for solid foods are expressed in both ounces and grams.
    b.   small bags of individually wrapped food items must contain only one serving.
    c.   serving sizes on food labels may not be the same as those of the Food Pyramid.
    d.   for a given product, the serving size is the same, no matter how large the package.

b   58(K)   50.   On a food label, the "% Daily Value" table compares key nutrients per serving for a person consuming how many kcalories?
    a.   1,500
    b.   2,000
    c.   2,500
    d.   3,000

a   60(K)   51.   According to U.S. food labeling regulations, clear and convincing evidence has been found for all of the following health claims regarding nutrition and disease **except**
  a.   sugar and diabetes.
  b.   sodium and hypertension.
  c.   calcium and osteoporosis.
  d.   lipids and cancer and cardiovascular disease.

b   60(K)   52.   According to the FDA, which of the following diet-health messages requires a disclaimer on food labels?
  a.   Fiber and cancer
  b.   Lipids and obesity
  c.   Calcium and osteoporosis
  d.   Sodium and high blood pressure

b   60,61(K)   53.   Which of the following is a characteristic of structure-function claims on food labels?
  a.   They are allowed only for unprocessed food.
  b.   They can be made without any FDA approval.
  c.   They must conform to guidelines of the "A" list of health claims.
  d.   They must state the name of the disease or symptom for which a benefit is claimed.

MATCHING (Answers can be used only once.)

N   40   01.   The principle of consuming a number of foods in proportion to each other
R   40   02.   The principle of recognizing that a food has more iron than another food when expressed per kcalorie
J   42   03.   Origin of the Daily Food Guide
B   46   04.   Ounces of meat in one serving in the Daily Food Guide
M   50   05.   Legume belonging to the starch category of exchange lists
A   47   06.   Percentage of people surveyed whose eating habits conform to the Food Guide Pyramid
L   55   07.   Commonly used to make textured vegetable protein
Q   52   08.   Portion of grain containing most of the starch
H   52   09.   Portion of grain richest in fiber
I   52   10.   Nutrient added in grain enrichment process
P   55   11.   Common cow's milk fortification nutrient
O   46   12.   Common soy milk fortification nutrient
K   57   13.   Nutrient found on Daily Values label
D   58   14.   Maximum number of grams of fat recommended on a 2,000 kcalorie diet
C   58   15.   Grams of fat supplied by a 1,200 kcalorie diet that is 30% fat
G   57   16.   Agency that regulates food labeling
S   60   17.   Health claim allowed on food labels
T   61   18.   Health claim **not** allowed on food labels without a disclaimer
E   46   19.   Serving size of rice in the Food Pyramid
F   57   20.   Serving size of rice on a food label

A. 1	F. 1 cup	K. Sodium	P. Vitamin A
B. 3	G. FDA	L. Soybeans	Q. Endosperm
C. 40	H. Bran	M. Green peas	R. Nutrient density
D. 65	I. Iron	N. Balance	S. Sodium and hypertension
E. ½ cup	J. USDA	O. Vitamin B$_{12}$	T. Antioxidants and heart disease

23

Chapter 2, Planning a Healthy Diet

ESSAY QUESTIONS

PAGE(S)

40,41   01.   List and discuss the significance of six diet-planning principles.

40,41   02.   What is meant by the term "nutrient-dense food"? Give 3 examples each of foods with high nutrient density and low nutrient density.

42-48   03.   List the five food groups and describe how foods are classified in the Daily Food Guide and Food Guide Pyramid. What are the advantages and disadvantages of these plans?

43;48   04.   Discuss the disadvantages inherent in the Daily Food Guide and Food Guide Pyramid.

46   05.   How can vegetarians conform to the principles of the Food Guide Pyramid?

52-54   06.   Discuss the meaning and significance of foods that are refined, enriched, fortified, or whole-grain.

52-54   07.   Discuss the benefits and limitations of the U.S. grain enrichment legislation.

55-58   08.   Describe the major aspects of nutrition labeling regulations. List the information that must be displayed on food labels.

58   09.   Calculate a set of personal Daily Values for a person with a 3,000 kcal diet.

66-70;46,47   10.   Discuss ways in which dietary guidelines can be applied to ethnic diets.

60,61   11.   List 5 approved food label health claims from the "A" list and the criteria that support the claims.

66-70   12.   Compare and contrast food guides from other countries with those of the United States.

CHAPTER 3
DIGESTION, ABSORPTION, AND TRANSPORT

AN PAGE(S)

b 76(K) 01. What structure prevents food from entering the trachea when you swallow?
a. Tongue
b. Epiglottis
c. Esophagus
d. Cardiac sphincter

c 76(K) 02. A bolus is conducted past the diaphragm through the
a. epiglottis.
b. stomach.
c. esophagus.
d. large intestine.

b 76(K) 03. What is a bolus?
a. Enzyme that hydrolyzes starch
b. Portion of food swallowed at one time
c. Device used to analyze the contents of the stomach
d. Sphincter muscle separating the stomach from the small intestine

c 76(K) 04. What is one function of the pyloric sphincter?
a. Secretes acid into the stomach
b. Secretes hormones into the stomach
c. Prevents the contents of the intestines from backing up into the stomach
d. Prevents the contents of the intestine from emptying too quickly into the colon

b 77(K) 05. What structure controls the passage of material from the small intestines to the large intestines?
a. Pyloric valve
b. Ileocecal valve
c. Colonic sphincter
d. Jejunal sphincter

b 74(K) 06. What structure separates the colon from the small intestine?
a. Pylorus
b. Ileocecal valve
c. Gastric retainer
d. Rectal sphincter

d 76(K) 07. Into what region of the intestinal tract does the stomach empty?
a. Ileum
b. Cecum
c. Jejunum
d. Duodenum

b   76(K)   08.   Which of the following is a description of chyme?

a.   The semisolid mass of undigested food which passes through the ileocecal valve

b.   A semiliquid mass of partially digested food released by the stomach into the intestines

c.   The mixture of pancreatic juices containing enzymes for digestion of the macronutrients

d.   A thick, viscous material synthesized by mucosal cells for protection against digestive juices

c   76,77(A)   09.   After swallowing, in what order does food pass through the regions of the GI tract?

a.   Jejunum, duodenum, colon, ileum, rectum

b.   Jejunum, ileum, duodenum, rectum, colon

c.   Stomach, duodenum, jejunum, ileum, colon

d.   Stomach, jejunum, duodenum, colon, ileum

b   76(K)   10.   What structure functions to prevent entrance of food into the trachea?

a.   Tongue

b.   Epiglottis

c.   Cardiac sphincter

d.   Trachea sphincter

c   77(K)   11.   What is the primary function of the rectum?

a.   Controls functioning of the colon

b.   Absorbs minerals from waste materials

c.   Stores waste materials prior to evacuation

d.   Absorbs excess water from waste materials

a   76(K)   12.   What is the name given to partially digested food in the stomach?

a.   Chyme

b.   Liquid food

c.   Gastric mucus

d.   Semiliquid mass

b   75(K)   13.   Which of the following is a characteristic of the appendix?

a.   It ferments fiber

b.   It stores lymph cells

c.   It slows down peristalsis

d.   It stores preformed stools

c   76,77(K)   14.   Which of the following is **not** a sphincter muscle?

a.   Anus

b.   Cardiac

c.   Duodenum

d.   Ileocecal valve

a   76(K)   15.   What is mastication?

a.   The act of chewing

b.   The act of swallowing

c.   The wave-like contraction of the intestines

d.   The wave-like contraction of the esophagus

d   76(A)   16.   About how many more times sensitive is the sense of smell compared with the
                        sense of taste?
                        a.   2
                        b.   10
                        c.   100
                        d.   1,000

a   76(A)   17.   Which among the following is **not** considered one of the basic taste sensations?
                        a.   Hot
                        b.   Sour
                        c.   Salty
                        d.   Bitter

b   76(A)   18.   The food flavor enhancer monosodium glutamate is believed to promote a
                        unique taste sensation known as
                        a.   sushi.
                        b.   umami.
                        c.   chymos.
                        d.   sashimi.

d   77(A)   19.   Which of the following is a feature of peristalsis?
                        a.   With an empty GI tract, the intestines remain quiet until the next meal.
                        b.   The waves of contraction along the GI tract occur at a constant rate when
                                 food is present.
                        c.   Circular muscles associated with peristalsis are found in the walls of the
                                 intestines but not the stomach.
                        d.   Wavelike muscular contractions result from alternate tightening and
                                 relaxing of circular muscles and longitudinal muscles.

d   77,78(K)   20.   Which of the following is a feature of the muscular actions of digestion?
                        a.   Peristalsis begins first in the stomach upon the initiation of the swallowing
                                 reflex
                        b.   The colon has the thickest and strongest muscles of the GI organs to
                                 withstand the pressure of stool evaluation
                        c.   The jejunum has a third layer of diagonal muscles to enhance contraction
                                 and relaxation phases for enhanced digestion
                        d.   Segmentation in the intestines allows periodic squeezing along its length
                                 resulting in momentary reversal of the movement of intestinal contents

b   77(K)   21.   What is meant by the term "motility" in reference to the GI tract?
                        a.   The efficiency of lymph transport
                        b.   The ability of the GI tract muscles to move
                        c.   The speed of gastric digestive juice release
                        d.   The speed of pancreatic digestive juice release

a   77(K)   22.   Among the GI tract organs, which has the strongest muscles?
                        a.   Stomach
                        b.   Small intestine
                        c.   Large intestine
                        d.   Cardiac sphincter

d   78(K)   23.   Which of the following is a function of sphincter muscles?
                         a.   Control peristalsis
                         b.   Grind large food particles
                         c.   Secrete digestive juices into the GI tract
                         d.   Control the passage of food through the GI tract

a   79,80(K)   24.   Which of the following body organs does **not** secrete digestive enzymes?
                         a.   Liver
                         b.   Stomach
                         c.   Pancreas
                         d.   Salivary glands

b   78(K)   25.   What is reflux?
                         a.   Hard, dry, stools
                         b.   Backward flow of chyme
                         c.   Soft, poorly formed stools
                         d.   The mixture of bile and pancreatic juice

d   80(K)   26.   What is the function of mucus in the stomach?
                         a.   Emulsifies fats
                         b.   Neutralizes stomach acid
                         c.   Activates pepsinogen to pepsin
                         d.   Protects stomach cells from gastric juices

b   80(K)   27.   What substance protects the stomach lining from damage due to digestive juices?
                         a.   Water
                         b.   Mucus
                         c.   Pepsinogen
                         d.   Dietary fats

d   80(K)   28.   What is a function of hydrochloric acid in the stomach?
                         a.   Absorbs water
                         b.   Inhibits peristalsis
                         c.   Neutralizes the food mass
                         d.   Creates an optimum acidity

b   80(K)   29.   Important functions of hydrochloric acid in digestion/absorption include all the
                         following **except**
                         a.   it kills bacteria.
                         b.   it activates pancreatic lipase.
                         c.   it activates a proteolytic enzyme.
                         d.   it promotes hydrolysis of dietary protein.

d   80;99(K)   30.   All of the following are features of stomach acid **except**
                         a.   its secretion is stimulated by ingestion of regular coffee.
                         b.   its secretion is stimulated by ingestion of decaffeinated coffee.
                         c.   it destroys most of the bacteria entering the stomach from food ingestion.
                         d.   its potentially destructive action on stomach cells is prevented by the
                                 presence of bile.

a   80(K)   31.   Which of the following best describes the normal pH of the stomach?
a.   Very acidic
b.   Slightly acidic
c.   Neutral
d.   Slightly alkaline

d   80(A)   32.   Why is there little or no digestion of starch in the stomach?
a.   Mucus inhibits starch breakdown
b.   Stomach enzymes are dysfunctional
c.   Starch should not be eaten with protein
d.   Salivary enzymes do not work in an acid environment

a   80(A)   33.   What is the fate of any enzymes that are present in the foods we eat?
a.   Hydrolyzed in the GI tract
b.   Absorbed intact by the stomach
c.   Absorbed intact by the small intestine
d.   Passed through the GI tract and excreted in the stool

c   80(K)   34.   Which part of the GI tract contains highly acidic digestive juices?
a.   Colon
b.   Ileum
c.   Stomach
d.   Duodenum

b   80(K)   35.   What is the substance that protects the stomach walls from digestion?
a.   Tums
b.   Mucus
c.   Pepsin
d.   Hydrochloric acid

a   81(A)   36.   The purpose of bicarbonate in the digestive process is to
a.   raise the pH of chyme.
b.   lower the pH of chyme.
c.   hydrolyze large peptides.
d.   provide a little fizz in your life.

a   80,81(K)   37.   Which of the following is **not** a component of pancreatic juice?
a.   Bile
b.   Water
c.   Lipase
d.   Sodium bicarbonate

b   80,81(K)   38.   Which of the following is **not** a component of pancreatic juice?
a.   Lipase
b.   Maltase
c.   Amylase
d.   Bicarbonate

d   81(A)   39   After the pancreatic juices have mixed with chyme in the intestine, which of the following describes the pH of the resulting mixture?
a.   Very acidic
b.   Moderately acidic
c.   Strongly alkaline
d.   Approximately neutral

b   80,81(A)   40.   Which of the following would **not** be acted upon by pancreatic juice secreted into the intestinal tract?
a.   Fats
b.   Fiber
c.   Proteins
d.   Carbohydrates

a   81(K)   41.   What is one function of the gallbladder?
a.   Stores bile
b.   Produces bile
c.   Reabsorbs water and salts
d.   Performs enzymatic digestion

a   81(K)   42.   What is the function of bile?
a.   Emulsifies fats
b.   Initiates digestion of protein
c.   Enhances absorption of complex carbohydrates
d.   Protects the stomach and small intestine from the action of hydrochloric acid

c   81(A)   43.   Which of the following is **not** a typical component of stools?
a.   Water
b.   Fiber
c.   Starch
d.   Bacteria

b   81(A)   44.   What is the **primary** role of the normal, thriving intestinal bacterial population?
a.   Helps degrade meat and dairy proteins
b.   Helps prevent infectious bacteria from attacking the system
c.   Synthesizes vitamin D which can be absorbed into the body
d.   Synthesizes several amino acids which can be absorbed into the body

d   81(K)   45.   Which of the following is known to be produced by small intestinal bacteria?
a.   Mucus
b.   Chyme
c.   Glucose
d.   Vitamins

c   81(K)   46.   Which of the following classes of nutrients requires the least amount of digestion?
a.   Lipids
b.   Proteins
c.   Vitamins
d.   Carbohydrates

b   81(A)   47.   Which of the following nutrients requires the least amount of digestion?
a.   Starch
b.   Calcium
c.   Animal fats
d.   Animal proteins

b   81(K)   48.   Which of the following is generally **not** digested but does stimulate intestinal muscle contractions?
- a.   Bile
- b.   Fiber
- c.   Starch
- d.   Amylase

b   81(K)   49.   Which of the following is a significant property of dietary fiber?
- a.   Inhibits protease activity
- b.   Promotes water retention of stools
- c.   Inhibits large intestinal contractions
- d.   Promotes vitamin excretion in stools

d   81(A)   50.   An example of an important function of the colon would be its absorption of
- a.   bile.
- b.   fats.
- c.   hormones.
- d.   sodium chloride.

c   81(A)   51.   A solution with a pH of 7 is how many times more alkaline than one with a pH of 6?
- a.   1
- b.   5
- c.   10
- d.   100

b   84(K)   52.   Which of the following is an important function of the intestinal villi crypts?
- a.   Synthesis of chylomicrons
- b.   Secretion of juices into the small intestine
- c.   Synthesis of fragments of fat for use by the colon
- d.   Transport of fat-soluble nutrients into the circulation

a   84(K)   53.   What is the name of the projections on the inner surface of the small intestine?
- a.   Villi
- b.   Cilia
- c.   Mesenteric vessels
- d.   Vascular projectiles

c   84(K)   54.   Which of the following is a function of the intestinal microvilli?
- a.   Secretion of bile salts
- b.   Secretion of digestive acid
- c.   Transport of nutrient molecules
- d.   Transport of pancreatic enzymes

c   84(K)   55.   What is the primary site for absorption of nutrients?
- a.   Crypt
- b.   Villus
- c.   Microvillus
- d.   Macrovillus

c   84-86(K)   56.   Which of the following are found on the microvilli and function to break apart
                     small nutrients into the final products of digestion?
                     a.   Mucus
                     b.   Micelles
                     c.   Enzymes
                     d.   Hormones

b   84(K)   57.   Absorption of nutrients by intestinal cells occurs by all of the following
                     mechanisms **except**
                     a.   diffusion.
                     b.   transmigration.
                     c   active transport.
                     d.   facilitated diffusion.

a   86(A)   58.   To assist the process of digestion and absorption, it is usually best to
                     a.   combine different food types to enhance the absorption process.
                     b.   avoid eating meat and fruit at the same meal to prevent competition.
                     c.   eat several snacks per day so the system is not overwhelmed.
                     d.   take enzyme pills or powder periodically so the system can rest and
                             rejuvenate.

a   85-86(A)   59.   What is the first vessel to receive absorbed water-soluble vitamins?
                     a.   Portal vein
                     b.   Hepatic vein
                     c.   Mesenteric vein
                     d.   Mesenteric artery

a   87,88(A)   60.   When nutrients are transported from intestinal epithelial cells to the vascular
                     system, what organ is first to receive them?
                     a.   Liver
                     b.   Heart
                     c.   Lungs
                     d.   Kidneys

a   88,89(A)   61.   When alcohol and barbiturates are ingested, they are absorbed from the
                     gastrointestinal tract and transported first to the
                     a.   liver.
                     b.   heart.
                     c.   spleen.
                     d.   kidneys.

a   88,89(K)   62.   Which of the following products of digestion is **not** normally released directly into
                     the bloodstream?
                     a.   Fats
                     b.   Minerals
                     c.   Vitamin C
                     d.   Carbohydrates

c   89(K)   63.   Immediately after absorption, what circulatory system carries the fat soluble
                     vitamins and large fats?
                     a.   Vascular
                     b.   Mesenteric
                     c.   Lymphatic
                     d.   Enterohepatic

c   89(K)   64.   Which of the following conducts lymph into the vascular system?
                         a.   Villi
                         b.   Mesentery
                         c.   Subclavian vein
                         d.   Common bile duct

a   89(K)   65.   Which of the following is a feature of the lymphatic system?
                         a.   It carries fats away from the intestines
                         b.   It contains a fluid with a composition similar to pancreatic fluid
                         c.   It circulates via a one-way pump at the junction to the subclavian vein
                         d.   It serves to transport fat-soluble and water-soluble vitamins to the vascular system

b   89(K)   66.   What is the first major organ to receive nutrients that are absorbed into the lymph?
                         a.   Liver
                         b.   Heart
                         c.   Spleen
                         d.   Pancreas

b   90(K)   67.   What is the normal pH of the stomach?
                         a.   0.25-0.50
                         b.   1.5-1.7
                         c.   7.0-7.5
                         d.   9.5-9.75

a   90(K)   68.   Which of the following regulates the pH of the stomach?
                         a.   Gastrin
                         b.   Insulin
                         c.   Secretin
                         d.   Cholecystokinin

b   90(A)   69.   Which of the following substances functions to control the release of hydrochloric acid to prevent excessive acidity?
                         a.   Fiber
                         b.   Gastrin
                         c.   Secretin
                         d.   Bicarbonate

a   90,91(A)   70.   All of the following are important enterogastrone hormones **except**
                         a.   pepsin.
                         b.   secretion.
                         c.   cholecystokinin.
                         d.   gastric-inhibitory peptide.

a   91(A)   71.   Which of the following nutrients requires the greatest time for digestion?
                         a.   Fats
                         b.   Water
                         c.   Minerals
                         d.   Carbohydrates

b 90(K) 72. Which of the following stimulates the pancreas to release bicarbonate-rich juice?
   a. Gastrin
   b. Secretin
   c. Glucagon
   d. Gastric-inhibitory peptide

d 87(K) 73. Exchange of oxygen, nutrients, and waste materials takes place across the walls of small vessels called
   a. ducts.
   b. venules.
   c. arterioles.
   d. capillaries.

c 90(K) 74. Which of the following is a characteristic of pancreatic digestive enzyme function?
   a. The major hormone controlling the release of pancreatic enzymes is gastrin.
   b. The release of pancreatic enzymes is controlled primarily by a pancreatic sphincter.
   c. The pancreas can increase the activity of fat-degrading enzymes in response to more fat in the diet.
   d. In general, the amounts of digestive enzymes secreted by the pancreas remain constant over a wide range of nutrient intake.

a 91(K) 75. Which of the following is a feature of gastric-inhibitory peptide?
   a. It is produced by the intestine
   b. It inhibits digestion in the stomach
   c. It stimulates secretion of gastric juices
   d. It is synthesized and released from the stomach

d 91(K) 76. The presence of fat in the intestines stimulates cells of the intestinal wall to release
   a. lipase.
   b. gastrin.
   c. secretin.
   d. cholecystokinin.

c 91(K) 77 What substance controls the release of bile into the small intestines?
   a. Gastrin
   b. Secretin
   c. Cholecystokinin
   d. Gastric-inhibitory peptide

b 91(K) 78. Which of the following is associated with the presence of fat in the GI tract?
   a. Inhibition of mucosal enzyme activities
   b. Slowing of the process of digestion and absorption
   c. Inhibition of thiamin, riboflavin, and niacin absorption
   d. Stimulation and hastening of digestion and absorption

d   94(A)   79.   What is the very first thing you should do if you suspect someone is choking on food?
- a.   Perform the Heimlich maneuver
- b.   Strike the person sharply on the back
- c.   Attempt to dislodge the food with your fingers
- d.   Ask the person to make sounds from the throat

b   94(A)   80.   Choking occurs when a piece of food becomes firmly lodged in the
- a.   larynx.
- b.   trachea.
- c.   epiglottis.
- d.   esophagus.

c   94(K)   81.   Which of the following results from reverse peristalsis?
- a.   Gas
- b.   Choking
- c.   Vomiting
- d.   Diarrhea

a   95,96(A)   82.   Chronic diarrhea may result in which of the following?
- a.   Dehydration
- b.   Constipation
- c.   Peptic ulcers
- d.   Heimlich's disease

a   94(K)   83.   The Heimlich maneuver may be helpful in conditions associated with
- a.   choking.
- b.   vomiting.
- c.   heartburn.
- d.   constipation.

a   96,97(A)   84.   People are said to be constipated when they experience
- a.   painful or difficult bowel movements.
- b.   more than a day without a bowel movement.
- c.   more than three days without a bowel movement.
- d.   soft or watery bowel movements with little notice.

b   97,98(A)   85.   Therapy for constipation would include **all** of the following **except**
- a.   increasing water intake.
- b.   decreasing fiber intake.
- c.   increasing physical activity.
- d.   responding promptly to the defecation signal.

c   97(A)   86.   Which of the following is most likely to result from insufficient intake of fiber?
- a.   Diarrhea
- b.   Bloating
- c.   Constipation
- d.   Pancreatitis

c   97(A)   87.   In general, which of the following is associated with the fewest adverse effects from the treatment of constipation in adults?
   a.   Taking an enema
   b.   Taking a laxative
   c.   Ingestion of honey
   d.   Ingestion of mineral oil

c   97(K)   88.   Which of the following is a common cause of constipation?
   a.   High-fat diet
   b.   High-carbohydrate diet
   c.   Lack of physical activity
   d.   Excessive mineral oil intake

b   98(K)   89.   All of the following are common causes of heartburn **except**
   a.   bending over.
   b.   eating too slowly.
   c.   drinking too much.
   d.   wearing tight clothes.

b   98(A)   90.   Holding the breath for as long as possible is considered an effective treatment for
   a.   colitis.
   b.   hiccups.
   c.   belching.
   d.   gastro-esophogeal reflux.

d   98(A)   91.   People who have frequent regular bouts of heartburn and indigestion have a medical condition known as
   a.   colitis.
   b.   watery stools.
   c.   lymphatic malabsorption.
   d.   gastroesophageal reflux.

c   97(A)   92.   All of the following dietary measures are known to help relieve constipation **except**
   a.   eating honey.
   b.   eating prunes.
   c.   eating less fat.
   d.   drinking more water.

d   98(A)   93.   The use of an antacid is indicated **primarily** for
   a.   excessive gas.
   b.   acid indigestion.
   c.   excessive belching.
   d.   active ulcer in the stomach.

b   94(K)   94.   All of the following are major causes of ulcer formation **except**
   a.   bacterial infection.
   b.   excessive use of antacids.
   c.   excessive gastric acid secretion.
   d.   use of certain anti-inflammatory medicines.

b   99(A)   95.   Which of the following is **least** likely to aggravate an existing ulcer?
  a.   Beer
  b.   Raw carrots
  c.   Regular coffee
  d.   Decaffeinated coffee

d   99(A)   96.   The organism *H. pylori* has been identified as one of the major causes of
  a.   hiccups.
  b.   hemorrhoids.
  c.   diverticulosis.
  d.   gastric ulcers.

a   99(K)   97.   The most common **cause** for the development of ulcers is
  a.   infection from *H. pylori*.
  b.   excess consumption of spicy foods.
  c.   failure to adapt to a high-stress lifestyle.
  d.   prolonged excess intake of hot beverages.

a   99,100(A)   98.   All of the following are important issues in the treatment or management of existing ulcers **except**
  a.   diet therapy plays a major role.
  b.   alcohol intake should be curtailed.
  c.   antibiotics are frequently administered.
  d.   anti-inflammatory drug use should be curtailed.

MATCHING (Answers can be used only once.)

D	74	01.	Controls the entry of chyme into the duodenum
O	74	02.	Controls the entry of chyme into the colon
J	74	03.	Prevents food from entering the windpipe when swallowing
H	74	04.	Organ that stores lymph cells
L	79	05.	Enzyme that digests starch
E	79	06.	Substance that helps make or break a chemical bond
R	80	07.	A component of gastric juice
K	81	08.	Organ that releases bile into intestines
A	81	09.	Organ that synthesizes bile
B	84	10.	Fingerlike projection of small intestinal lining
C	85	11.	Type of cell that secretes mucus
Q	84	12.	Absorption mechanism that requires energy
I	84	13.	Absorption mechanism that does not require energy
G	87	14.	Connects an artery to a vein
N	87	15.	Vessel that carries blood from liver to heart
M	88	16.	Vessel that carries blood from GI tract to liver
S	89	17.	Carries fat soluble vitamins
F	90	18.	Hormone that signals release of pancreatic bicarbonate
T	91	19.	Hormone that slows acid output of stomach
P	91	20.	Hormone that signals release of bile

A.	Liver	F.	Secretin	K.	Gallbladder	P.	Cholecystokinin
B.	Villus	G.	Capillary	L.	Carbohydrase	Q	Active transport
C.	Goblet	H.	Appendix	M.	Portal vein	R.	Hydrochloric acid
D.	Pylorus	I.	Diffusion	N.	Hepatic vein	S.	Lymphatic system
E.	Enzyme	J.	Epiglottis	O	Ileocecal valve	T.	Gastric inhibitory peptide

ESSAY QUESTIONS

PAGE(S)

74-77 01. Name and describe the functions of the four major sphincter muscles which divide the GI tract into its principal regions.

76-81 02. Describe the major events of digestion that occur in the mouth, stomach, and small intestines.

80 03. What is the function of hydrochloric acid and why is it necessary in the process of digestion?

80,81 04. Discuss the defenses of the GI tract against bacteria that cause infection.

81 05. List several beneficial roles for the intestinal flora.

77;81,82 06. What is the primary function of the colon? What are the effects on colonic function from insufficient fluid intake, insufficient fiber intake, or intestinal infection?

83-86 07. Describe features of the small intestines that facilitate absorption.

90,91 08. Name and describe the functions of four major hormones involved in digestion/absorption.

90 09. Discuss the response of the pancreas to enzyme secretion upon exposure to diets differing in the amounts of protein, fat, and carbohydrate.

81 10. Discuss the role of bacteria in the GI tract and factors that help regulate their proliferation.

90 11. What is the most likely explanation for the observation that a person may experience "upset digestion" upon changing the diet?

90-91 12. Why does the pancreas not "digest itself"?

94-100 13. Describe four common digestive problems and their recommended treatments or therapies.

98-99 14. In the treatment of heartburn or "acid indigestion," which therapies are recommended and which are not?

99,100 15. Describe the three major causes of peptic ulcers and the recommended therapies.

CHAPTER 4
THE CARBOHYDRATES: SUGARS, STARCHES, AND FIBERS

AN PAGE(S)

a 103(A) 01. In which of the following are ample amounts of carbohydrates almost always found?
a. Plant foods
b. Health foods
c. Animal products
d. Protein-rich foods

d 104(K) 02. What type of nutrient is starch?
a. Fiber
b. Gluten
c. Simple carbohydrate
d. Complex carbohydrate

b 104,105(K) 03. How many carbon atoms are found in the ring structure of the most common dietary monosaccharides?
a. 5
b. 6
c. 8
d. 12

a 105(K) 04. Which of the following is **not** a simple carbohydrate?
a. Starches
b. White sugar
c. Disaccharides
d. Monosaccharides

c 104(K) 05. The types of atoms found in a glucose molecule include all of the following **except**
a. carbon.
b. oxygen.
c. nitrogen.
d. hydrogen.

c 104-108(K) 06. Typical dietary sources of carbohydrate include all of the following **except**
a. starch.
b. maltose.
c. glycogen.
d. hemicellulose.

d 105(A) 07. Which of the following is **not** a characteristic of glucose?
a. Monosaccharide
b. Soluble in water
c. Part of the sucrose molecule
d. Sweeter tasting than sucrose

c 104,105(K) 08. What component accounts for the usually sweet taste of fruits?
a. Fats
b. Fiber
c. Simple sugars
d. Complex carbohydrates

a 106,107; 09. Milk that has been treated with a commercially available lactase
   111;114(A)   preparation undergoes which of the following changes?
                    a.   Increase in sweetness
                    b.   Decrease in sweetness
                    c.   Increase in carbohydrate content
                    d.   Decrease in carbohydrate content

a 105(K) 10. Which of the following is known as blood sugar or dextrose?
                a.   Glucose
                b.   Maltose
                c.   Sucrose
                d.   Fructose

b 105,106(K) 11. Which of the following is a component of all three dietary disaccharides?
                    a.   Sucrose
                    b.   Glucose
                    c.   Fructose
                    d.   Galactose

c 105(K) 12. Which of the following is known as fruit sugar or levulose?
                a.   Maltose
                b.   Glucose
                c.   Fructose
                d.   Galactose

c 105(K) 13. What is the sweetest tasting simple carbohydrate in the diet?
                a.   Glucose
                b.   Lactose
                c.   Fructose
                d.   Sucrose

d 106(K) 14. What is the reaction that links two monosaccharides together?
                a.   Hydrolysis
                b.   Absorption
                c.   Disaccharide
                d.   Condensation

a 106(A) 15. Which of the following is a byproduct of the condensation of two molecules of glucose?
                a.   Water
                b.   Oxygen
                c.   Hydrogen
                d.   Carbon dioxide

b 106(K) 16. What is the composition of sucrose?
                a.   Two fructose units
                b.   One glucose and one fructose unit
                c.   One glucose and one galactose unit
                d.   One galactose and one fructose unit

a   106(K)   17.   What is the composition of maltose?
                       a.   Two glucose units
                       b.   One glucose and one fructose unit
                       c.   One glucose and one galactose unit
                       d.   One galactose and one fructose unit

d   106(K)   18.   What is the composition of lactose?
                       a.   Two glucose units
                       b.   Two fructose units
                       c.   One glucose and one fructose unit
                       d.   One glucose and one galactose unit

a   106(K)   19.   What is the principle carbohydrate of milk?
                       a.   Lactose
                       b.   Sucrose
                       c.   Maltose
                       d.   Glycogen

a   106(K)   20.   What is another name for lactose?
                       a.   Milk sugar
                       b.   Fruit sugar
                       c.   Table sugar
                       d.   Artificial sugar

b   106(K)   21.   Which of the following sugars is **not** found in plants?
                       a.   Glucose
                       b.   Lactose
                       c.   Sucrose
                       d.   Fructose

d   108,109(K) 22.   What is the name of the animal polysaccharide composed of glucose units?
                       a.   Fiber
                       b.   Enzyme
                       c.   Dextrin
                       d.   Glycogen

a   108,109(K) 23.   Glycogen is stored mainly in which of the following tissues?
                       a.   Muscle and liver
                       b.   Pancreas and kidneys
                       c.   Stomach and intestine
                       d.   Brain and red blood cells

b   108-110(A) 24.   Which of the following is **not** a rich source of dietary starch?
                       a.   Grains
                       b.   Fruits
                       c.   Tubers
                       d.   Legumes

c   108,109(K) 25.   Which of the following is a feature of glycogen?
                       a.   Found in plants
                       b.   Important as a dietary nutrient
                       c.   Virtually absent from animal meats
                       d.   Plays an insignificant role in the body

d   108,109(K)   26.   What is the primary storage form of carbohydrate in the body?
a.   Fiber
b.   Starch
c.   Glucose
d.   Glycogen

d   108(K)   27.   What is the staple grain of Canada, the United States, and Europe?
a.   Oats
b.   Rice
c.   Corn
d.   Wheat

b   108(K)   28.   What is the predominant grain product in much of South and Central America?
a.   Rice
b.   Corn
c.   Millet
d.   Wheat

a   108,109(K)   29.   What are cellulose, pectin, hemicellulose, and lignin?
a.   Fibers
b.   Starches
c.   Sugar alcohols
d.   Artificial sweeteners

d   109(A)   30.   Which of the following is an example of the difference between the chemical bonds in starch and those in cellulose?
a.   Starch bonds are single
b.   Starch bonds are fatty acids
c.   Cellulose bonds release energy
d.   Cellulose bonds are not hydrolyzed by human enzymes

c   109,110(K)   31.   Which of the following fibers is water **insoluble**?
a.   Gums
b.   Pectins
c.   Cellulose
d.   Mucilages

c   108-110;   32.   With few exceptions, all of the following characteristics are shared by water-soluble
     124,125(A)   and water-insoluble fibers **except**
a.   they are found only in plant-derived foods.
b.   they consist primarily of nonstarch polysaccharides.
c.   neither has an appreciable effect on glucose absorption.
d.   their consumption enhances stool formation and evacuation.

a   109(K)   33.   Which of the following plays a major role in the breakdown of certain types of dietary fiber in the large intestines?
a.   Bacteria
b.   Pancreas
c.   Colonic cells
d.   Small intestinal villus cell

d   109,110(K)   34.   Which of the following is a characteristic of dietary fiber?
a.   Causes diverticulosis
b.   Usually found in high fat foods
c.   Raises blood cholesterol levels
d.   Classified according to solubility in water

d   108-110;124(A) 35.   Which of the following contains the **least** amount of fiber?
a.   Apples
b.   Prunes
c.   Potatoes
d.   White rice

a   109(K)   36.   Which of the following is a feature of the pectins?
a.   They are used to thicken jelly.
b.   They are classified as insoluble fibers.
c.   They are resistant to intestinal bacterial fermentation.
d.   They are found in the small seeds of fruits such as strawberries.

c   109,110(K)   37.   Water soluble fibers include all of the following **except**
a.   gums.
b.   pectins.
c.   lignins.
d.   mucilages.

d   109(K)   38.   What type of fiber is found chiefly in the cereal fibers?
a.   Pectin
b.   Lignin
c.   Mucilage
d.   Hemicellulose

d   109(A)   39.   Which of the following is a common source of resistant starch?
a.   Apple
b.   Orange
c.   Baked potato
d.   Unripe bananas

c   109(A)   40.   Which of the following is a feature of resistant starch?
a.   It is common in overripe bananas.
b.   Excessive intake promotes constipation.
c.   It resists hydrolysis by digestive enzymes.
d.   It cannot be fermented by large intestinal bacteria.

c   109(K)   41.   Which of the following statements is **not** characteristic of fibers?
a.   Most fibers consist of linked monosaccharides.
b.   An example of a nonstarch polysaccharide fiber is pectin.
c.   An example of a nonpolysaccharide fiber is hemicellulose.
d.   Most soluble fibers are easily digested by the bacteria in the colon.

c   110(K)   42.   A "functional fiber" is one that
a.   occurs naturally in the intact plant.
b.   performs a specific function in the plant.
c.   is extracted from plants and has a beneficial health effect.
d.   is a polysaccharide that is stored primarily in muscle and liver of animals.

a   110(K)   43.   Characteristics of dietary phytic acid include all of the following **except**
      a.   it is classified as a fiber.
      b.   it is found in the husks of grains.
      c.   it is synonymous with the term phytate.
      d.   it inhibits absorption of several minerals.

b   110(K)   44.   Which of the following describes the compound phytic acid?
      a.   Product of starch digestion
      b.   Nonnutrient component of plant seeds
      c.   Found in gastric juice and helps to lower pH of chyme
      d.   Found in high concentrations in the blood of people with diabetes

a   106(A)   45.   The chemical reaction by which starch is split into monosaccharides is termed
      a.   hydrolysis.
      b.   condensation.
      c.   gluconeogenesis.
      d.   homeostatic balancing.

a   111(K)   46.   Digestion of starches takes place in the small intestines and also in the
      a.   mouth.
      b.   colon.
      c.   stomach.
      d.   pancreas.

d   111(K)   47.   What is the name of the short chains of glucose units that result from starch breakdown?
      a.   Sucrose
      b.   Lignins
      c.   Pectins
      d   Dextrins

c   111-113(K)   48.   Which of the following enzymes does **not** act on simple sugars?
      a.   Lactase
      b.   Sucrase
      c.   Amylase
      d.   Maltase

d   111-113(K)   49.   What is the primary absorption site for digestible carbohydrates?
      a.   Mouth
      b.   Stomach
      c.   Large intestines
      d.   Small intestines

d   111(K)   50.   Where is the location of enzymes that digest dietary sugars?
      a.   Mouth
      b.   Stomach
      c.   Pancreas
      d.   Small intestines

a   113(K)   51.   What is the primary organ that converts fructose to glucose following absorption?
      a.   Liver
      b.   Pancreas
      c.   Skeletal muscle
      d.   Small intestines

b   112,113(K)   52.   What is the first organ to receive carbohydrates absorbed from the intestine?
a.   Heart
b.   Liver
c.   Pancreas
d.   Skeletal muscle

d   113(K)   53.   All of the following are symptoms of lactose intolerance **except**
a.   nausea.
b.   diarrhea.
c.   cramping.
d.   constipation.

a   113(K)   54.   What percentage of the world's **adult** population shows good tolerance to lactose ingestion?
a.   30
b.   55
c.   80
d.   95

b   113,114(A)   55.   Which of the following would **least** likely be connected with the development of lactose intolerance?
a.   Medicines
b.   Milk allergy
c.   Prolonged diarrhea
d.   Inherited lactase deficiency

c   113(A)   56.   A person diagnosed with milk allergy would be sensitive to the milk's
a.   fat.
b.   lactose.
c.   protein.
d.   minerals.

d   114(K)   57.   Among the following population groups, which shows the highest prevalence of lactose intolerance?
a.   Hispanics
b.   Caucasians
c.   Scandinavians
d.   African Americans

b   113(A)   58.   For most of the world's population, what is the effect of aging on the activity of lactase?
a.   Declines by 30-40%
b.   Declines by 90-95%
c.   Increases by 30-40%
d.   Increases by 90-95%

c   114(A)   59.   Which of the following ingredients listed on food labels would be acceptable to the person who is highly intolerant to lactose in the diet?
a.   Whey
b.   Casein
c.   Dextrins
d.   Milk solids

d   113,114(K)   60.   Which of the following is a feature of lactose?
a.   Its digestion begins in the mouth.
b.   It is found in various amounts in most animal foods.
c.   It causes frequent allergies in certain population groups.
d.   It is used as a filler in one out of five prescription drugs.

d   114(K)   61.   Among the following foods, which contains the lowest amount of lactose per serving?
a.   Doughnut
b.   Ice cream
c.   Yogurt
d.   American cheese

b   114(A)   62.   Which of the following is a feature of acidophilus milk?
a.   It is virtually free of lactose.
b.   It contains live bacterial organisms.
c.   Its low pH inactivates lactose.
d.   It is a recommended substitute for people with milk allergy.

b   114(K)   63.   Why are hard cheeses lower in lactose than soft cheeses?
a.   The lactose molecules bond to casein.
b.   More lactose is removed during manufacturing.
c.   The bacterial culture is selected to degrade more of the lactose.
d.   The lactose molecules condense to form a poorly digested oligosaccharide.

a   114(K)   64.   Which of the following is a characteristic of yogurt?
a.   Bacteria in the product produce lactase.
b.   It is poorly tolerated in lactose-intolerant people.
c.   There are only trace amounts of lactose present.
d.   The lactose content is about one-half that of milk.

a   114(K)   65.   What is the chief reason that many people with lactose-intolerance can nonetheless consume foods containing some lactase without suffering any symptoms?
a.   A change occurs in the GI bacteria.
b.   Intestinal lactase enzyme can re-appear in adequate amounts.
c.   The lactose-containing foods must be eaten only as part of a full meal.
d.   The lactose-containing foods must first be heated to 100° C to degrade lactose.

d   115(A)   66.   Gluconeogenesis is a term that describes the synthesis of
a.   amino acids from glucose.
b.   lactose from a source of sucrose.
c.   fat from excess carbohydrate intake.
d.   glucose from a noncarbohydrate substance.

b   115(K)   67.   At rest, the typical body stores of glycogen can provide energy for a maximum of about
a.   4 hours.
b.   1 day.
c.   3 days.
d.   1 week.

b   116(K)   68.   What is the minimum daily amount of dietary carbohydrate necessary to spare body protein from excessive breakdown?
- a.   10-25 g
- b.   50-100 g
- c.   150-175 g
- d.   200-400 g

b   116(K)   69.   What is the primary function of insulin?
- a.   Raises blood glucose levels
- b.   Lowers blood glucose levels
- c.   Stimulates glycogen breakdown
- d.   Stimulates intestinal carbohydrate absorption

b   116,117(A)   70.   Which of the following is a typical response of the body to changes in blood glucose?
- a.   Blood glucose levels that fall too low signal the release of insulin
- b.   Blood glucose levels that fall too low signal the release of glucagon
- c.   Blood glucose levels that rise too high signal the release of glycogen
- d.   Blood glucose levels that rise too high signal the release of epinephrine

d   116(A)   71.   What is the first organ to respond to an increase in blood glucose concentration?
- a.   Brain
- b.   Liver
- c.   Muscle
- d.   Pancreas

b   116,117(A)   72.   When blood glucose concentration falls, what pancreatic hormone is secreted to stimulate release of stored glucose?
- a.   Insulin
- b.   Glucagon
- c.   Epinephrine
- d.   Cholecystokinin

c   116(A)   73.   Which of the following values falls within the normal range of blood glucose?
- a.   40 mg/dL
- b.   60 mg/dL
- c.   110 mg/dL
- d.   140 mg/dL

b   116(K)   74.   What is a normal range for blood glucose?
- a.   60-80 mg/dL
- b.   70-110 mg/dL
- c.   120-140 mg/dL
- d.   140-180 mg/dL

d   116,117(A)   75.   When you are under physical stress, what hormone is released quickly to stimulate an increase in blood glucose concentration?
- a.   Insulin
- b.   Secretin
- c.   Glucogen
- d.   Epinephrine

d   118(K)   76.   Which of the following is a feature of diabetes?
                         a.   Type 1 diabetes is also known as adult-onset diabetes.
                         b.   It is believed to be caused by abnormal intake of dietary carbohydrates.
                         c.   The insulin-dependent type is more common than the noninsulin-
                               dependent type.
                         d.   Dietary management should focus on total carbohydrate intake rather than
                               the type of carbohydrate consumed.

a   118(K)   77.   Which of the following is a feature of diabetes?
                         a.   Many people with type 2 diabetes are obese.
                         b.   Most people who have diabetes require insulin therapy.
                         c.   Diabetes results chiefly from excess dietary intake of simple carbohydrates.
                         d.   People with type 1 diabetes fail to respond to the insulin made by the
                               pancreas.

a   118(K)   78.   Which of the following statements describes the glycemic effect of foods?
                         a.   A measure of how fast and high the food causes the blood glucose to rise
                         b.   The newest, most practical means for planning diets for people with
                               diabetes
                         c.   A well-utilized, highly valued mechanism to control the intake of simple
                               sugars
                         d.   A measure of the percentage of digestible carbohydrates in relation to total
                               energy content of the food

c   118,119(K)   79.   In a person with type 2 diabetes, which of the following foods would ordinarily
                         promote the **least** favorable glycemic effect?
                         a.   Chocolate
                         b.   Ice cream
                         c.   Baked potato
                         d.   Baked beans

b   118(K)   80.   Type 2 diabetes is also known as
                         a.   prediabetes.
                         b.   adult-onset diabetes.
                         c.   anti-glycemic intolerance.
                         d.   insulin-dependent diabetes.

a   118(A)   81.   Which of the following blood glucose concentrations is most consistent with
                         hypoglycemia?
                         a.   40 mg/dL
                         b.   80 mg/dL
                         c.   115 mg/dL
                         d.   150 mg/dL

b   123(K)   82.   Approximately how many pounds of added sugars are **consumed** by the average
                         U.S. resident each year?
                         a.   25
                         b.   65
                         c.   105
                         d.   190

b   120(A)   83.   What is the name of the sweetener consisting of a mixture of glucose and fructose formed by chemical hydrolysis of sucrose?
a.   Molasses
b.   Invert sugar
c.   Turbinado sugar
d.   High-fructose syrup

d   120(K)   84.   What is the predominant sweetener used in formulating beverages?
a.   Glucose
b.   Sucrose
c.   Invert sugar
d.   High-fructose corn syrup

a   120(K)   85.   Which of the following sweeteners contains a significant amount of calcium?
a.   Molasses
b.   Brown sugar
c.   Maple sugar
d.   Invert sugar

c   121,122(A) 86.   Which of the following is best known to result from regular ingestion of sugar?
a.   Ulcers
b.   Diabetes
c.   Dental caries
d.   Cardiovascular disease

d   121,122(K) 87.   Which of the following is among food intake recommendations for reducing the incidence of dental caries when the diet contains sugary foods?
a.   Eat sugary foods separate from meals.
b.   Eat dried fruits in place of whole fruits.
c.   Sip a sugary soft drink slowly rather than quickly.
d.   Eat a sugary snack all at one time rather than in parts throughout the day.

c   121,122(A) 88.   Which of the following describes a relationship between carbohydrate intake and dental health?
a.   Starches can not promote the formation of dental caries.
b.   After exposure to a single snack, mouth bacteria produce acid for 50-60 minutes.
c.   Eating a sugary dessert at the beginning of a meal, rather than the end, is less likely to promote dental caries.
d.   Sugar consumed in a soft drink promotes more bacterial fermentation than the same amount of sugar in a doughnut.

a   123,124(K) 89.   Which of the following is known to correlate most strongly with reduced risk of deaths from heart disease?
a.   High fiber intake
b.   High sugar intake
c.   High levulose intake
d.   High corn syrup intake

d   123(K)   90.   According to the current dietary recommendations, what is the maximum percentage of total energy intake that added sugar should contribute in the diet?
a.   2
b.   10
c.   15
d.   25

d   124,125(K) 91.   Which of the following is **not** a feature of high-fiber foods?
a.   Effective in weight control
b.   Provide feeling of fullness
c.   Usually lower in fat and simple sugars
d.   Provide more energy per gram than processed foods

b   124,125(A) 92.   In general, a diet that is modified by substituting complex carbohydrates for pure sugars results in a diet that is higher in
a.   fat.
b.   fiber.
c.   energy.
d.   refined foods.

c   126(K)   93.   According to most dietary guidelines, what percentage of the day's total energy intake should be furnished by carbohydrates?
a.   10-15
b.   30-35
c.   45-65
d.   90-95

c   126(K)   94.   What is the RDA for carbohydrate?
a.   10 g
b.   45 g
c.   130 g
d.   250 g

a   127(K)   95.   According to the American Dietetic Association, what is the recommended daily intake of dietary fiber?
a.   20-35 g
b.   40-50 g
c.   55-70 g
d.   75-100 g

d   127(A)   96.   What is the DRI for fiber for a person consuming 2,500 kcal?
a.   5 g
b.   15 g
c.   25 g
d.   35 g

c   127(K)   97.   Which of the following provides the most fiber?
a.   1 orange
b.   1 serving oatmeal
c.   1 serving split peas
d.   1 serving whole wheat bread

c 134-138(K) 98. All of the following are features of artificial sweeteners **except**
- a. there is a lack of scientific consensus on their benefits for weight reduction.
- b. there is an Acceptable Daily Intake which provides a wide margin of safety.
- c. they provide about one-half the energy of carbohydrates plus small amounts of vitamins and minerals.
- d. if used, the American Dietetics Association advises moderate intake and only in a well-balanced, nutritious diet.

a 134;137(K) 99. What is stevia?
- a. An herb-derived sweetener
- b. An FDA-approved sugar alcohol
- c. A poorly digested polysaccharide
- d. An inhibitor of lactase enzyme activity

a 134-137(K) 100. Which of the following artificial sweeteners has a composition similar to aspartame?
- a. Neotame
- b. Sucralose
- c. Saccharin
- d. Acesulfame-K

d 135,136(K) 101. Which of the following is a feature of aspartame?
- a. Its sweetness increases with heat
- b. It is made up of three amino acids
- c. It is recommended for people with PKU
- d. Two of its breakdown products include methanol and formaldehyde

b 135(K) 102. Among the following approved sweeteners, which has the highest relative sweetness?
- a. Saccharin
- b. Sucralose
- c. Aspartame
- d. Acesulfame-K

b 137(K) 103. Among the alternative sweeteners available in the United States, which has a structure that integrates chlorine atoms?
- a. Saccharin
- b. Sucralose
- c. Aspartame
- d. Acesulfame-K

d 138(K) 104. Which of the following is a general feature of the sugar alcohols (sugar replacers)?
- a. They provide less than 1 kcal/g.
- b. They elicit a high glycemic index.
- c. They are rapidly absorbed from the intestines.
- d. They cannot be metabolized by caries-causing bacteria.

d 134;138(K) 105. Which of the following is **not** a classification for the food additives mannitol, sorbitol, and xylitol?
- a. Carbohydrates
- b. Sugar alcohols
- c. Sugar replacers
- d. Artificial sweeteners

c   138,139(K)   106.   Which of the following is a characteristic of the sugar alcohols?
                a.   Not sweet
                b.   Not metabolized
                c.   Contain kcalories
                d.   Promote dental caries

c   139(K)   107.   When consumed in excess, which of the following is most likely to lead to diarrhea?
                a.   Fiber
                b.   Sucrose
                c.   Sorbitol
                  d.   Wheat starch

b   138(K)   108.   What is the approximate energy content of most sugar alcohols?
                a.   0 kcal/g
                b.   2 kcal/g
                c.   4 kcal/g
                d.   7 kcal/g

a   138,139(K)   109.   Which of the following is a characteristic of the sugar replacers (sugar alcohols)?
                a.   They promote a low glycemic index
                b.   They promote constipation in children
                c.   They are less effective than alternative sweeteners in inhibiting dental caries
                d.   They demonstrate fewer GI side effects than the alternative sweeteners

MATCHING (Answers can be used only once.)

H	105	01.	Disaccharide containing fructose
R	106	02.	Chemical reaction that links two molecules together
O	106	03.	Chemical reaction that splits a larger molecule into smaller molecules
L	108	04.	A complex carbohydrate in muscle
G	108	05.	A complex carbohydrate in legumes
N	109	06.	Structurally similar to starch but resistant to digestion
D	109	07.	A water-soluble fiber
J	109	08.	A water-insoluble fiber
S	111	09.	Site where digestion of disaccharides takes place
F	111	10.	Site where digestion of starch begins
T	111	11.	Site where fibers may be metabolized to short-chain fatty acids
I	111	12.	When digested, yields galactose
M	116	13.	Substance that signals the release of glucose **into** blood
E	116	14.	Substance that signals removal of glucose from the blood
Q	117	15.	Stress hormone that modulates blood glucose
B	120	16.	Number of kcal in a 16-ounce regular soda
C	126	17.	Recommended intake of total carbohydrate, in grams, from a 2,600 kcal diet
P	136	18.	Safe sweetener, except for children with PKU
K	138	19.	A sugar alcohol
A	116	20.	Normal blood glucose level, in mg per 100 ml blood

A.	100	F.	Mouth	K.	Sorbitol	P.	Aspartame
B.	200	G.	Starch	L.	Glycogen	Q.	Epinephrine
C.	422	H.	Sucrose	M.	Glucagon	R.	Condensation
D.	Pectin	I.	Lactose	N.	Cellulose	S.	Small intestine
E.	Insulin	J.	Lignin	O.	Hydrolysis	T.	Large intestine

Essay Questions

Page(s)

104-113   01.   Compare and contrast the chemical makeup, major food sources, and digestion/absorption of simple and complex carbohydrates.

108-110;124-126 02.   Give several examples of soluble and insoluble dietary fibers. List food sources of these fibers. Contrast the physical characteristics and features of these two types of fiber and their effects on gastrointestinal tract function.

108-110;124-126 03.   List and discuss seven benefits of fiber.

109-110   04.   Compare and contrast the terms total fiber, dietary fiber, and functional fiber.

113,114   05.   Discuss the meaning, significance, and features of lactose intolerance.

116-118   06.   Describe the body's mechanisms for controlling blood glucose levels under normal and stress conditions.

118,119   07.   Discuss the pros and cons of using the glycemic index in meal planning for people with diabetes.

122,123   08.   List four common accusations made against dietary sugar. What is the evidence for and against these accusations?

122,123   09.   Discuss the relation between carbohydrate craving and brain serotonin levels.

124,125   10.   Discuss the interactions between fiber and bile.

124   11.   Discuss the possible reasons why diets rich in complex carbohydrates may lower the risk of heart disease.

124,125   12.   How is fiber thought to exert an influence over cancer of the colon?

125-127   13.   What are potential hazards of consuming too much fiber? Give examples of the circumstances, conditions, and forms in which a person might ingest large amounts of fiber.

134-138   14.   Discuss the contribution of artificial sweeteners to the diet and their role in weight control.

138,139   15.   Describe the benefits and adverse effects of the common sugar replacers (sugar alcohols).

CHAPTER 5
THE LIPIDS: TRIGLYCERIDES, PHOSPHOLIPIDS, AND STEROLS

AN PAGE(S)

c 141(K) 01. Approximately what percentage of the lipids in foods are triglycerides?
  a. 5
  b. 30
  c. 95
  d. 100

c 142(K) 02. What is the chemical composition of fats?
  a. Hexose polymers
  b. Glycogen granules
  c. Fatty acids and glycerol
  d. Combinations of long chain fatty acids

b 141,142(A) 03. A compound composed of carbon, hydrogen, and oxygen with 3 fatty acids attached to a molecule of glycerol would be known as a
  a. diglyceride.
  b. triglyceride.
  c. phospholipid.
  d. monoglyceride.

c 141,142(K) 04. What compound is composed of 3 fatty acids and glycerol?
  a. Steroid
  b. Lecithin
  c. Triglyceride
  d. Monoglyceride

c 141(K) 05. In which form are most dietary lipids found?
  a. Sterols
  b. Glycerols
  c. Triglycerides
  d. Monoglycerides

d 141(K) 06. What percentage of stored body fat is in the form of triglycerides?
  a. 2
  b. 50
  c. 78
  d. 99

b 142(K) 07. What is the simplest fatty acid found in the diet?
  a. Oleic acid
  b. Acetic acid
  c. Linoleic acid
  d. Palmitic acid

c 143(K) 08. Which of the following describes a fatty acid that has one double bond?
  a. Saturated
  b. Hydrogenated
  c. Monounsaturated
  d. Polyunsaturated

b   142,143(K) 09.   Lipids differ in their degree of saturation or unsaturation due to their number of
a.   amino acids.
b.   double bonds.
c.   saccharide units.
d.   peptide linkages.

b   143(K)   10.   What type of fatty acid is found in high amounts in olive oil?
a.   Saturated
b.   Monounsaturated
c.   Polyunsaturated
d.   Partially hydrogenated

b   142-144(A) 11.   Which one of the following compounds is missing 4 or more hydrogen atoms?
a.   Monounsaturated fatty acid
b.   Polyunsaturated fatty acid
c.   Long chain saturated fatty acid
d.   Short chain saturated fatty acid

b   142,143(K) 12.   Which of the following is a common dietary saturated fatty acid?
a.   Oleic acid
b.   Stearic acid
c.   Linolenic acid
d.   Arachidonic acid

b   142(K)   13.   Approximately how many carbons are contained in a medium-chain fatty acid?
a.   2-4
b.   6-10
c.   12-22
d.   24-26

d   142(A)   14.   Which of the following is a source of medium-chain fatty acids?
a.   Fish oils
b.   Beef products
c.   Vegetable oils
d.   Dairy products

b   143,144(A) 15.   Which of the following chemical characteristics of fatty acids determines their
susceptibility to spoilage by oxygen?
a.   Chain length
b.   Number of double bonds
c.   Position of first saturated bond
d.   Size of adjacent fatty acids on the triglyceride molecule

d   142-144(K) 16.   Which of the following is a polyunsaturated fatty acid in foods?
a.   Oleic acid
b.   Acetic acid
c.   Stearic acid
d.   Linoleic acid

c   144,145(A)   17.   Of the following foods, which has the highest percentage of its fat in saturated form?
                         a.   Butter
                         b.   Soybean
                         c.   Coconut
                         d.   Beef tallow

b   144,145(A)   18.   Of the following foods, which has the highest percentage of its fat in polyunsaturated form?
                         a.   Butter
                         b.   Soybean
                         c.   Coconut
                         d.   Beef tallow

a   144(K)   19.   Which of the following is considered a major source of polyunsaturated fat?
                         a.   Corn oil
                         b.   Palm oil
                         c.   Peanut oil
                         d.   Chicken fat

d   145;141(A)   20.   Which of the following sources would yield the softest lipids at room temperature?
                         a.   Lard
                         b.   Beef
                         c.   Pork
                         d.   Safflower

a   145,146(A)   21.   Which of the following is a feature of polyunsaturated fats?
                         a.   Low melting point
                         b.   High melting point
                         c.   Solid at room temperature
                         d.   Solid at refrigerator temperature

a   144-146(A)   22.   All of the following are rich sources of polyunsaturated fatty acids **except**
                         a.   palm oil.
                         b.   fish oils.
                         c.   soybean oil.
                         d.   safflower oil.

d   144-146(A)   23.   Which of the following characteristics is **shared** by olive oil and canola oil?
                         a.   Neither is liquid at room temperature.
                         b.   Neither contains saturated fatty acids.
                         c.   Both contain high levels of polyunsaturated fatty acids.
                         d.   Both contain high levels of monounsaturated fatty acids.

b   145(A)   24.   Which of the following is a factor that determines the hardness of a fat at a given temperature?
                         a.   Origin of the fat
                         b.   Degree of saturation
                         c.   Number of acid groups
                         d.   Number of oxygen atoms

a   145,146(A) 25.   A major cause of rancidity of lipids in foods is exposure to
                      a.   heat and oxygen.
                      b.   fluorescent lighting.
                      c.   freezer temperatures.
                      d.   enrichment additives.

c   145,146(A) 26.   When stored at room temperature in loosely capped containers, which of the
                      following dietary lipids would turn rancid in the shortest time?
                      a.   Lard
                      b.   Peanut oil
                      c.   Soybean oil
                      d.   Coconut oil

d   145,146(A) 27.   Characteristics of hydrogenated oils include all of the following **except**
                      a.   they are stored in adipose tissue.
                      b.   they lower HDL and raise LDL cholesterol in the body.
                      c.   some of their fatty acids change shape from *cis* to *trans*.
                      d.   products containing them become rancid sooner, contributing to a shorter
                              shelf life.

d   146(A)   28.   All of the following are methods used by food processors to stabilize the lipids in
                      food products **except**
                      a.   refrigeration.
                      b.   hydrogenation.
                      c.   tightly sealed packaging.
                      d.   addition of oxidizing chemicals.

d   146(A)   29.   Which of the following would be **least** effective at preventing oxidation of the
                      polyunsaturated fatty acids in processed foods?
                      a.   Refrigeration
                      b.   Addition of BHT
                      c.   Partial hydrogenation
                      d.   Addition of phosphorus

b   146(A)   30.   In the process of fat hydrogenation, hydrogen atoms are added to which part of the
                      molecule?
                      a.   Oxygen
                      b.   Carbon
                      c.   Glycerol
                      d.   Other hydrogens

a   146,147(A) 31.   An oil that is partially hydrogenated sometimes changes one or more of its double
                      bond configurations from
                      a.   *cis* to *trans*.
                      b.   solid to liquid.
                      c.   covalent to ionic.
                      d.   saturated to unsaturated.

d   146,147(K) 32.   Which of the following is descriptive of fatty acid configuration?
                      a.   A *cis*-fatty acid has an extended, linear formation.
                      b.   A *trans*-fatty acid has a folded, U-shape formation.
                      c.   *Trans*-fatty acids are made only from polyunsaturated fats.
                      d.   Naturally occurring *trans*-fatty acids are found in dairy products.

d   146-147(K)   33.   Which of the following describes a feature of *cis*-fatty acids and *trans*-fatty acids?
  a.   In nature, most double bonds are *trans*.
  b.   Hydrogenation converts *trans*-fatty acids to *cis*-fatty acids.
  c.   The conversion of *cis*-fatty acids to *trans*-fatty acids is inhibited by the presence of antioxidants.
  d.   In the body, *trans*-fatty acids are metabolized more like saturated fats than like unsaturated fats.

b   148(K)   34.   Which of the following is a feature of phospholipids?
  a.   Resistant to digestion
  b.   Soluble in both water and fat
  c.   Highly susceptible to oxidation
  d.   Found naturally only in animal foods

d   148(K)   35.   The composition of lecithin could include all of the following **except**
  a.   choline.
  b.   phosphate.
  c.   fatty acids.
  d   magnesium.

d   148(K)   36.   What type of compound is lecithin?
  a.   Bile salt
  b.   Glycolipid
  c.   Lipoprotein
  d.   Phospholipid

d   148,149(A)   37.   Which of the following is **not** a feature of lecithin?
  a.   Widespread in foods
  b.   Found in cell membranes
  c.   Manufactured by the body
  d.   Dietary supplements inhibit fat absorption

d   148;150-52(A)   38.   Each of the following may act as an emulsifier in the intestinal tract **except**
  a.   lecithin.
  b.   bile acids.
  c.   bile phospolipids.
  d.   pancreatic lipase.

d   150(A)   39.   What is the **usual** fate of dietary lecithin?
  a.   Unabsorbed and passes out in the feces
  b.   Absorbed intact and incorporated into tissues
  c.   Absorbed intact and broken down by the liver
  d.   Hydrolyzed by the intestinal enzyme lecithinase

d   148,149(A)   40.   How much energy is contributed by one gram of lecithin in a dietary supplement?
  a.   0 kcal
  b.   4 kcal
  c.   7 kcal
  d.   9 kcal

c   148,149(A)   41.   What is the approximate energy value of one teaspoon of liquid lecithin
                          supplement?
                          a.   0 kcal
                          b.   2 kcal
                          c.   45 kcal
                          d.   200 kcal

c   149(K)   42.   What is the major sterol in the diet?
                          a.   Palm oil
                          b.   Lecithin
                          c.   Cholesterol
                          d.   Arachidonic acid

a   149(A)   43.   Which of the following is a feature of cholesterol?
                          a.   Synthesized by the body
                          b.   No relation to heart disease
                          c.   Recommended intake is zero
                          d.   No function in the human body

a   149(K)   44.   Which of the following is a feature of cholesterol?
                          a.   Its Daily Value is 300 mg.
                          b.   Its structure is similar to that of lecithin.
                          c.   Most of the body's cholesterol is found circulating in the bloodstream.
                          d.   The amount consumed in the diet usually exceeds the amount synthesized
                                  in the body.

c   149(K)   45.   Which of the following is a feature of cholesterol?
                          a.   Good cholesterol is a form of cholesterol found in plant foods.
                          b.   Bad cholesterol is a form of cholesterol found in plant foods.
                          c.   Only about 10% of the body's total cholesterol is extracellular.
                          d.   Exogenous cholesterol absorption is reduced by lecithin supplements.

b   149(K)   46.   Which of the following is a characteristic of cholesterol?
                          a.   It is absorbed directly into the blood.
                          b.   It is a precursor for bile and vitamin D synthesis.
                          c.   It is not formed in the body when provided by the diet.
                          d.   It is found in abundance in tropical fats such as palm oil.

d   148,149(A)   47.   Which of the following characteristics are **shared** by cholesterol and lecithin?
                          a.   Both are sterols.
                          b.   Both are phospholipids.
                          c.   Both are essential nutrients.
                          d.   Both are synthesized in the body.

b   149(K)   48.   All of the following compounds may be synthesized from cholesterol **except**
                          a.   bile.
                          b.   glucose.
                          c.   vitamin D.
                          d.   sex hormones.

c   149-151;   49.   Which of the following is **not** a destination for cholesterol?
     159,160(A)
                                  a.   Synthesized into bile
                                    b.   Excreted in the feces
                                    c.   Accumulates on walls of veins
                                    d.   Accumulates on walls of arteries

c   149(A)   50.   Which of the following foods contains cholesterol?
                                    a.   Corn
                                    b.   Olives
                                    c.   Roasted turkey
                                    d.   Roasted peanuts

a   149(A)   51.   Which of the following **cannot** be found in plants?
                                    a.   Cholesterol
                                    b.   Triglycerides
                                    c.   Essential fatty acids
                                    d.   Nonessential fatty acids

b   149(A)   52.   Which of the following contains the **least** cholesterol per serving size?
                                    a.   Steamed fish
                                    b.   Steamed corn
                                    c.   Broiled chicken
                                    d.   Very lean grilled steak

b   160(K)   53.   Which of the following foods contains the **least** amount of cholesterol per serving?
                                    a.   Cod
                                    b.   Butter
                                    c.   Shrimp
                                    d.   Hamburger

b   160(K)   54.   Approximately how many milligrams of cholesterol is found in an egg?
                                    a.   100
                                    b.   200
                                    c.   300
                                    d.   450

b   159(K)   55.   Among the following dietary fatty acids, which has been found to raise blood cholesterol level by the **least** amount?
                                    a.   Lauric
                                    b.   Stearic
                                    c.   Myristic
                                    d.   Palmitic

b   158-162(A)   56.   Among the following, which would be the **least** effective method to control blood cholesterol levels?
                                    a.   Control body weight
                                    b.   Eat more insoluble fiber
                                    c.   Consume less saturated fat
                                    d.   Exercise intensely and frequently

d   150,151(A)   57.   How is soluble fiber in the diet thought to help lower blood cholesterol level?
a.   It denatures cholesterol in the stomach.
b.   It hydrolyzes cholesterol in the intestinal tract.
c.   It traps cholesterol in the intestinal tract and thus inhibits its absorption.
d.   It enhances excretion of bile leading to increased cholesterol turnover.

a   162(A)   58.   Surveys show that U.S. adults' average daily cholesterol intake (mg) is
a.   300.
b.   400.
c.   750.
d.   1,000.

a   150(K)   59.   What term may be used to describe a substance that is hydrophobic?
a.   Lipophilic
b.   Lipophobic
c.   Glycerophilic
d.   Glycerophobic

c   150(K)   60.   Which of the following is characteristic of the lipase enzymes?
a.   Gastric lipase plays a significant role in fat digestion in adults.
b.   Intestinal mucosal lipase is responsible for most dietary fat digestion.
c.   Salivary gland lipase (lingual lipase) plays a significant role in fat digestion in infants.
d.   Pancreatic lipase hydrolyzes most dietary triglycerides completely to glycerol and free fatty acids.

c   150,151(K) 61.   What part of the gastrointestinal tract is the predominant site of dietary fat hydrolysis?
a.   Mouth
b.   Stomach
c.   Small intestine
d.   Large intestine

c   149-152(K) 62.   Which of the following is **not** a feature of the bile acids?
a.   Stored in the gallbladder
b.   Synthesized from cholesterol
c.   Manufactured by the gallbladder
d.   Released into the intestines whenever fat is present

a   150,152(A) 63.   Bile is known to assist in the absorption of
a.   fat only.
b.   all nutrients.
c.   carbohydrate and fat only.
d.   carbohydrate, fat, and protein only.

c   150,151(K) 64.   What is the storage site of bile?
a.   Liver
b.   Pancreas
c.   Gallbladder
d.   Intestinal epithelial cells

a   152(K)   65.   Spherical complexes of emulsified fats are known as
a.   micelles.
b.   chylomicrons.
c.   monolipomicrons.
d.   endogenous bilayer aggregates.

c   152(K)   66.   In the digestion of fats, emulsifiers function as
a.   enzymes.
b.   hormones.
c.   detergents.
d.   chylomicrons.

b   152(A)   67.   Which of the following substances **cannot** be absorbed directly into the blood?
a.   Glycerol
b.   Long-chain fatty acids
c.   Short-chain fatty acids
d.   Medium-chain fatty acids

b   152(K)   68.   After a meal, most of the fat that eventually empties into the blood is in the form of particles known as
a.   micelles.
b.   chylomicrons.
c.   low-density lipoproteins.
d.   very-low-density lipoproteins.

b   153,154(K)   69.   Which of the following lipoproteins contains the highest percentage of cholesterol?
a.   Chylomicron
b.   Low-density lipoprotein
c.   High-density lipoprotein
d.   Very-low-density lipoprotein

a   153(K)   70.   What lipoprotein is largest in size?
a.   Chylomicron
b.   High-density lipoprotein
c.   Low-density lipoprotein
d.   Very-low-density lipoprotein

a   154(A)   71.   In comparison to a low-density lipoprotein, a high-density lipoprotein contains
a.   less lipid.
b.   less protein.
c.   more cholesterol.
d.   more carbohydrate.

a   154(A)   72.   What tissue contains special receptors for removing low-density lipoproteins from the circulation?
a.   Liver
b.   Adipose
c.   Arterial walls
d.   Skeletal muscle

c   154(K)   73.   What lipoprotein is responsible for transporting cholesterol back to the liver from
                         the periphery?
                         a.   Chylomicron
                         b.   Low-density lipoprotein
                         c.   High-density lipoprotein
                         d.   Very-low density lipoprotein

c   154 (K)   74.   A **low** risk of cardiovascular disease correlates with high blood levels of
                         a.   triglycerides.
                         b.   free fatty acids.
                         c.   high-density lipoproteins.
                         d.   very-low-density lipoproteins.

b   156(K)   75.   A **major** function of fat in the body is to
                         a.   build muscle tissue.
                         b.   protect vital organs.
                         c.   regulate blood glucose levels.
                         d.   provide precursors for glucose synthesis.

d   163(A)   76.   Which of the following does **not** describe a function of fat?
                         a.   Adds flavor to food
                         b.   Serves as a carrier of fat-soluble vitamins
                         c.   Is an essential constituent of body tissues
                         d.   Supplies up to 25% of the body's energy needs during rest

c   163(K)   77.   Which of the following is the most desirable quality that fat adds to foods?
                         a.   Color
                         b.   Sweetness
                         c.   Palatability
                         d.   Hydrogenation

d   156(K)   78.   Which of the following lipids is an essential nutrient?
                         a.   Lecithin
                         b.   Cholesterol
                         c.   Stearic acid
                         d.   Linoleic acid

b   156(K)   79.   Which of the following is used by the body to synthesize arachidonic acid?
                         a.   Oleic acid
                         b.   Linoleic acid
                         c.   Palmitic acid
                         d.   Linolenic acid

d   156(K)   80.   Which of the following is an omega-3 fat?
                         a.   Acetic acid
                         b.   Palmitic acid
                         c.   Linoleic acid
                         d.   Docosahexaenoic acid

d   161(K)   81.   All of the following foods contain liberal amounts of eicosapentaenoic and
                         docosahexaenoic acid **except**
                         a.   tuna.
                         b.   salmon.
                         c.   human milk.
                         d.   soybean oil.

c   156,157(A) 82.   What is the immediate precursor for the eicosanoids?
                         a.   Glucose
                         b.   Hormones
                         c.   Fatty acids
                         d.   Cholesterol

b   156-157(A) 83   Aspirin works to reduce the symptoms of infection or pain by retarding the
                         synthesis of
                         a.   arachidonic acid.
                         b.   certain eicosanoids.
                         c.   certain saturated fatty acids.
                         d.   certain unsaturated fatty acids.

d   156;161(A) 84.   Where can essential fatty acids be found?
                         a.   Fish only
                         b.   Beef only
                         c.   Plants only
                         d.   Fish, beef, and plants

d   156,157(K) 85.   What are the precursors for synthesis of the thromboxanes?
                         a.   Steroids
                         b.   Short-chain fatty acids
                         c.   Medium-chain saturated fatty acids
                         d.   Long-chain polyunsaturated fatty acids

a   156-158(K) 86.   Which of the following is a feature of the lipid content of foods?
                         a.   Omega-3 fats are found in fish.
                         b.   Cholesterol is found in peanuts.
                         c.   Essential fatty acids are found in olestra.
                         d.   Low-density lipoproteins are found in coconut oil.

b   160,161(A) 87.   Which of the following vegetable oils is a good source of omega-3 fatty acids?
                         a.   Corn
                         b.   Canola
                         c.   Sesame
                         d.   Coconut

a   161(A)   88.   Which of the following is a good source of eicosapentanoic acid?
                         a.   Tuna
                         b.   Butter
                         c.   Salad oil
                         d.   Shortening

c   158(K)   89.   Which of the following is a feature of adipose cell lipoprotein lipase?
  a.   The enzyme's activity is reduced by high-fat diets.
  b.   The enzyme's activity is increased by signals from epinephrine and glucagon.
  c.   The enzyme works to promote uptake of circulating triglycerides into storage triglycerides.
  d.   The enzyme is involved in release of free fatty acids from stored triglyceride into the bloodstream.

d   158(K)   90.   What is the function of lipoprotein lipase?
  a.   Synthesizes lipoproteins in liver cells
  b.   Synthesizes triglycerides in adipose cells
  c.   Assembles lipid particles into chylomicrons
  d.   Hydrolyzes blood triglycerides for uptake into cells

d   158(A)   91.   Approximately what percentage of the body's energy needs at rest is supplied by fat?
  a.   5
  b.   25
  c.   40
  d.   60

c   158(K)   92.   What is the function of adipose cell hormone-sensitive lipase?
  a.   Hydrolyzes hormones involved in fat breakdown
  b.   Synthesizes new adipose cells from simple fatty acids
  c.   Hydrolyzes triglycerides to provide fatty acids for other cells
  d.   Synthesizes long-chain fatty acids to provide precursors for other cells

a   158(A)   93.   What nutrient is used to form ketones?
  a.   Fat
  b.   Protein
  c.   Simple carbohydrates
  d.   Complex carbohydrates

c   158(K)   94.   Approximately how many kcalories are contained in a pound of body fat?
  a.   1,000
  b.   2,500
  c.   3,500
  d.   4,000

b   156(K)   95.   What are the building blocks in the body's synthesis and elongation of fatty acids?
  a.   1-carbon fragments
  b.   2-carbon fragments
  c.   4-carbon fragments
  d.   7-carbon fragments

a   159(K)   96.   The results of blood tests that reveal a person's total cholesterol and triglycerides are called a
  a.   lipid profile.
  b.   circulating fat count.
  c.   personal lipids count.
  d.   degenerative disease assessment.

d   159-162(A)   97.   Each of the following is known to be linked to excessive intake of fats **except**
a.   cancer.
b.   obesity.
c.   diabetes.
d.   lactose intolerance.

a   159-162(A)   98.   Features consistent with the ingestion of high-fat diets include all of the following **except**
a.   the diets initiate but do not promote cancer formation.
b.   the diets lead to a greater efficiency of body fat storage.
c.   people on these diets typically exceed their energy intake and gain weight.
d.   people on these diets tend to have more body fat than predicted from their total energy intake.

c   162,163;159(K)   99.   All of the following statements are characteristics of lipid intake of U.S. adults **except**
a.   cholesterol intake averages 350 mg per day for men.
b.   energy from fat provides about 35% of total energy intake.
c.   *trans*-fatty acid intake accounts for 1-2% of total fat intake.
d.   saturated fat intake represents about one–third of total fat intake.

a   159,162(K)   100.   Which of the following is a feature of fat intake and health?
a.   Intake of saturated fat raises blood cholesterol more so than intake of cholesterol.
b.   High intakes of fish oil lower bleeding time and improve diabetes and wound healing.
c.   High intakes of short and medium-chain fatty acids raise high-density lipoprotein levels.
d.   *Trans*-fatty acids contained in polyunsaturated fats but not in monounsaturated fats alter blood cholesterol levels.

c   159(A)   101.   Important factors in the selection of a margarine product include all of the following **except**
a.   it should be *trans* fat free.
b.   it should be soft instead of hard.
c.   it contains primarily omega-3 fatty acids.
d.   it lists liquid vegetable oil as first ingredient.

b   161(A)   102.   The oils found in walnuts, soybeans, flaxseed, and wheat germ represent a good source of preformed
a.   eicosanoids.
b.   linolenic acid.
c.   docosahexanoic acid.
d.   eicosapentanoic acid.

b   161,162(K)   103.   Which of the following describes a recognized relationship between dietary fat and cancer?
a.   Dietary fat initiates rather than promotes cancer formation.
b.   High saturated fat intake raises the risk for prostate cancer.
c.   High intakes of omega-3 fatty acids promote cancer development in animals.
d.   The evidence linking fat intake with cancer is stronger than that linking it with heart disease.

a   160-162(K)   104.   Studies show that regular consumption of fatty fish leads to
- a.   lower blood pressure.
- b.   higher blood cholesterol.
- c.   greater tendency of the blood to clot.
- d.   decreased storage of omega-3 fatty acids.

d   160(K)   105.   Which of the following fatty acids leads to reduction in the tendency of blood to clot?
- a.   Oleic acid
- b.   Stearic acid
- c.   Arachidonic acid
- d.   Eicosapentaenoic acid

d   162(A)   106.   According to the DRI, what is the upper limit of fat (g) that may be consumed by a healthy person requiring 3,000 kcalories per day?
- a.   33
- b.   66
- c.   83
- d.   117

c   162(K)   107.   According to the Dietary Guidelines, what should be the maximum total fat intake as a percent of energy intake?
- a.   10
- b.   20
- c.   30
- d.   40

c   162(K)   108.   Surveys show that U.S. adults' average intake of fat as a percentage of total energy intake is
- a.   20.
- b.   27.
- c.   35.
- d.   55.

c   163(K)   109.   For most adults, what is the recommended minimum amount of fat that should be consumed, as a percentage of total energy intake?
- a.   5
- b.   15
- c.   20
- d.   35

b   162(K)   110.   As a percentage of daily energy intake, what is the recommended range for the essential fatty acids?
- a.   2.5-5.5
- b.   5.6-11.2
- c.   12-19
- d.   20-35

c   162(A)   111.   According to the Dietary Guidelines, what should be the maximum daily intake of cholesterol on a 2,500 kcal diet?
- a.   50 mg
- b.   150 mg
- c.   300 mg
- d.   1,000 mg

c   162(A)   112.   Approximately how many **grams** of fat would be contained in an 800 kcalorie meal which provides 50% of the energy from carbohydrate, 20% from protein, and the remainder from fat?

    a.   15
    b.   22
    c.   27
    d.   35

b   162(A)   113.   A meal providing 1200 kcalories contains 10 g of saturated fats, 14 g of monounsaturated fats, and 20 g of poly-unsaturated fats. What is the percentage of energy supplied by the lipids?

    a.   22
    b.   33
    c.   44
    d.   55

d   160(K)   114.   Which of the following is a characteristic of eggs in nutrition?

    a.   The cholesterol is found in approximately equal amounts in the yolk and the white (albumin).
    b.   The omega-3 fatty acid content of eggs is increased by feeding hens more corn oil.
    c.   The amount of cholesterol in one egg is about the same as in one serving of ice cream.
    d.   Consumption of four eggs per week has been approved by the American Heart Association.

b   163(K)   115.   Which of the following is a feature of fat in the diet of athletes?

    a.   A minimum of 20% fat energy in the diet is needed by athletes.
    b.   Greater endurance is found on a 50% fat diet than on a 10% fat diet.
    c.   Optimal performance is found with a high carbohydrate, 15% total fat kcalories diet.
    d.   Diets with at least 10% total kcalories from fat are able to provide the recommended amounts of micronutrients.

a   161(A)   116.   Which of the following is a likely explanation for the imbalance between omega-6 and omega-3 lipids in the U.S. diet?

    a.   High intakes of vegetable oils and low intakes of fish
    b.   Low intakes of vegetable oils and high intakes of fish
    c.   High intakes of beef fat and low intakes of vegetable oils
    d.   Low intakes of beef fat and high intakes of vegetable oils

b   164(A)   117.   A food that represents a visible fat would be

    a.   nuts.
    b.   butter.
    c.   avocados.
    d.   chocolate.

b   165,166(A)   118.   Which of the following is **not** a feature of the artificial fat replacer olestra?

    a.   It can be used in the frying of foods
    b.   It leads to constipation in some individuals
    c.   Its chemical structure is similar to a triglyceride
    d.   It lowers absorption of vitamins A and K from foods

d   165,166(K)   119.   Which of the following is a drawback of olestra consumption?
        a.   It yields 9 kcalories per gram
        b.   It imparts off-flavors to foods
        c.   It raises blood glucose levels
        d.   It inhibits absorption of vitamin E

d   174(K)   120.   Of the total average fat content of the most commonly eaten nuts in the United States, what is the approximate percentage of monounsaturated fat?
        a.   5
        b.   30
        c.   45
        d.   60

a   175(A)   121.   Why does the FDA advise against consumption of certain fish such as swordfish and shark by women of childbearing age?
        a.   These fish are a major source of toxic mercury.
        b.   The omega-3 fatty acids may induce premature labor.
        c.   The omega-3 fatty acids prolong bleeding time during delivery.
        d.   These fish contain unusually high amounts of medium-chain triglycerides.

c   176(K)   122.   Studies show that a 1% increase in dietary saturated fatty acids will raise the risk of heart disease by what percentage?
        a.   0.5
        b.   1.0
        c.   2.0
        d.   5.0

b   177-178(A)   123.   A major feature of the Mediterranean diet is liberal amounts of
        a.   eggs.
        b.   olive oil.
        c.   lean meat.
        d.   fortified butter.

MATCHING (Answers can be used only once.)

J	142	01.	The simplest dietary fatty acid
K	142	02.	A long-chain saturated fatty acid
L	145	03.	A source of short- and medium-chain fatty acids
H	146	04.	A good source of monounsaturated fats
O	146	05.	Common source of *trans*-fatty acids
P	156	06.	Example of an eicosanoid
Q	156	07.	An essential fatty acid
C	160	08.	Good food source of omega-3 fatty acids
E	161	09.	Good food source of omega-6 fatty acids
D	148	10.	A phospholipid
I	149	11.	Major dietary precursor for vitamin D synthesis
G	150	12.	Major source of lipase
A	150	13.	Source of bile
R	150	14.	Signals the release of bile
M	152	15.	A lipoprotein synthesized within intestinal absorptive cells
B	152	16.	Structure assisting absorption of long-chain fats
T	153	17.	A lipoprotein made primarily by the liver
S	155	18.	The lipoprotein type with the highest percentage of protein
F	165	19.	Fat replacement product made from fat
N	174	20.	Oil that is characteristic of the Mediterranean diet

A.	Liver		K.	Stearic acid
B.	Micelle		L.	Tropical oils
C.	Sardines		M.	Chylomicron
D.	Lecithin		N.	Olive oil
E.	Corn oil		O.	Potato chips
F.	Olestra		P.	Thromboxane
G.	Pancreas		Q.	Linolenic acid
H.	Canola oil		R.	Cholecystokinin
I.	Cholesterol		S.	High-density lipoprotein
J.	Acetic acid		T.	Very-low density lipoprotein

ESSAY QUESTIONS

PAGE(S)

145,146	01.	What methods are used by the food industry to inhibit rancidity of the unsaturated lipids in foods?
142-146	02.	List the major differences in the characteristics that define the chemical structures of fatty acids differing in chain length, saturation and unsaturation, position of the first double bond and effects of partial hydrogenation.
146,147;159	03.	Discuss the meaning and significance of *trans*-fatty acids in the diet. List four common food sources.
145,146;159	04.	Describe the process of fat hydrogenation and discuss its advantages and disadvantages.
147-149;153-157	05.	Discuss the functions of lipids in the body. What is the role of the liver in metabolizing and processing fats?

149;153-155;159,160	06.	Discuss the role of dietary cholesterol and the endogenous production of cholesterol and heart disease. What is meant by "good" and "bad" cholesterol?
150-153	07.	Compare and contrast the digestion-absorption mechanisms for long-chain vs. short-chain fatty acids.
150-155	08.	Discuss in detail the digestion, absorption, and transport of dietary lipids, including the sterols.
152-154	09.	Discuss the composition and function of the major circulating lipoproteins.
156-157	10.	Explain the chemical differences between fish oil and corn oil. Discuss the health benefits of fish oil. What are some of the possible disadvantages of increasing the consumption of fish and fish oil supplements?
156,157;161-163	11.	List the essential fatty acids (EFA) for human beings. What are the signs of EFA deficiency? What is the minimum amount of EFA required to prevent a deficiency? What foods are rich sources of EFA?
156-157	12	How do eicosanoids differ from hormones?
157,158	13.	Discuss the roles of hormone-sensitive lipase and lipoprotein lipase in the metabolism of fats.
159-161;162-165	14.	Discuss the relationship of dietary fats to atherosclerosis. What dietary changes bring about the greatest reductions in blood lipids?
163-168	15.	List strategies for lowering fat intake with minimal impact on diet palatability.
164	16.	What is meant by invisible fat? List 3 common sources in the diet.
165,166	17.	Discuss the benefits and possible hazards of dietary fat replacers in the diet.
174	18.	Discuss the potential health benefits of substituting olive oil for other cooking fats.
174-175	19.	Discuss the health benefits of substituting nuts for other sources of fat in the diet.

CHAPTER 6
PROTEIN: AMINO ACIDS

AN PAGE(S)

d   181(K)   01.   What element is found in proteins but **not** in carbohydrates and fats?
a.   Carbon
b.   Oxygen
c.   Calcium
d.   Nitrogen

d   182(K)   02.   How many different kinds of amino acids make up proteins?
a.   8
b.   10
c.   14
d.   20

c   181(K)   03.   In comparison to the composition of carbohydrates and fats, which element found in proteins makes them unique?
a.   Carbon
b.   Oxygen
c.   Nitrogen
d.   Hydrogen

c   182(K)   04.   All of the following are contained in an amino acid **except**
a.   an acid group.
b.   an amino group.
c.   an aldehyde group.
d.   a central carbon atom.

a   182(K)   05.   Which of the following is the primary factor that differentiates one amino acid from another?
a.   The side group
b.   The central carbon atom
c.   The number of oxygen atoms
d.   The number of nitrogen atoms

c   182(A)   06.   Approximately how many different amino acids are used in the synthesis of body proteins?
a.   5
b.   10
c.   20
d.   35

c   182,183(K)   07.   Terms used to classify amino acids in the diet include all of the following **except**
a.   essential.
b.   nonessential.
c.   partially essential.
d.   conditionally essential.

b   182(K)   08.   What is the simplest amino acid?
a.   Valine
b.   Glycine
c.   Alanine
d.   Methionine

a   182(K)   09.   Which of the following is **not** an essential amino acid in human nutrition?
a.   Proline
b.   Threonine
c.   Methionine
d.   Tryptophan

b   182(K)   10.   Which of the following elements is found in certain amino acids?
a.   Iron
b.   Sulfur
c.   Calcium
d.   Potassium

b   182(A)   11.   Any of the following can be used by the body for the synthesis of a nonessential amino acid **except**
a.   a fragment of fat.
b.   an essential mineral.
c.   an essential amino acid.
d.   a fragment of carbohydrate.

b   182,183(A)   12.   What amino acid is classified as conditionally essential when dietary intake of phenylalanine is insufficient or the body cannot normally metabolize phenylalanine?
a.   Cysteine
b.   Tyrosine
c.   Glutamine
d.   Isoleucine

b   182(K)   13.   Which of the following is a feature of an essential amino acid?
a.   It is not necessary in the diet.
b.   It must be supplied by the diet.
c.   It can be made from fat in the body.
d.   It can be made from glucose in the body.

d   183(A)   14.   What type of reaction is required to bind two molecules of glycine together and release a molecule of water?
a.   Hydrolysis
b.   Deamination
c.   Denaturation
d.   Condensation

a   183(K)   15.   When two amino acids are chemically joined together, the resulting structure is called a
a.   dipeptide.
b.   diglyceride.
c.   polypeptide.
d.   polysaccharide.

b   183(K)   16.   What is the composition of a tripeptide?
a.   One amino acid with three carbons
b.   Three amino acids bonded together
c.   One amino acid with three acid groups
d.   Three small protein chains bonded together

c   183,184(K) 17.   What is meant by the amino acid sequence of a protein?
    a.   Number of side chains in the protein
    b.   Folding arrangement of the peptide chain
    c.   Order of amino acids in the peptide chain
    d.   Order of only the essential amino acids in the protein

a   187-189(K) 18.   Which of the following describes a process in protein synthesis?
    a.   The code to make a protein is carried by a strand of messenger RNA.
    b.   The final step in completing the protein is carried out in the mitochondria.
    c.   The function of transfer RNA is to assist in absorption of amino acids into the cell.
    d.   The DNA binds to ribosomes and directs uptake of specific amino acids to form the peptide chain.

d   187-189(K) 19.   A common genetic variation which causes a change in the amino acid sequence in the structure of hemoglobin leads to the disease
    a.   diabetes.
    b.   marasmus.
    c.   kwashiorkor.
    d.   sickle-cell anemia.

b   183,184(A) 20.   In comparison to the well-defined structure of starch, which of the following is the most important factor that allows for the synthesis of thousands of different proteins?
    a.   Number of cell ribosomes
    b.   Number of different amino acids
    c.   Availability of amino acids containing sulfur
    d.   Availability of amino acids containing hydroxyl groups

c   184(K) 21.   What is the process by which heat or acidity disrupts the normal shape of a protein chain?
    a.   Digestion
    b.   Condensation
    c.   Denaturation
    d.   Hydrogenation

c   184(K) 22.   The application of heat or acid to a protein that causes its shape to change is known as
    a.   stiffening.
    b.   condensation.
    c.   denaturation.
    d.   destabilization.

b   184(A) 23.   What is the process that results in the hardening of an egg when it is exposed to heat?
    a.   Solidification
    b.   Denaturation
    c.   Condensation
    d.   Protein interaction

b   185(A)   24.   Upon eating a hamburger, in what organ is the hydrolysis of its proteins initiated?
       a.   Mouth
       b.   Stomach
       c.   Small intestine
       d.   Large intestine

a   185(A)   25.   In what organ is pepsin active?
       a.   Stomach
       b.   Pancreas
       c.   Small intestine
       d.   Large intestine

a   185(A)   26.   What digestive enzyme would be most affected in people who are unable to produce hydrochloric acid?
       a.   Pepsin
       b.   Transaminase
       c.   Pancreatic protease
       d.   Intestinal peptidase

c   185(K)   27.   What is the name given to the inactive form of a protein splitting enzyme in the stomach?
       a.   Peptidase
       b.   Propepsin
       c.   Pepsinogen
       d.   Propeptidase

b   185(A)   28.   Which of the following describes the structure of pepsin?
       a.   Lipid
       b.   Protein
       c.   Nucleic acid
       d.   Carbohydrate

d   185,86(K)   29.   What is the chief function of pepsin?
       a.   Emulsifies dietary proteins
       b.   Activates hydrochloric acid
       c.   Activates pancreatic proteases
       d.   Cleaves proteins into smaller polypeptides

a   185,186(A)   30.   What percentage of dietary protein is hydrolyzed in the mouth?
       a.   0
       b.   5-10
       c.   15-20
       d.   25-30

d   185(A)   31.   After digestion of proteins, what products are absorbed into the circulation?
       a.   Free amino acids only
       b.   Free amino acids and oligopeptides
       c.   Free amino acids and dipeptides only
       d.   Free amino acids, and some dipeptides and tripeptides

a   185(A)   32.   What is the usual fate of orally ingested enzyme supplements?
　　　　　　　　　　　a.   Digested by gastrointestinal proteases
　　　　　　　　　　　b.   Rapidly degraded by salivary secretions
　　　　　　　　　　　c.   Mostly absorbed in original form from stomach
　　　　　　　　　　　d.   Completely absorbed in original form from jejunum

a   185,186(A) 33.   Of the following **sources** of amino acids, which would show the highest absorption in normal, healthy people?
　　　　　　　　　　　a.   Whole proteins
　　　　　　　　　　　b.   Raw protein foods
　　　　　　　　　　　c.   Predigested proteins
　　　　　　　　　　　d.   Mixture of free amino acids

d   185;187(K) 34.   Which of the following statements is **not** characteristic of enzymes?
　　　　　　　　　　　a.   They are all catalysts.
　　　　　　　　　　　b.   They have a protein structure.
　　　　　　　　　　　c.   They can be destroyed by heat.
　　　　　　　　　　　d.   They are involved in synthesis reactions only.

b   190(K)   35.   What is the structure of an enzyme?
　　　　　　　　　　　a.   Lipid
　　　　　　　　　　　b.   Protein
　　　　　　　　　　　c.   Nucleic acid
　　　　　　　　　　　d.   Carbohydrate

a   185(K)   36.   Protein hydrolyzing enzymes are commonly known as
　　　　　　　　　　　a.   proteases.
　　　　　　　　　　　b.   hydrolyzers.
　　　　　　　　　　　c.   prodigestins.
　　　　　　　　　　　d.   denaturases.

a   185(K)   37.   The function of a protease is to
　　　　　　　　　　　a.   hydrolyze proteins.
　　　　　　　　　　　b.   synthesize proteins.
　　　　　　　　　　　c.   hydrolyze ribosomes.
　　　　　　　　　　　d.   synthesize ribosomes.

c   189(K)   38.   What **protein** is intimately involved in the formation of scar tissue in wound healing?
　　　　　　　　　　　a.   Albumin
　　　　　　　　　　　b.   Thrombin
　　　　　　　　　　　c.   Collagen
　　　　　　　　　　　d.   Hydroxyproline

c   189(A)   39.   What type of protein would the body make to heal a wound?
　　　　　　　　　　　a.   Ferritin
　　　　　　　　　　　b.   Albumin
　　　　　　　　　　　c.   Collagen
　　　　　　　　　　　d.   Hemoglobin

b   190(K)   40.   Which of the following is a characteristic of hormones?
      a.   Inactivate bacteria
      b.   Act as messenger molecules
      c.   Coordinate visual response
      d.   Act as buffers in the bloodstream

a   190,191(A)   41.   What is the relationship between body proteins and water?
      a.   Proteins attract water.
      b.   Water attracts proteins.
      c.   Water degrades proteins.
      d.   Proteins form polymers of water.

a   190(K)   42.   Tissue swelling that results from water that accumulates between cells is known as
      a.   edema.
      b.   acidosis.
      c.   alkalosis.
      d.   extravascularization.

a   191;189(K)   43.   Which of the following does **not** function as a transport protein?
      a.   Collagen
      b.   Transferrin
      c.   Hemoglobin
      d.   Lipoproteins

b   191(A)   44.   Proteins, because they attract hydrogen ions, can act as
      a.   acids.
      b.   buffers.
      c.   enzymes.
      d.   antibodies.

b   191(K)   45.   What function does a buffer perform?
      a.   Helps emulsify fats
      b.   Helps maintain a constant pH
      c.   Facilitates chemical reactions
      d.   Helps protect against plaque buildup

a   191(K)   46.   Which of the following processes is regulated primarily by the buffering action of proteins?
      a.   pH balance
      b.   Fluid balance
      c.   Blood clotting
      d.   Synthesis of visual pigments

d   192((K)   47.   Which of the following are proteins that inactivate foreign bacteria and viruses?
      a.   Enzymes
      b.   Collagen
      c.   Hormones
      d.   Antibodies

c   192(K)   48.   Which of the following proteins inactivates foreign bacteria and viruses?
      a.   Enzymes
      b.   Hormones
      c.   Antibodies
      d.   Lipoproteins

c   192(K)   49.   Which of the following describes the structure of an antibody?
                      a.   Tripeptide
                      b.   Small nucleic acid
                      c.   Huge protein molecule
                      d.   Large peptide molecule

b   192(K)   50.   Which of the following is involved in the clotting of blood?
                      a.   Opsin
                      b.   Fibrin
                      c.   Collagen
                      d.   Transferrin

d   193(K)   51.   The body's amino acid pool consists of
                      a.   essential amino acids only.
                      b.   endogenous amino acids only.
                      c.   nonessential amino acids only.
                      d.   both essential and nonessential amino acids.

d   193(K)   52.   What amino acid is used to synthesize the important neurotransmitter serotonin
                      and the vitamin niacin?
                      a.   Glycine
                      b.   Tyrosine
                      c.   Methionine
                      d.   Tryptophan

d   193-195(A)   53.   Protein sparing in the body is best achieved under which of the following
                          circumstances?
                          a.   Ingesting proteins of plant origin only
                          b.   Ingesting proteins of animal origin only
                          c.   Ingesting mixed protein sources on alternate days
                          d.   Ingesting adequate levels of carbohydrate and fat

a   193,194(A)   54.   Which of the following are precursors of urea synthesis?
                          a.   All amino acids
                          b.   Animal proteins only
                          c.   Essential amino acids only
                          d.   Nonessential amino acids only

d   192,193(A)   55.   How many grams of nitrogen are contained in a 2,500 kcal diet that provides 15%
                          of the energy as protein?
                          a.   2.5
                          b.   5
                          c.   10
                          d.   15

b   193(A)   56.   Which of the following may be used to determine protein utilization?
                      a.   Calorimetry
                      b.   Nitrogen balance
                      c.   Amino acid pool
                      d.   Supplementary value

c   193(A)   57.   When nitrogen taken into the body exceeds nitrogen losses, we say the person is in
      a.   a healthy state.
      b.   nitrogen equilibrium.
      c.   positive nitrogen balance.
      d.   negative nitrogen balance.

b   193(K)   58.   Which of the following defines protein turnover?
      a.   The sum of protein in food and the body
      b.   The sum of protein synthesis and degradation
      c.   The amount of protein absorbed from the diet
      d.   The amount of protein used to synthesize glucose

d   193(K)   59.   What is the amino acid pool?
      a.   The total amino acid content derived from a 24-hour dietary intake
      b.   A measure of the circulating essential amino acid levels available for protein synthesis
      c.   The total amount of free amino acids in the circulation destined for deamination and excretion
      d.   A mix of essential and nonessential amino acids derived from protein breakdown and dietary protein intake

a   193(A)   60.   Which of the following describes the state of nitrogen balance for a normal, healthy 35-year-old person who weighs 60 kg and consumes a diet that provides 75 g of protein and adequate energy?
      a.   Equilibrium
      b.   Positive balance
      c.   Negative balance
      d.   Endogenous balance

d   193(A)   61.   What is the nitrogen balance of a person who consumed a 3,500 kcalorie diet containing 10% **protein** and excreted a total of 12 grams of **nitrogen**?
      a.   0 g
      b.   -3 g
      c.   -1 g
      d.   +2 g

c   193(A)   62.   Which of the following would describe the state of nitrogen balance of a person who ingested 16 g of food nitrogen and lost 19 g of nitrogen?
      a.   Equilibrium
      b.   Positive balance
      c.   Negative balance
      d.   Exogenous balance

c   193(A)   63.   What would be the usual state of nitrogen balance for healthy infants, children, and pregnant women?
      a.   Equilibrium
      b.   Metabolic
      c.   Positive
      d.   Negative

a   194(A)   64.   Which of the following illustrates a deamination reaction?
      a.   Removal of the amino group from an amino acid
      b.   Separation of an amino acid from a peptide chain
      c.   Addition of an amino group to form a new amino acid
      d.   Addition of an amino acid to form a larger peptide chain

d   193,194(A) 65.   Which of the following compounds does **not** contain nitrogen?
      a.   Urea
      b.   Enzymes
      c.   Ammonia
      d.   Cholesterol

b   193,194(A) 66.   What is the fate of excess dietary protein?
      a.   After absorption, the liver will store the extra amino acids.
      b.   After absorption, the extra amino acids will be rapidly degraded.
      c.   Digestion will be decreased by 30 to 60%, resulting in less absorption.
      d.   After absorption, extra proteins will be synthesized and stored for use when protein intake returns to normal.

b   194(K)   67.   What is the chief factor that governs the quality of a food protein?
      a.   Fat content
      b.   Essential amino acid content
      c.   Complex carbohydrate content
      d.   Nonessential amino acid content

b   193-195;182(A) 68.   Which of the following could **not** be a limiting amino acid in the diet?
      a.   Lysine
      b.   Glycine
      c.   Threonine
      d.   Tryptophan

b   194,195(A) 69.   If the diet is lacking an essential amino acid, what will be the course of action?
      a.   Body cells will synthesize it.
      b.   Protein synthesis will be limited.
      c.   Health will not be affected as long as other nutrients are adequate.
      d.   Proteins will be made but they will lack that particular amino acid.

c   195(K)   70.   What is a "limiting" amino acid in a protein?
      a.   A nonessential amino acid present in high amounts, which inhibits protein synthesis
      b.   An amino acid of the wrong structure to be utilized for protein synthesis efficiently
      c.   An essential amino acid present in insufficient quantity for body protein synthesis to take place
      d.   An amino acid that limits the absorption of other essential amino acids by competing with them for transport sites within the GI tract

b   195(K)   71.   What is complementary protein nutrition?
                        a.   A dietary program involving consumption of vegetable and animal
                                proteins on alternating days
                        b.   A strategy of combining plant proteins in the same meal to improve the
                                balance of essential amino acids
                        c.   A technique developed specifically for the elderly that involves optimizing
                                protein intake to energy intake
                        d.   A body process involving synthesis of crucial proteins from amino acids
                                made available by breakdown of storage proteins

a   195(A)   72.   In general, the protein quality in grains would be most improved by the addition of
                        a plant protein rich in
                        a.   lysine.
                        b.   tryptophan.
                        c.   phenylalanine.
                        d.   glutamic acid.

c   195(A)   73.   Which of the following food proteins has the best assortment of essential amino
                        acids for the human body?
                        a.   Corn
                        b.   Rice
                        c.   Egg
                        d.   Gelatin

a   195(A)   74.   Which of the following is related to the quality of a food protein?
                        a.   Essential amino acid balance
                        b.   Nonessential amino acid balance
                        c.   Total amino acids per gram of food
                        d.   Quantity of nonessential amino acids that can be converted to glucose

a   194(K)   75.   In the study of protein nutrition, what is the term given to the amount of amino
                        acids absorbed as a percentage of the amount of protein consumed?
                        a.   Digestibility
                        b.   Completeness
                        c.   Complementary Index
                        d.   Comparative Equivalence

b   194,195(K) 76.   Which of the following is a common measure of protein quality?
                        a.   LAAS
                        b.   PDCAAS
                        c.   Amino acid pool
                        d.   Digestibility-corrected complementary score

c   195(A)   77.   Which of the following is **not** considered to be a source of high-quality protein in
                        human nutrition?
                        a.   Soy
                        b.   Egg
                        c.   Corn
                        d.   Fish

c   195(K)   78.   Which of the following animal-derived proteins is classified as a poor-quality protein?
a.   Fish
b.   Cheese
c.   Gelatin
d.   Turkey

c   195(A)   79.   In general, the protein quality of legumes would be most improved by the addition of a plant protein rich in
a.   lysine.
b.   tryptophan.
c.   methionine.
d.   glutamic acid.

d   197(K)   80.   What protein quality measure is used to assess the protein in foods for the Daily Value percentages seen on food labels?
a.   Biological value
b.   Ratio of animal to plant protein
c.   Net protein utilization efficiency ratio
d.   Protein-digestibility-corrected amino acid score

c   195(A)   81.   Relative to animal proteins, which of the following amino acids is present in lesser amounts in proteins of legumes?
a.   alanine.
b.   tryptophan.
c.   methionine.
d.   glutamic acid.

d   197(K)   82.   Approximately how many millions of children worldwide have protein-energy malnutrition?
a.   10
b.   100
c.   250
d.   500

a   199(K)   83.   Which of the following is a feature of malnutrition?
a.   Dysentery is a common occurrence and leads to diarrhea and nutrient depletion.
b.   Intestinal villi grow slightly larger to provide additional absorptive surfaces for nutrients.
c.   Digestive enzyme production increases in order to extract as much of the ingested nutrients as possible.
d.   Infections are uncommon due to insufficient availability of nutrients in the body to support growth of bacteria and viruses.

b   198(K)   84.   Which of the following is **not** a characteristic of marasmus?
a.   Results in a low resistance to disease
b.   Affects brain development only minimally
c.   Occurs most commonly in children aged 6 to 18 months
d.   Results in little or no fat under the skin to insulate against cold

b   198(K)   85.   Marasmus occurs most commonly in children of ages
      a.   1-5 months.
      b.   6-18 months.
      c.   1½-3 years.
      d.   4-10 years.

b   198,199(A) 86.   Which of the following conditions is associated with edema?
      a.   Excessive use of certain drugs which causes high excretion of water and amino acids
      b.   Below-normal concentration of blood protein, which causes fluid to leak from the blood vessels
      c.   Above-normal concentration of blood protein, which causes fluid to leak from the blood vessels
      d.   Excessive protein in the diet leading to increased retention of fluid, especially in the extravascular spaces

b   198,199(A) 87.   What term describes the following quote: "The evil spirit that infects the first child when the second child is born"?
      a.   Marasmus
      b.   Kwashiorkor
      c.   Psychomalnutrition
      d.   Postbirth malnutrition

d   199(A)   88.   What is the most likely explanation for the fatty liver that develops from protein deficiency?
      a.   Increased uptake of circulating fats
      b.   Increased absorption of dietary fats
      c.   Inability of adipose tissue to remove circulating fats
      d.   Inability of the liver to synthesize lipoproteins for fat export

d   198,199(A) 89.   Which of the following would you **not** expect to see in a person with kwashiorkor?
      a.   Edema
      b.   Dysentery
      c.   Increased infection rate
      d.   increased physical activity

c   198,199(A) 90.   Which of the following is associated with the presence of tissue edema in kwashiorkor?
      a.   Inadequate intake of water
      b.   Excessive intake of dietary protein
      c.   Low concentration of blood protein
      d.   High concentration of blood protein

d   198,199(K) 91.   Which of the following is a feature of kwashiorkor?
      a.   It makes the child appear grossly dehydrated.
      b.   It usually occurs prior to the onset of marasmus.
      c.   It is usually found in communities where marasmus is present.
      d.   It is typically precipitated in the undernourished child who has an infection.

d   199,200(A)   92.   What is the usual initial therapy for the treatment of kwashiorkor?
     a.   Fat replacement
     b.   Energy replacement
     c.   Protein replacement
     d.   Fluid balance restoration

c   200(K)   93.   Excessive amounts of homocysteine in the blood are thought to increase the risk for
     a.   cancer.
     b.   diabetes.
     c.   heart disease.
     d.   protein-energy malnutrition.

c   200(K)   94.   Which of the following is a feature of homocysteine?
     a.   It is found only in animal foods.
     b.   It is a risk factor for osteoporosis.
     c.   It is increased in the blood of coffee drinkers.
     d.   It is increased in the blood of vitamin C-deficient people.

d   200(K)   95.   Which of the following describes a relationship between protein/amino acid intake and heart disease?
     a.   Substituting soy protein for animal protein raises blood cholesterol levels.
     b.   High blood levels of the amino acid arginine are a risk factor for atherosclerosis.
     c.   High levels of homocysteine in food promote elevation of blood low-density lipoproteins.
     d.   Elevated blood homocysteine levels are associated with smoking cigarettes and drinking alcohol.

b   200-202(K)   96.   What would be the primary principle of wise diet planning as related to protein nutrition?
     a.   Variety
     b.   Moderation
     c.   Nutrient density
     d.   kCalorie control

b   201,202(K)   97.   Which of the following describes a relationship between protein intake and calcium metabolism?
     a.   Calcium **excretion** falls with increasing intake of animal- derived proteins.
     b.   Calcium **excretion** rises with increasing intake of animal-derived proteins.
     c.   Calcium **absorption** declines with higher intakes of plant-derived proteins.
     d.   Calcium **absorption** increases with higher intakes of animal-derived proteins.

d   201(A)   98.   In relation to the range of protein intake as a percentage of energy intake, what would be the highest safe level of protein intake for a 60 kg adult ingesting 2,500 kcalories?
     a.   48 g
     b.   96 g
     c.   120 g
     d.   219 g

a   201(A)   99.   Which of the following is a feature of the protein RDA?
                        a.   The recommendations are generous.
                        b.   It is highest proportionately for adult males.
                        c.   It is established at 8 grams per kilogram of ideal body weight.
                        d.   An assumption is made that dietary protein is from animal sources only.

c   201(A)   100.   What is the RDA for protein for a 48 kg woman?
                        a.   24 g
                        b.   34 g
                        c.   38 g
                        d.   40 g

c   202(A)   101.   Which of the following is an assumption made in the formulation of the RDA for
                        protein?
                        a.   Dietary protein is of high quality only.
                        b.   Dietary protein is of animal origin only.
                        c.   Dietary carbohydrate and fat intakes are adequate.
                        d.   Dietary protein should represent 12% of total energy.

c   201,202(K)   102.   All of the following assumptions are made by the committee in setting the RDA for
                        protein **except**
                        a.   adequate kcalories will be consumed.
                        b.   protein eaten will be of mixed quality.
                        c.   the fat content of the diet will be high.
                        d.   other nutrients in the diet will be adequate.

a   201(K)   103.   Which of the following is a known consequence of excess protein intake in animals
                        or human beings?
                        a.   Increased excretion of water
                        b.   Decreased excretion of calcium
                        c.   Decreased size of the liver and kidneys
                        d.   Increased protein storage by the liver and kidneys

c   201(A)   104.   If proteins needs are expressed per kilogram of body weight, which of the
                        following describes the requirements of infants?
                        a.   Less than adults
                        b.   Similar to adults
                        c.   Greater than adults
                        d.   Less than adolescents

c   201,202(A)   105.   What is the percentage of total energy derived from protein in a diet containing 50
                        grams of protein and 2,000 kcal?
                        a.   2.5
                        b.   5
                        c.   10
                        d.   20

b   201,202(A)   106.   If a person consumes 65 grams of protein and a total of 2,700 kcal per day,
                        approximately what percentage of energy would be derived from protein?
                        a.   7
                        b.   10
                        c.   14
                        d.   20

d   202(A)   107.   According to the Food Guide Pyramid, an adult who consumes the minimum recommended number of servings of each food group would obtain the RDA level of protein for a body weight of about
a.   75 lbs.
b.   110 lbs.
c.   160 lbs.
d.   200 lbs.

c   203(K)   108.   What amino acid has been linked to the development of the rare blood disorder eosinophilia myalgia in people who took it as a supplement?
a.   Glycine
b.   Arginine
c.   Tryptophan
d.   Phenylalanine

a   203(K)   109.   What amino acid supplement has been reported to show some success in suppressing herpes infections?
a.   Lysine
b.   Arginine
c.   Tryptophan
d.   Phenylalanine

c   208,209(A)   110.   All of the following are advantages of vegetarian diets **except**
a.   fat content is lower.
b.   fiber content is higher.
c.   vitamin B$_{12}$ intake is higher.
d.   vitamins A and C are found in generous quantities.

b   208-210(A)   111.   All of the following are documented benefits for people following a vegetarian diet **except**
a.   better digestive function.
b.   lower rates of osteoporosis.
c.   lower blood cholesterol levels.
d.   lower rates of certain types of cancer.

d   210(A)   112.   Which of the following are allowed in the diet of a lactovegetarian?
a.   Plant foods only
b.   Eggs and plant foods only
c.   Meat, eggs, and plant foods only
d.   Milk products and plant foods only

b   209(A)   113.   Which of the following ingredients found on a food label is a protein?
a.   BHT
b.   Tofu
c.   Corn starch
d.   Diglycerides

a   210(K)   114.   Studies reveal that many vegetarian women have intakes of vitamins and minerals that are at least equal to the recommended intake except for
a.   iron.
b.   calcium.
c.   folate.
d.   vitamin A.

b   210(A)   115.   Which of the following is a feature of iron nutrition in vegetarians?
a.   The bioavailability of iron is high.
b.   Vegetarians absorb iron more efficiently.
c.   The high zinc content in grains inhibits iron utilization.
d.   Vegetarians show more iron deficiency than people eating a mixed diet.

a   210(K)   116.   Textured vegetable protein is usually made of
a.   soy protein.
b.   fish protein.
c.   bean plus rice proteins.
d.   bean plus cheese proteins.

c   211(A)   117.   Which of the following is a feature of vitamin B_{12} nutrition in vegetarians?
a.   The B_{12} in fortified cereals has low bioavailability.
b.   Vegan mothers need only infrequent intake of B_{12}-fortified cereals.
c.   Much of the B_{12} in fermented soy products may have low bioavailability.
d.   Infants born to vegan mothers are resistant to the development of B_{12} deficiency.

d   211(K)   118.   In general, a newborn infant is able to thrive during the early months by ingesting only breast milk and a source of
a.   iron.
b.   calcium.
c.   vitamin C.
d.   vitamin D.

b   212(K)   119.   What is the primary reason that vegan children are shorter and weigh less than meat-eating children?
a.   Deficiency of vitamin D
b.   Insufficient energy intake
c.   Inherited growth disorders
d.   Deficiencies of calcium and iron

MATCHING (Answers can be used only once.)

F	182	01.	A dietary nonessential amino acid
I	183	02.	A conditionally essential amino acid
G	183	03.	A small protein
Q	184	04.	A large protein that carries oxygen
R	184	05.	Substances repelled by water
K	184	06.	The result of protein exposed to severe heat
C	172	07.	An active protease
L	187	08.	A cell structure where protein synthesis takes place
J	189	09.	A connective tissue protein
M	190	10.	A protein catalyst
P	190	11.	Fluid situated between cells
T	190	12.	Fluid within blood vessels
O	193	13.	A condition that favors positive nitrogen balance
H	193	14.	A condition that favors negative nitrogen balance
B	194	15.	A product of amino acid breakdown
E	195	16.	A dietary protein lacking tryptophan
A	195	17.	A good quality protein source
D	195	18.	A typical limiting amino acid
N	198	19.	A condition of protein malnutrition
S	200	20.	An amino acid associated with heart disease

A.	Soy	K.	Denatured
B.	Urea	L.	Ribosome
C.	Pepsin	M.	Enzyme
D.	Lysine	N.	Kwashiorkor
E.	Gelatin	O.	Pregnancy
F.	Alanine	P.	Intercellular
G.	Insulin	Q.	Hemoglobin
H.	Infection	R.	Hydrophobic
I.	Tyrosine	S.	Homocysteine
J.	Collagen	T.	Intravascular

ESSAY QUESTIONS

PAGE(S)

182,183   01.   Explain the differences among amino acids that are classified as essential, nonessential, or conditionally essential.

185-187   02.   Explain the processes of protein digestion and absorption.

187-189;193, 194;202   03.   Describe the processes involved in cellular protein synthesis. How would synthesis be affected by intake of an otherwise adequate diet which is very low in glycine or low in tryptophan? How would synthesis be affected by a diet that is low in energy?

187-189   04.   Explain the manner by which a gene becomes expressed to direct the synthesis of a protein.

193   05.   What is meant by nitrogen balance? How does it differ among infants and adults, and among those who are injured or on weight loss diets?

195   06.   Explain the rationale for the selection of a reference protein for the comparison of protein quality. Why is this reference protein considered to be superior to that of egg protein?

195   07.   What is the meaning and significance of the protein digestibility-corrected amino acid score?

197-199   08.   Compare and contrast the features of kwashiorkor and marasmus.

200,201   09.   Explain the proposed relationships between:
                     A.   Body homocysteine levels and heart disease.
                     B.   Protein intake and calcium metabolism

200-203   10.   What are the possible consequences of consuming too much protein? What are the hazards of consuming amino acid supplements?

203   11.   List population groups for which amino acid dietary supplements are especially inappropriate.

208-213   12.   List the advantages of a vegetarian diet. What nutrient requirements are more difficult to meet on this diet, and what precautions are needed to prevent insufficient intakes in the child, in the adult, and in the pregnant woman?

CHAPTER 7
METABOLISM: TRANSFORMATIONS AND INTERACTIONS

AN PAGE(S)

b   215(K)   01.   Which of the following describes the sum of all chemical reactions that go on in living cells?
- a.   Digestion
- b.   Metabolism
- c.   Absorption
- d.   Catabolism

a   216(A)   02.   What term is specific to reactions in which simple compounds are combined into more complex molecules?
- a.   Anabolic
- b.   Catabolic
- c.   Ergogenic
- d.   Gluconeogenic

c   216(A)   03.   Which of the following reactions is an example of an anabolic reaction?
- a.   Pyruvate synthesis from glucose
- b.   Carbon dioxide synthesis from citric acid
- c.   Cholesterol synthesis from acetyl-CoA molecules
- d.   Acetyl-CoA synthesis from cholesterol

c   216(A)   04.   The formation of glycogen by the liver cell is an example of
- a.   oxidation.
- b.   glycolysis.
- c.   anabolism.
- d.   catabolism.

b   216(A)   05.   Which of the following is an example of a catabolic reaction?
- a.   Glucose formation from glycerol
- b.   Urea formation from an amino acid
- c.   Albumin formation from amino acids
- d.   Palmitic acid formation from acetate

a   216(K)   06.   Which of the following is a feature of catabolic reactions?
- a.   Involve release of energy
- b.   Occur only in mitochondria
- c.   Involve consumption of energy
- d.   Occur only during loss of body weight

a   216,217(K) 07.   What is the major energy carrier molecule in most cells?
- a.   ATP
- b.   Glucose
- c.   Pyruvate
- d.   A kcalorie

c   216,217(A) 08.   Which of the following metabolic reactions occurs when a cell uses energy?
- a.   ATP gains a phosphate group and becomes ADP
- b.   ADP gains a phosphate group and becomes ATP
- c.   ATP releases a phosphate group and becomes ADP
- d.   ADP releases a phosphate group and becomes ATP

a   218(K)   09.   What is the approximate percent efficiency of conversion of food energy to ATP energy in the body?
- a.   40
- b.   60
- c.   85
- d.   99

a   218(A)   10.   In the adult body, food energy not stored as fat or glycogen is lost as
- a.   heat.
- b.   photons.
- c.   carbon dioxide.
- d.   electromagnetic radiation.

b   219(K)   11.   Which of the following defines a coenzyme?
- a.   A unit consisting of an enzyme bound to reactants plus ATP
- b.   A small organic molecule required for the functioning of an enzyme
- c.   The small, active part of an enzyme that binds to the organic reactants
- d.   An inactive enzyme that becomes functional upon contact with specific cofactors

c   219(K)   12.   All of the following are among the functions of the liver **except**
- a.   synthesis of urea.
- b.   synthesis of glycogen.
- c.   production of red blood cells.
- d.   conversion of fructose to glucose.

c   221(K)   13.   Glycolysis is the conversion of
- a.   glycogen to fat.
- b.   glycogen to protein.
- c.   glucose to pyruvate.
- d.   glucose to glycogen.

b   221(K)   14.   The series of reactions involving the conversion of glucose to pyruvate is known as
- a.   pyrolysis.
- b.   glycolysis.
- c.   beta-oxidation.
- d.   coupled reaction.

a   221(K)   15.   Which of the following is **not** an aspect of glycolysis?
- a.   It is irreversible
- b.   It generates ATP
- c.   It occurs in the absence of oxygen
- d.   It generates two molecules of pyruvate for each molecule of glucose

b   221(A)   16.   An aerobic reaction is one that requires
- a.   alcohol.
- b.   oxygen.
- c.   nitrogen.
- d.   ammonia.

a   223(K)   17.   Which of the following can **not** be formed from acetyl-CoA molecules?
                         a.   Glucose
                         b.   Cholesterol
                         c.   Stearic acid
                         d.   Carbon dioxide

d   222-224(A) 18.   Which of the following can **not** be formed from pyruvate in human beings?
                         a.   Glucose
                         b.   Fructose
                         c.   Lactic acid
                         d.   Linoleic acid

a   222(K)   19.   The Cori cycle involves the interconversion of
                         a.   lactic acid and glucose.
                         b.   glucose and amino acids.
                         c.   pyruvate and citric acids.
                         d.   fatty acids and acetyl-CoA.

c   222(A)   20.   When a person is performing intense physical exercise and begins to feel fatigue
                         and a burning pain in the muscles, it is most likely due to the muscles'
                         accumulation of
                         a.   ammonia.
                         b.   citric acid.
                         c.   lactic acid.
                         d.   pyruvic acid.

c   222,224(A) 21.   Which of the following is a possible fate of acetyl CoA?
                         a.   Degradation to urea
                         b.   Synthesis to glycerol
                         c.   Synthesis to fatty acids
                         d.   Degradation to ammonia

c   224(A)   22.   What is the first product of fatty acid catabolism?
                         a.   Glycerol
                         b.   Pyruvate
                         c.   Acetyl CoA
                         d.   Triglycerides

d   212-213(A) 23.   Which of the following nutrients can be made from compounds composed of 2-
                         carbon skeletons?
                         a.   Glucose
                         b.   Fructose
                         c.   Glycogen
                         d.   Fatty acids

b   224(A)   24.   Which of the following dietary components **cannot** be used to synthesize and store
                         glycogen?
                         a.   Lactose
                         b.   Animal fats
                         c.   Wheat starch
                         d.   Plant protein

a   224(K)   25.   In a triglyceride that contains 54 carbon atoms, how many can become part of glucose?
a.   3
b.   9
c.   54
d.   108

b   224(K)   26.   Which of the following compounds **cannot** be formed from fatty acids?
a.   Ketones
b.   Glucose
c.   Acetyl CoA
d.   Carbon dioxide

a   223,224(A) 27.   Production of excessive amounts of acetyl-CoA molecules leads to the synthesis of
a.   fatty acids only.
b.   fatty acids and glucose only.
c.   fatty acids and fructose only.
d.   fatty acids, glucose, and amino acids.

d   224(K)   28.   Approximately what percentage of triglycerides **cannot** be converted to glucose?
a.   70
b.   80
c.   90
d.   95

b   224(A)   29.   What percent (by weight) of a triglyceride molecule can be converted to glucose?
a.   0
b.   5
c.   50
d.   100

c   221-226(A) 30.   Which of the following **cannot** be used to make body proteins?
a.   Glucose
b.   Glycerol
c.   Fatty acids
d.   Amino acids

d   226,227(A) 31.   What is the immediate fate of excess dietary protein in the body?
a.   Stored
b.   Reduced
c.   Oxidized
d.   Deaminated

a   226,227(A) 32.   After digestion and absorption, an amino acid not used to build protein will first be subjected to
a.   removal of its amino group.
b.   removal of its carboxyl group.
c.   hydrolysis of its peptide bond.
d.   condensation of its peptide bond.

c   225,226(A)   33.   If the carbohydrate content of the diet is insufficient to meet the body's needs for glucose, which of the following can be converted to glucose?
a.   Fatty acids
b.   Acetyl-CoA
c.   Amino acids
d.   Carbon dioxide

b   225-227(A)   34.   Which of the following leads to the production of urea?
a.   Oxidation of glucose
b.   Oxidation of amino acids
c.   Incomplete oxidation of fatty acids
d.   Synthesis of protein from amino acids

d   224-226(A)   35.   When protein consumption is in excess of body needs and energy needs are met, the excess amino acids are metabolized and the energy in the molecules is
a.   stored as fat only.
b.   excreted in the feces.
c.   stored as amino acids only.
d.   stored as glycogen and fat.

c   227(K)   36.   What is the process whereby an amino group is combined with a keto acid to form an amino acid?
a.   Deamination
b.   Ureagenesis
c.   Transamination
d.   Ammoniogenesis

a   226-228(K)   37.   In the metabolism of amino acids for energy, what is the fate of the amino group?
a.   Excreted as urea
b.   Burned for energy
c.   Stored in the liver
d.   Converted to glucose

a   223-228(A)   38.   Which of the following is **not** a possible fate of metabolized glucose?
a.   Urea
b.   Acetyl CoA
c.   Amino acids
d.   Muscle glycogen

c   229-231(A)   39.   Which of the following products is **not** generated via TCA cycle or electron transport chain?
a.   Water
b.   Energy
c.   Ammonia
d.   Carbon dioxide

a   228(K)   40.   The body's need for water increases on a diet high in
a.   protein.
b.   carbohydrate.
c.   saturated fat.
d.   unsaturated fat.

c   228(A)   41.   Which of the following is the most likely side effect of a high-protein, low-carbohydrate diet?
a.   Edema
b.   Diarrhea
c.   Dehydration
d.   Nitrogen toxicity

a   227,228(A) 42.   What is the most likely cause for a person to have abnormally high blood ammonia levels?
a.   Liver dysfunction
b.   Kidney dysfunction
c.   Protein intake twice the RDA
d.   Protein intake one-tenth the RDA

b   227,228(A) 43.   What is the most likely reason for having an abnormally high blood urea level?
a.   Liver dysfunction
b.   Kidney dysfunction
c.   Protein intake twice the RDA
d.   Protein intake one-tenth the RDA

d   228(A)   44.   When energy-yielding nutrients are consumed in excess, which one(s) can lead to storage of fat?
a.   Fat only
b.   Carbohydrate only
c.   Fat and carbohydrate only
d.   Fat, carbohydrate, and protein

a   229-231(K) 45.   In addition to energy, what are the principal end products of cellular oxidation of carbohydrates?
a.   Water and carbon dioxide
b.   Carbon, hydrogen, and urea
c.   Indigestible fiber and nitrogen
d.   Monosaccharides and amino acids

d   224;229-   46.   What are the products from the complete oxidation of fatty acids?
     232(K)   a.   Urea and acetone
b.   Fatty acids and glycerol
c.   Carbon, hydrogen, and oxygen
d.   Water, carbon dioxide, and energy

b   230-233(A) 47.   Which of the following outlines the overall sequence of events in the complete oxidation of glucose?
a.   Cori cycle, TCA cycle, glycolysis
b.   Glycolysis, TCA cycle, electron transport chain
c.   Electron transport chain, TCA cycle, Cori cycle
d.   TCA cycle, electron transport chain, glycolysis

b   231,232(K)   48.   Which of the following accounts for the higher energy density of a fatty acid compared with the other energy-yielding nutrients?
  a.   Fatty acids have a lower percentage of hydrogen-carbon bonds
  b.   Fatty acids have a greater percentage of hydrogen-carbon bonds
  c.   Other energy-yielding nutrients have a lower percentage of oxygen-carbon bonds
  d.   Other energy-yielding nutrients undergo fewer metabolic reactions thereby lowering the energy yield

d   232,232(A)   49.   The number of ATPs that can be produced from a molecule of protein, fat, or carbohydrate is generally related to the number of atoms of
  a.   carbon.
  b.   oxygen.
  c.   nitrogen.
  d.   hydrogen.

b   234,235(K)   50.   All of the following are features of the metabolism of surplus dietary carbohydrate in human beings **except**
  a.   excess glucose suppresses fat oxidation.
  b.   excess glucose is oxidized only very slowly.
  c.   excess glucose is first used to fill glycogen reserves.
  d.   conversion of excess glucose to fat occurs only to a very limited extent.

a   234,235(K)   51.   Which of the following is a feature of the metabolism of **surplus** dietary fat?
  a.   Excess fat is almost all stored.
  b.   Excess fat promotes increased fat oxidation.
  c.   Excess fat spares breakdown of body proteins.
  d.   Conversion of excess fat to storage fat is inefficient.

a   235,236(A)   52.   After the first day or so of fasting, which of the following is most depleted in the body?
  a.   Glycogen
  b.   Fatty acids
  c.   Amino acids
  d.   Triglycerides

d   236(A)   53.   If a normal person expends 1500 kcal while at rest, approximately how many are used by the brain?
  a.   40
  b.   100
  c.   200
  d.   300

a   236(K)   54.   During the first few days of a fast, what energy source provides about 90% of the **glucose** needed to fuel the body?
  a.   Protein
  b.   Ketones
  c.   Glycogen
  d.   Triglycerides

a   236(A)   55.   How soon would death occur from starvation if the body was unable to shift to a state of ketosis?
- a.   Within 3 weeks
- b.   Less than 2 weeks
- c.   Between 5 and 6 weeks
- d.   Between 2 and 3 months

d   236,237(K)   56.   Which of the following is classified as a ketone body?
- a.   Sorbitol
- b.   Pyruvate
- c.   Acetyl-CoA
- d.   Acetoacetate

a   236,237(A)   57.   Which of the following is used to supply some of the fuel needed by the brain only after the body has been fasting for a while?
- a.   Ketones
- b.   Glycerol
- c.   Fatty acids
- d.   Amino acids

b   237(K)   58.   How are ketones formed?
- a.   Condensation of lactic acid molecules
- b.   Condensation of acetyl CoA molecules
- c.   Hydrolysis of excess glycerol fragments
- d.   Hydrolysis of excess pyruvate fragments

a   236,237(A)   59.   Which of the following is a feature of ketosis?
- a.   Occurs when fats are partially oxidized
- b.   Occurs from lack of protein in the diet
- c.   Results from excess acetoacetate in the diet
- d.   Results from excess carbohydrate in the diet

d   236-238(A)   60.   Which of the following dietary nutrients would most **rapidly** reverse a state of ketosis in a starving person?
- a.   Fat
- b.   Protein
- c.   Amino acids
- d.   Carbohydrate

a   236-238(K)   61.   Which of the following is a characteristic of ketosis?
- a.   It may lead to a lowering of blood pH.
- b.   It leads to increased appetite in most individuals.
- c.   It may be alleviated quickly by ingestion of some dietary fat.
- d.   It is a necessary physiological adjustment for maximum weight loss.

b   236-238(A)   62.   All of the following are general features of starvation in people **except**
- a.   a decrease in metabolic rate.
- b.   a decrease in mental alertness.
- c.   a decrease in immune function.
- d.   a decrease in body temperature.

a   237(A)   63.   A person with fruity odor on the breath demonstrates evidence of metabolic
  a.   ketosis.
  b.   alkalosis.
  c.   transamination.
  d.   anaerobic breakdown.

b   240(A)   64.   With alcohol beverages, the ratio of proof to alcohol percentage is
  a.   1:1.
  b.   2:1.
  c.   4:1.
  d.   8:1.

c   240(A)   65.   What is the percentage of ethanol in 120-proof scotch whiskey?
  a.   5
  b.   30
  c.   60
  d.   95

c   240,241(K)   66.   One average-sized can of beer contains about the same amount of alcohol as
  a.   ½ ounce of rum.
  b.   ½ quart of wine.
  c.   1 ounce of vodka.
  d.   1 quart of wine cooler.

c   241,242(K)   67.   Which of the following statements is **not** characteristic of alcohol metabolism?
  a.   There are gender differences in the rate of breakdown.
  b.   The average person needs about 3 hours to metabolize two drinks.
  c.   Alcohol is metabolized by muscle and brain cells as well as by the liver.
  d.   The amount of alcohol in the breath is proportional to the amount in the blood.

a   240(A)   68.   Which of the following defines a moderate level of alcohol intake per day for the average-sized woman?
  a.   Up to 1 drink
  b.   Up to 2 drinks
  c.   Up to 3 drinks
  d.   Up to 5 drinks

b   240(K)   69.   Which of the following defines a moderate level of alcohol intake per day for the average-sized man?
  a.   Up to 1 drink
  b.   Up to 2 drinks
  c.   Up to 3 drinks
  d.   Up to 5 drinks

c   241,242(K)   70.   The metabolism of alcohol begins in the
  a.   liver.
  b.   brain.
  c.   stomach.
  d.   intestines.

b   241,242(A)   71.   What organ is first to absorb alcohol after taking a drink?
  a.   Colon
  b.   Stomach
  c.   Jejunum
  d.   Duodenum

a   241,242(K)   72.   Which of the following is characteristic of alcohol absorption?
  a.   It is increased about 20% on an empty stomach.
  b.   It is increased from the GI tract by high-fat snacks.
  c.   It is increased from the GI tract by carbohydrate snacks.
  d.   It is lower in women than in men of the same body weight.

b   242,242(K)   73.   What is the primary organ that oxidizes alcohol for fuel?
  a.   Brain
  b.   Liver
  c.   Pancreas
  d.   Digestive tract

d   242(A)   74.   Which of the following is/are best suited for slowing alcohol absorption?
  a.   Not eating
  b.   Protein snacks
  c.   Caffeine drinks
  d.   Carbohydrate snacks

c   242(K)   75.   Which of the following plays a major role in regulating the elimination of alcohol from the body?
  a.   Lung respiratory rate
  b.   Kidney antidiuretic hormone
  c.   Liver alcohol dehydrogenase
  d.   Brain acetaldehyde dehydrogenase

c   242(A)   76.   In the average healthy person, about how much time is required by the liver to process the alcohol in a typical drink?
  a.   15 minutes
  b.   30 minutes
  c.   1 hour
  d.   2 hours

d   243(K)   77.   What is the sequence of stages that brings about advanced liver disease caused by chronic alcohol toxicity?
  a.   Fibrosis, gout, cirrhosis
  b.   Fibrosis, cirrhosis, fat depletion
  c.   Cirrhosis, fat accumulation, fibrosis
  d.   Fat accumulation, fibrosis, cirrhosis

b   243(K)   78.   Excess alcohol intake leads to a reduction in the synthesis rate of
  a.   liver fat.
  b.   liver glucose.
  c.   ketone bodies.
  d.   acetyl CoA molecules.

d   244(K)   79.   What is MEOS?
                     a.   An advanced liver disorder
                     b.   A drug that inhibits alcohol absorption
                     c.   A waste product of alcohol metabolism
                     d.   A system of enzymes that oxidizes alcohol and drugs

a   245(K)   80.   What **minimum** concentration of alcohol in the blood is usually fatal?
                     a.   0.5%
                     b.   1%
                     c.   5%
                     d.   50%

a   245(A)   81.   Chronic excess alcohol intake leads to all of the following effects on folate **except**
                     a.   the intestines recycle more folate.
                     b.   the liver releases more folate into the blood.
                     c.   the kidney excretes more folate via the urine.
                     d.   the intestines absorb less folate from the diet.

b   245-246(K) 82.   The Wernicke-Korsakoff syndrome in people with chronic alcohol abuse stems primarily from a deficiency of
                     a.   folate.
                     b.   thiamin.
                     c.   antidiuretic hormone.
                     d.   alcohol dehydrogenase.

a   246(K)   83.   Which of the following is a feature of ethanol metabolism?
                     a.   It increases gastric acid output.
                     b.   It decreases activity of the MEOS.
                     c.   It decreases secretion of gastric histamine.
                     d.   It increases secretion of antidiuretic hormone.

c   246(A)   84.   Approximately how many kcalories from **ethanol** are contained in one standard alcoholic drink?
                     a.   25
                     b.   50
                     c.   100
                     d.   200

c   237(K)   85.   What percentage of all traffic fatalities involve alcohol?
                     a.   5
                     b.   25
                     c.   50
                     d.   75

a   247(K)   86.   What is the median weekly number of alcoholic drinks consumed by college students?
                     a.   1½
                     b.   3
                     c.   5
                     d.   10

Chapter 7, Metabolism: Transformations and Interactions

MATCHING (Answers can be used only once.)

S	216	01.	Example of an anabolic reaction
R	216	02.	Example of a catabolic reaction
F	219	03.	A protein that accelerates a chemical reaction
J	219	04.	A small non-protein organic substance that promotes optimal activity of an enzyme
O	220	05.	A product of glycolysis
N	220	06.	The oxidation product of pyruvate
L	222	07.	A product of pyruvate metabolism when oxygen is limited
K	222	08.	A recycling process of converting lactic acid to glucose
T	224	09.	An irreversible reaction
H	224	10.	The part of a triglyceride that is convertible to glucose
I	227	11.	A product of deamination
P	227	12.	An enzyme involved in synthesis of amino acids
B	228	13.	The principal nitrogen-containing waste product
D	231	14.	Waste product of the electron transport chain
G	234	15.	A storage form of carbohydrate
E	236	16.	The major energy fuel for the central nervous system
M	237	17.	A ketone
C	244	18.	A system for metabolizing drugs and alcohol
Q	242	19.	An enzyme with activity levels related to a person's sex
A	243	20.	A coenzyme required for metabolism of alcohol

A.	NAD	K.	Cori cycle
B.	Urea	L.	Lactic acid
C.	MEOS	M.	Acetoacetate
D.	Water	N.	Acetyl-CoA
E.	Glucose	O.	Pyruvate
F.	Enzyme	P.	Transaminase
G.	Glycogen	Q.	Alcohol dehydrogenase
H.	Glycerol	R.	Synthesis of pyruvate from glycogen
I.	Ammonia	S.	Synthesis of cholesterol from acetate
J.	Coenzyme	T.	Synthesis of acetyl-CoA from glucose

ESSAY QUESTIONS

PAGE(S)

216-219   01.   Compare and contrast the various ways in which the body uses carbohydrate, fat, and amino acids.

220-223   02.   What are the major differences between aerobic and anaerobic metabolism? Give an example of an aerobic reaction and an anaerobic reaction.

227,228   03.   What is urea? How and where is it synthesized and how is it removed from the body?

236-238   04.   Discuss ways in which the body's metabolism adapts to conditions of fasting/starvation. How do these adaptations affect the rate of weight loss when dieting?

2224-227;232-238	05.	Explain the roles of protein and fat as nutrients for gluconeogenesis. What are the circumstances that favor low and high rates of gluconeogenesis?
234-236	06.	Describe interactions among the energy nutrients when each is consumed in excess.
236-238	07.	What is ketosis and how can it be identified? What conditions typically induce a state of ketosis? What are the adverse effects of this abnormality?
242-244;245,246	08.	Discuss ways in which alcohol interferes with metabolism of proteins, fats, carbohydrates, vitamins, minerals, and water.
241-246	09.	Describe the two major pathways for metabolism of alcohol in the liver. How does the liver adapt when forced to metabolize high quantities of alcohol on a daily basis?
241,242	10.	Compare and contrast the metabolism of alcohol in men versus women.
245,246	11.	Describe the effects of excess alcohol intake on folate utilization.
248	12.	List 6 common myths concerning alcohol use and discuss ways to dispel them.

CHAPTER 8
ENERGY BALANCE AND BODY COMPOSITION

AN PAGE(S)

d   252(A)   01.   What would be the approximate weight gain of a person who consumes an excess of 500 kcal daily for one month?
a.   0.5 lb
b.   2 lbs
c.   3 lbs
d.   4 lbs

d   252(A)   02.   Approximately what percentage of weight loss during starvation is lean body mass?
a.   0
b.   20
c.   35
d.   50

c   252(A)   03.   In an adult who gains 20 pounds of excess body weight, about how much of this is lean tissue?
a.   0 lbs
b.   2 lbs
c.   5 lbs
d.   10 lbs

b   252(A)   04.   When an adult gains an extra 10 pounds of body weight, approximately how much of this weight is fat?
a.   5 lbs
b.   7.5 lbs
c.   9.5 lbs
d.   10 lbs

c   252(K)   05.   What instrument is used to measure the energy content of foods?
a.   Energy chamber
b.   Exothermic meter
c.   Bomb calorimeter
d.   Combustion chamber

a   253,254(K)   06.   Which of the following identifies a specific food intake behavior?
a.   Appetite can be experienced without hunger
b.   A physiological need to eat is called satiety
c.   A pleasurable desire for food is called hunger
d.   An intense feeling of hunger is called insatiable nervosa

d   253(A)   07.   Which of the following describes an association between energy measurement and foods?
a.   Indirect calorimetry cannot be used to determine the energy value of alcohol
b.   A bomb calorimeter measures the amount of oxygen released when a food is oxidized
c.   Direct calorimetry and indirect calorimetry of the same food rarely give similar values
d.   The physiological fuel value of a food is almost always lower than the energy value of that food as determined by bomb calorimetry

c   253(A)   08.   After consuming a very large meal, the desire to eat a slice of chocolate cake is an
                      example of behavior known as
                      a.   satiety.
                      b.   hunger.
                      c.   appetite.
                      d.   pigging out.

a   253,254(A) 09.   A person who eats in response to arousal is most likely experiencing
                      a.   stress eating.
                      b.   sensory influences.
                      c.   physiological influences.
                      d.   postabsorptive influences.

a   253(K)   10.   The feeling of satisfaction resulting from consumption of a meal is termed
                      a.   satiety.
                      b.   appetite.
                      c.   postabsorptive hunger.
                      d.   resting postabsorptive increment.

d   254(A)   11.   An emotionally insecure person might eat for all of the following reasons **except**
                      a.   to relieve boredom.
                      b.   to ward off depression.
                      c.   in preference to socializing.
                      d.   to satisfy energy needs only.

b   254(K)   12.   External cues that may cause an obese person to respond helplessly to food
                      typically include all of the following **except**
                      a.   TV commercials.
                      b.   outdoor exercises.
                      c.   availability of food.
                      d.   "time of day" patterns.

c   254,255(K) 13.   What is the most satiating macronutrient?
                      a.   Fat
                      b.   Water
                      c.   Protein
                      d.   Carbohydrate

a   254,255(A) 14.   Among the following, which has the greatest power to suppress hunger?
                      a.   Apples
                      b.   Peanuts
                      c.   Doughnuts
                      d.   Potato chips

d   255(K)   15.   The brain chemical neuropeptide Y is known to specifically enhance the craving for
                      a.   fat.
                      b.   salt.
                      c.   protein.
                      d.   carbohydrate.

b   255(K)   16.   All of the following are characteristics of neuropeptide-Y **except**
a.   it stimulates appetite.
b.   it reduces fat storage.
c.   it is synthesized in the brain.
d.   it increases carbohydrate cravings.

c   255(A)   17.   All of the following are characteristics related to the fat content in food **except**
a.   high-fat foods are energy dense.
b.   it has a weak effect on satiation.
c.   eating high-fat foods typically leads to underconsumption of kcalories.
d.   in the intestine it triggers release of a hormone that inhibits food intake.

c   256(K)   18.   Which of the following describes the process of thermogenesis?
a.   Burning of fat
b.   Synthesis of fat
c.   Generation of heat
d.   Generation of water

c   256(K)   19.   What method is used to measure the amount of heat given off by the body?
a.   Bomb calorimetry
b.   Basal calorimetry
c.   Direct calorimetry
d.   Indirect calorimetry

a   256(K)   20.   Which of the following may be used to calculate the amount of energy expended by the body?
a.   Oxygen consumed
b.   Total air exchanged
c.   Intestinal gas expelled
d.   Carbon dioxide consumed

c   256(A)   21.   What fraction of the day's energy expenditure of the average person is represented by the basal metabolism?
a.   about 1/10
b.   up to 1/2
c.   about 2/3
d.   over 9/10

c   257(K)   22.   Which of the following is a feature of the basal metabolic rate (BMR)?
a.   Fever decreases the BMR
b.   Fasting increases the BMR
c.   Pregnancy increases the BMR
d.   Females have a higher BMR than males on a body weight basis

b   257(K)   23.   For every decade beyond the age of 30, what is the percentage decrease in the need for total kcalories?
a.   2
b.   5
c.   10
d.   15

c   256,257(K)   24.   Among the following groups, which has the highest metabolic rate?
                          a.   Females
                          b.   Older individuals
                          c.   Younger individuals
                          d.   People with smaller surface areas

d   256,257(K)   25.   What is the major factor that determines metabolic rate?
                          a.   Age
                          b.   Gender
                          c.   Amount of fat tissue
                          d.   Amount of lean body tissue

a   257(K)   26.   Which of the following does **not** decrease the metabolic rate?
                          a.   Fever
                          b.   Injury
                          c.   Fasting
                          d.   Malnutrition

c   257(A)   27.   If a normal 30 year-old woman has a daily energy expenditure of 2,200 kcal, what
                          would be her expected output when she reaches 60 years of age?
                          a.   1210 kcal
                          b.   1450 kcal
                          c.   1885 kcal
                          d.   2275 kcal

d   256,257(A)   28.   If a dancer and a typist are the same height and have the exact same body build, the
                          dancer will be heavier because she has
                          a.   more body fat.
                          b.   stronger bones.
                          c.   stronger muscles.
                          d.   more muscle mass.

c   257(K)   29.   What is the main explanation for the difference in basal metabolic rates between
                          males and females of the same body weight?
                          a.   Males are usually taller than females.
                          b.   Females have lower levels of thyroid hormones.
                          c.   Males have a higher percentage of lean body mass.
                          d.   Females have a lower percentage of adipose tissue.

d   258(A)   30.   If a normal 60 kg person has a resting energy expenditure of 1300 kcal/day, about
                          how many total kilocalories are needed to sustain 4 hours of studying?
                          a.   50
                          b.   120
                          c.   260
                          d.   350

b   257;259(A)   31.   What is the approximate value for the thermic effect of a 2,500 kcal diet?
                          a.   25 kcal
                          b.   250 kcal
                          c.   400 kcal
                          d.   500 kcal

a   257(K)   32.   The weight of the body less the fat content is known as the
                      a.   lean body mass.
                      b.   body mass index.
                      c.   ideal body weight.
                      d.   water of metabolism.

d   259(A)   33.   What is the term that describes the increase in energy expenditure that occurs in a
                      person who fractures a leg?
                      a.   Febrile hyperthermia
                      b.   Physical hyperthermia
                      c.   Specific thermogenesis
                      d.   Adaptive thermogenesis

a   259(K)   34.   To estimate the basal metabolic rates of individuals, which of the following was
                      used in the equations by the DRI Committee?
                      a.   Weight
                      b.   Surface area
                      c.   Activity level
                      d.   Fat-fold thickness

b   259(K)   35.   The thermic effect of foods is highest for what nutrient?
                      a.   Fat
                      b.   Protein
                      c.   Vitamins
                      d.   Carbohydrate

b   256(A)   36.   What is the approximate daily basal metabolism of a 110-pound woman?
                      a.   500 kcal
                      b.   1,000 kcal
                      c.   1,500 kcal
                      d.   2,000 kcal

a   262(A)   37.   An index of a person's weight in relation to height is called
                      a.   body mass index.
                      b.   height to weight index.
                      c.   ideal body weight index.
                      d.   desirable body weight index.

a   262(K)   38.   Which of the following is a feature of the body mass index?
                      a.   It correlates with disease risks
                      b.   It decreases by 1 unit for every 10 years of life
                      c.   It provides an estimate of the fat level of the body
                      d.   It is defined as the person's height divided by the square of the weight

a   262(A)   39.   What is the approximate body mass index of a woman who is 5'5" and 125 lbs?
                      a.   21
                      b.   26
                      c.   31
                      d.   36

d 262,263(K) 40. Which of the following is a characteristic associated with using weight measures to assess risk of disease?
  a. They are expensive to perform.
  b. They are complicated to perform.
  c. They are able to quantitate total body fat.
  d. They are subject to gross inaccuracies.

d 262,263(K) 41. All of the following are features of using weight measures to assess risk of disease **except**
  a. they are inexpensive.
  b. they are very accurate.
  c. they are easy to perform.
  d. they provide information on body composition.

b 263(K) 42. What is the range of body fat content for normal weight women?
  a. 9-17%
  b. 23-31%
  c. 33-37%
  d. 38-44%

b 263(K) 43. What is the range of body fat content for normal weight men?
  a. 5-10%
  b. 13-21%
  c. 22-30%
  d. 32-40%

d 263 (K) 44. Which of the following is a disadvantage of using weight measures for the assessment of disease risk?
  a. Cost
  b. Accuracy
  c. Complexity
  d. Limited amount of body composition data

c 264(A) 45. Which of the following is **not** a known side effect of having insufficient fat stores?
  a. Infertility
  b. Clinical depression
  c. Elevated body temperature
  d. Abnormal hunger regulation

b 263(A) 46. What is the weight classification assigned both to young women with 30% body fat and young men with 20% body fat?
  a. Obese
  b. Normal
  c. Mildly overweight
  d. Slightly underweight

b 264,265(K) 47. In what region of the body is the storage of excess body fat associated with highest risks for cardiovascular disease and diabetes?
  a. Neck
  b. Abdomen
  c. Hips and thighs
  d. Arms and shoulders

b   264(K)   48.   Which of the following defines central obesity?
                         a.   Accumulation of fat during the mid-years of life
                         b.   Storage of excess fat around the central part of the body
                         c.   Overfatness due to a large number of interacting behavioral problems
                         d.   Overfatness due to reliance on high fat foods as a central part of the diet

c   264,265(A)   49.   Research in obese people seems to show that there is no increase in the risks for
                         strokes and hypertension provided that the excess body fat is distributed around
                         the
                         a.   stomach.
                         b.   arms and chest.
                         c.   hips and thighs.
                         d.   neck and shoulders.

c   265(K)   50.   A high risk of weight-related health problems is seen in women whose waist
                         circumference begins to exceed
                         a.   24 inches.
                         b.   28 inches.
                         c.   35 inches.
                         d.   42 inches.

d   264,265(K)   51.   Which of the following is a characteristic of excess body fat that is distributed
                         primarily around the abdomen?
                         a.   It is related directly to exercise
                         b.   Its presence lowers the risk for diabetes
                         c.   It is less common in women past menopause
                         d.   It is associated with increased mortality for both sexes

d   265(A)   52.   Which of the following can be used to gauge the amount of a person's abdominal
                         fat?
                         a.   BMI
                         b.   Essential body fat
                         c.   Hydrodensitometry
                         d.   Waist circumference

b   266(K)   53.   Which of the following is a feature of fatfold **assessment** techniques?
                         a.   The device to measure fatfold thickness is called a lipidometer.
                         b.   The folds of fat increase in size in proportion to the gain in body fat.
                         c.   Measures taken from upper-body sites are more precise than those from
                               the lower-body sites.
                         d.   The principles are based on the assumption that subcutaneous fat mass
                               represents about 20% of total body fat.

a   267(K)   54.   The known health risks for being underweight include all of the following **except**
                         a.   diabetes.
                         b.   infertility in women.
                         c.   giving birth to unhealthy infants.
                         d.   increased cancer-induced wasting.

b   265(K)   55.   A high risk of weight-related health problems is seen in men whose waist circumference begins to exceed
    a.   34 inches
    b.   40 inches.
    c.   45 inches.
    d.   52 inches.

b   265;267,   56.   Which of the following describes an association between body weight and
    268(K)   mortality?
    a.   Obesity is the fourth leading cause of premature death.
    b.   Overweight men who are physically fit have a lower mortality risk than normal-weight, unfit men.
    c.   Normal-weight men who are physically unfit have a similar mortality risk versus normal-weight fit men.
    d.   The amount of weight gain in adulthood that is not associated with increased mortality is 20 pounds or less.

d   268(K)   57.   All of the following are an association between type 2 diabetes and body fat **except**
    a.   people with the disease often have central obesity rather than lower-body obesity.
    b   a woman who has gained 12 pounds since age 18 has double the risk of developing the disease.
    c.   an obese person is 3 times more likely to develop the disease than is a nonobese individual.
    d.   overweight people with the disease who lose weight show no improvement in glucose tolerance and insulin resistance.

d   267(K)   58.   The risks for dying prematurely are doubled when the body mass index first rises above
    a.   27.
    b.   30.
    c.   32.
    d.   35.

a   267(A)   59.   A graph of the relationship between mortality (left axis) and body mass index is shaped like a(n)
    a.   J.
    b.   S.
    c.   backslash.
    d.   inverted U.

a   267(K)   60.   The yearly death toll in the United States from obesity-related diseases is estimated at
    a.   300,000.
    b.   1 million.
    c.   10 million.
    d.   20 million.

c   267(K)   61.   All of the following are features of the health risks associated with excessive body fat **except**
  a.   obesity is now classified as a disease.
  b.   obese women have elevated levels of estrogen.
  c.   the risks are higher in black women than in white women.
  d.   people with a BMI higher than 35 have twice the risk of dying prematurely.

b   268;273(K) 62.   What term best describes a failure of the body's cells to respond to secretion of insulin?
  a.   Central obesity
  b.   Insulin resistance
  c.   Thyroid insufficiency
  d.   Hypothalamic impedance

c   273(K)   63.   The major cause of insulin resistance is related to
  a.   low protein diets.
  b.   high protein diets.
  c.   excess body weight.
  d.   prolonged excess carbohydrate intake.

d   273(A)   64.   Current dietary trends in fat and/or energy intake for adult Americans include all of the following **except**
  a.   our actual fat intake has increased by 3 g per day.
  b.   our average daily energy intake has risen by 200 kcalories.
  c.   our fat intake has decreased from 35% to 33% of daily energy intake.
  d.   our higher prevalence of obesity is due primarily to excess carbohydrate intake.

c   273-275(A) 65.   All of the following are features of high-protein diets **except**
  a.   they have a high satiety index.
  b.   they advise dieters to not count kcalories.
  c.   they provide for long-term weight maintenance.
  d.   they typically recommend intakes of 800 to 1200 kcal/day.

d   273-276(K) 66.   The dieter's typical responses to a high-protein diet include all of the following **except**
  a.   a state of ketosis.
  b.   a loss of appetite.
  c.   a loss of glycogen.
  d.   a slow re-gain of the lost weight.

d   275,276(K) 67.   Adverse side effects of typical low-carbohydrate diets include all of the following **except**
  a.   fatigue.
  b.   nausea.
  c.   constipation.
  d.   high blood pressure.

a   273,274(A) 68.   What is the primary reason for the weight loss seen on common high-protein diets?
  a.   Low energy intake
  b.   A fall in the rate of de novo lipogenesis
  c.   Liberal intake of low glycemic index foods
  d.   Low blood insulin levels which favors fat oxidation

d   275(K)   69.   Which of the following is characteristic of dieting and ketosis?
                  a.   Ketogenic diets typically reduce urine production.
                  b.   There is a strong relationship between ketosis and weight loss.
                  c.   Body fat losses on a ketogenic diet are initially high but then taper off
                           after one week.
                  d.   Body fat losses on a ketogenic diet are not higher than on other diets of
                           equivalent kcalories.

MATCHING (Answers can be used only once.)

G   252   01.   Approximate number of kcal in 2 lbs of body fat
Q   253   02.   Technique used to measure the amount of heat given off when a food burns
R   253   03.   Technique used to measure the amount of oxygen consumed when a food burns
D   259   04.   Thermic effect of alcohol as percent
L   253   05.   Response to the smell of favorite food
J   253   06.   Irritating sensation that initiates thoughts of food
I   253   07.   A feeling of fullness after eating
N   254   08.   Eating in response to arousal
M   254   09.   Eating in response to the time of day
P   256   10.   Energy needed to maintain the body at rest
B   257   11.   The percentage decline in basal metabolism per decade of adult life
H   259   12.   A factor that lowers basal metabolism
K   259   13.   A factor that raises basal metabolism
O   257   14.   Term that describes the energy needed to process food
T   259   15.   Changes in energy expenditure consequent to changes in environment
F   259   16.   The amount of kcal in a 1,000 kcal meal that is expended as specific dynamic
                 activity
A   259   17.   Maximum amount of kcal expended during one minute of studying
S   259   18.   Synonymous with the thermic effect of food
E   262   19.   Body mass index of an adult of 180 lbs and 5 ft 11 in
C   263   20.   Lower range of body fat percentage in normal-weight men

A.   2   K.   Caffeine
B.   5   L.   Appetite
C.   13   M.   External cue
D.   20   N.   Stress eating
E.   25   O.   Thermic effect
F.   100   P.   Basal metabolism
G.   7,000   Q.   Direct calorimetry
H.   Fasting   R.   Indirect calorimetry
I.   Satiety   S.   Specific dynamic effect
J.   Hunger   T.   Adaptive thermogenesis

ESSAY QUESTIONS

PAGE(S)

252,253   01.   Discuss common methods for determining the energy content of foods and energy
                 expenditure of individuals.

253,254   02.   Discuss factors that affect the sensations of hunger and appetite.

253-255	03.	Explain the difference between satiety and satiation. Give examples of nutrients with a high or low satiating index.
226,257	04.	Define basal metabolic rate and discuss factors that increase and decrease it.
256-260	05.	List the major components that contribute to the body's daily expenditure of energy. Compare the relative contributions of a sedentary person with a marathon runner of the same body weight.
257;259	06.	Explain the meaning and significance of A. the thermic effect of food. B. adaptive thermogenesis.
2559-265	07.	What factors should be considered in determining healthy body fat levels in people or population groups?
263,264	08.	Explain the adverse effects of excess body fat deposited around the abdominal region.
266	09.	Briefly explain the following techniques for the estimation of body composition: a) fatfold measures, b) hydrodensitometry, c) bioelectrical impedance, d) air displacement plethysmography, and e) dual energy X-ray absorptiometry.
267,268	10.	List several health risks associated with being underweight and with being overweight.
272-274	11.	Explain the connection between fad diets and high-protein diets.
274-276	12.	Discuss the pros and cons of high-protein diets.
264	13.	List circumstances under which some people would benefit from having more body fat.
275	14.	Discuss the appeal of ketogenic diets as well as adverse side effects.

CHAPTER 9
WEIGHT MANAGEMENT: OVERWEIGHT AND UNDERWEIGHT

AN PAGE(S)

c 280(K) 01. What is the rationale for the fat cell theory of obesity?
   a. Fat cell number increases dramatically after puberty.
   b. Fat cell number in an adult can decrease only by fasting.
   c. Fat cell number increases most readily in late childhood and early puberty.
   d. Weight gain from overeating in adults takes place primarily by increasing the number of fat cells.

d 279(K) 02. According to body mass index values, what fraction of the U.S. adult population is considered overweight?
   a. 1/10
   b. 1/6
   c. 1/3
   d. 1/2

a 280(K) 03. All of the following describe the behavior of fat cells **except**
   a. the number decreases when fat is lost from the body.
   b. the storage capacity for fat depends on both cell number and cell size.
   c. the size is larger in obese people than in normal-weight people.
   d. the number increases several-fold during the growth years and tapers off when adult status is reached.

d 280,281(A) 04. In the quest for achieving desirable body weight, adults have control over all of the following **except**
   a. diet.
   b. behavior.
   c. physical activity.
   d. adipocyte number.

b 281(K) 05. Obesity resulting from an increase in the **size** of fat cells is termed
   a. hyperplastic obesity.
   b. hypertrophic obesity.
   c. idiopenthic leptinemia.
   d. anaplastic hypometabolism.

a 281(K) 06. Obesity resulting from an increase in the **number** of fat cells is termed
   a. hyperplastic obesity.
   b. hypertrophic obesity.
   c. idiopenthic leptinemia.
   d. anaplastic hypometabolism.

b 280,281(K) 07. Which of the following is known to promote fat storage in adipocytes?
   a. Glucagon
   b. Lipoprotein lipase
   c. Cellulite synthetase
   d. Lipoprotein synthetase

b   280,281(A) 08.   What is the most likely explanation for why women readily store fat around the
                        hips whereas men readily store fat around the abdomen?
                        a.   Differences in blood insulin levels
                        b.   Differences in the activity of lipoprotein lipase
                        c.   Differences in circulating lipid transport proteins
                        d.   Differences in the activity of lipoprotein synthetase

d   281(K)   09.   Which of the following defines the body's set point?
                        a.   Minimum weight of a person
                        b.   Maximum weight of a person
                        c.   Point at which a dieter plateaus and then drops weight quickly
                        d.   Point above which the body tends to lose weight and below which it tends
                              to gain weight

a   281(A)   10.   Adverse effects on organs such as the liver from the presence of excess body fat is
                        known as
                        a.   lipotoxicity.
                        b.   hyperplastic lipase.
                        c.   set point susceptibility.
                        d.   hyper-responsive ghrelin.

a   282(K)   11.   What is the chief factor that determines a person's risk for obesity?
                        a.   Heredity
                        b.   Environment
                        c.   Metabolic rate
                        d.   Fat content of diet

a   282(K)   12.   Which of the following is known to cause a reduction in fat cell number?
                        a.   Injection of leptin
                        b.   Supplements of ghrelin
                        c.   Long-term resistance exercise
                        d.   Consumption of high-protein diets

c   282,833(K) 13.   Which of the following describes a relationship between leptin and energy balance?
                        a.   Fat cell sensitivity to leptin is higher in obese people.
                        b.   A deficiency of leptin is characteristic of all obese people.
                        c.   Blood levels of leptin usually correlate directly with body fat.
                        d.   Major functions of leptin include an increase in hunger and a decrease in
                              metabolic rate.

b   282,283(K) 14.   Which of the following is a feature of leptin?
                        a.   It is an enzyme.
                        b.   It acts primarily on the brain.
                        c.   It is usually deficient in obese people.
                        d.   It is secreted by the brain and acts on fat cells.

d   283-284(K) 15.   Which of the following is a feature of ghrelin?
                        a.   High blood levels are found in obese people.
                        b.   Its major role in the body is in suppressing appetite.
                        c.   It is secreted by adipocytes and promotes negative energy balance.
                        d.   Its blood concentration is very high in people with anorexia nervosa.

a   284(K)   16.   What is the significance of the uncoupling proteins in adipose tissue?
     a.   Increased loss of body heat
     b.   Reduction of fat cell number
     c.   Lowering of basal metabolism
     d.   Proliferation of fat cell number

c   284(K)   17.   What serves as the body's chief storage site for lipid?
     a.   Yellow fat
     b.   Brown adipose tissue
     c.   White adipose tissue
     d.   High-density lipoproteins

c   285(K)   18.   In comparison with non-obese people, obese people have a lower
     a.   basal metabolic rate.
     b.   thermic effect of food.
     c   physical activity level.
     d.   metabolic response to exercise.

b   285(K)   19.   What is the most important single contributor to the obesity problem in the United States?
     a.   High-fat diets
     b.   Physical inactivity
     c.   Environmental factors
     d.   Overabundance of foods

c   285(K)   20.   Television watching contributes to obesity for all of the following reasons **except** that
     a.   it promotes inactivity.
     b.   it promotes between-meal snacking.
     c.   it replaces time that could be spent eating.
     d.   it gives high exposure to energy-dense foods featured in the commercial advertisements.

b   285(K)   21.   To help prevent body fat gain, the DRI suggests daily, moderately intense, physical activities totaling
     a.   20 minutes.
     b.   60 minutes.
     c.   1 ½ hours.
     d.   3 hours.

a   288(K)   22.   What is the primary action of the substance benzocaine, found in certain candy and gum and used as an over-the-counter weight loss aid?
     a.   It reduces taste sensations.
     b.   It inhibits lipoprotein lipase.
     c.   It inhibits pancreatic lipase.
     d.   It alters circulating leptin concentrations.

c   290(K)   23.   What is the primary action of orlistat, a weight loss drug?
     a.   It reduces taste sensation.
     b.   It inhibits lipoprotein lipase.
     c.   It inhibits pancreatic lipase.
     d.   It alters circulating leptin concentrations.

d   290(K)   24.   The drug sibutramine reduces appetite by affecting
        a.   ketone production.
        b.   insulin to glucagon ratio.
        c.   leptin sensitivity of fat cells.
        d.   serotonin utilization in the brain.

a   290(K)   25.   The prescription drug sibutramine acts by regulating the utilization of
        a.   serotonin.
        b.   blood insulin.
        c.   hormone-sensitive lipase.
        d.   adipocyte lipoprotein lipase.

c   287,288(K) 26.   Which of the following is an FDA approved over-the-counter medication for weight loss?
        a.   Leptin
        b.   Ephedrine
        c.   Benzocaine
        d.   Tetrahydrolipostatin

d   288(K)   27.   Over-the-counter products labeled as "dieter's tea" are reported to lead to
        a.   leptin resistance.
        b.   ketone poisoning.
        c.   cravings for protein.
        d.   nausea and diarrhea.

c   289(K)   28.   Fraudulent weight reduction literature refers to visually apparent lumpy forms of body fat as
        a.   lipomas.
        b.   lipidosis.
        c.   cellulite.
        d.   hyperphagic deposits.

b   292-296(K) 29.   All of the following are sensible guidelines for diet plans **except**:
        a.   consume low-fat foods regularly.
        b.   eat rapidly to avoid prolonged contact with food.
        c.   adjust energy intake downward as weight loss progresses.
        d.   include vegetables, fruits, and grains as the mainstay of the diet.

a   292(K)   30.   What is a safe rate of weight loss on a long-term basis for most overweight people?
        a.   0.5-2 lbs/week
        b.   3-4 lbs/week
        c.   5% body weight per month
        d.   10% body weight per month

d   296(A)   31.   What is the best approach to weight loss?
        a.   Avoid foods containing carbohydrates.
        b.   Eliminate all fats from the diet and decrease water intake.
        c   Greatly increase protein intake to prevent body protein loss.
        d   Reduce daily energy intake and increase energy expenditure.

c   293(K)   32.   As a general rule, what minimum number of kcalories per day is necessary to assure nutritional adequacy in an eating plan for reducing body weight?
a.   500
b.   800
c.   1200
d.   1600

c   292(K)   33.   In a weight reduction regimen, the most realistic time frame for losing 10% of initial body weight is
a.   6 weeks.
b.   3 months.
c.   6 months.
d.   1 year.

a   291,292(K) 34.   Which of the following describes the research results of obese women in weight-loss programs?
a.   They initially expected to lose unrealistic amounts of weight.
b.   They were mostly satisfied with a 15% reduction in weight.
c.   They typically lost about 30% more weight than they predicted.
d.   They expressed far less psychological benefits than expected after losing weight.

d   298(A)   35.   All of the following are behavior modifications for losing weight **except**
a.   shopping only when not hungry.
b.   eating only in one place and in one room.
c.   participating in activities such as television viewing only when not eating.
d.   taking smaller portions of food but always eating everything on the plate quickly.

d   293,294(K) 36.   The feeling of satiety from weight-loss diets is best promoted by diets rich in
a.   fat.
b.   short-chain fats.
c.   simple carbohydrates.
d.   complex carbohydrates.

b   295(K)   37.   Upon beginning a meal, the satiety signal in the body is sent after a lag time of about
a.   10 minutes.
b.   20 minutes.
c.   40 minutes.
d.   60 minutes.

c   295(K)   38.   Which of the following describes the results of a weight loss study comparing a low-carbohydrate with a low-fat diet?
a.   On the low-fat diet, people complained more often of abdominal cramping and diarrhea.
b.   On the low-carb diet, people lost more weight due, in large part, to the nausea resulting from ketosis.
c.   On the low-carb diet, people lost more weight for the first 6 months but regained more weight during the next 6 months.
d.   On the low-fat diet, people lost approximately 30% more weight the first 3 months but thereafter the rate of weight loss was not different.

a 296,297(A) 39. Which of the following describes a connection between physical activity and energy expenditure?
    a.   Walking a mile uses about the same energy as running a mile.
    b.   Walking a mile uses about half as much energy as running a mile.
    c.   Exercising the leg muscles is effective at burning away fat primarily around the thighs and hips.
    d.   Exercising the abdominal muscles is effective at burning away fat primarily around the abdomen.

b 297-298(A) 40. A person weighing 150 lbs walking at a pace of 3 miles/hr expends about how many kcal in that hour?
    a.   100
    b.   200
    c.   300
    d.   800

b 297(K) 41. Features of the adaptive response to regular physical exercise include all of the following **except**
    a.   it curbs appetite.
    b.   it stimulates digestive function in the postexercise period.
    c.   it increases energy expenditure in the postexercise period.
    d.   it triggers release of lipids from adipocytes from all over the body.

a 297(K) 42. Which of the following is a feature of the body's response to engaging in physical activity?
    a.   After an intense and vigorous workout, basal metabolism remains elevated for several hours.
    b.   Lower body fat is more readily lost from vigorous exercises that work primarily the hip and leg muscles.
    c.   Blood glucose and fatty acid levels are low immediately after working out, but thereafter recover on their own.
    d.   After an intense workout, most people immediately feel the urge to eat a large carbohydrate meal to replace glycogen stores.

b 296,297(A) 43. An important aid in any weight-loss diet program is to
    a.   decrease water intake.
    b.   increase physical activity.
    c.   speed up thyroid activity with metabolic enhancers.
    d.   develop ketosis by maintaining carbohydrate intake as low as possible.

a 298(K) 44. Which of the following is a relation of "spot-reducing" to exercise?
    a.   No exercise can target fat removal from any specific area of the body.
    b.   Upper body fat is mostly unaffected by exercising lower body muscles.
    c.   Lower body fat in women is depleted at a faster rate than abdominal fat.
    d.   Abdominal fat in men is released more readily with anaerobic exercise.

b 298,299(A) 45. An example of a behavior modification technique for weight control is to
    a.   feel guilty after you overeat.
    b.   keep a record of your eating habits.
    c.   always clean your plate when you eat.
    d.   have someone watch you to prevent overeating.

a   298,299(A)   46.   To help maximize the long-term success of a person's weight-loss program, which of the following personal attitudes should be encouraged in the individual?
    a.   Strongly believing that weight can be lost
    b.   Viewing the body realistically as being fat rather than thin
    c.   Refraining from expressing overconfidence in ability to lose weight
    d.   Accepting that underexercising is a part of the lifestyle of most overweight people

c   300K)   47.   Which of the following is a feature of energy metabolism in formerly obese people who have lost weight?
    a.   Energy expenditure is the same as in people who were never obese.
    b.   Basal metabolic rates are higher than those during the obese state.
    c.   Energy requirements are lower than expected for their current body weight.
    d.   Energy expenditure is the same per kg body weight compared with the obese state.

c   300,301(K)   48.   Since obesity apparently has many causes, even in a single individual, the best approach to the condition seems to be
    a.   fasting.
    b.   medicines.
    c.   prevention.
    d.   genetic counseling.

a   300(K)   49.   Approximately what percentage of overweight people who intentionally lose weight are able to maintain the weight loss for at least 5 years?
    a.   20
    b.   40
    c.   60
    d.   80

a   301(K)   50.   Approximately what percentage of U.S. adults are classified as underweight?
    a.   5
    b.   10
    c.   20
    d.   25

b   301(K)   51.   The classification of underweight is defined when the BMI first drops below
    a.   14.
    b.   18.5.
    c.   20.
    d.   22.5.

c   302,303(A)   52.   Of the following, which is **not** among the recommended strategies for weight gain in an underweight person?
    a.   Behavior modification training
    b.   Increased physical activity, especially strength training
    c   Forced awakening during the night for supplemental meals and snacks
    d.   Consumption of regular meals and snacks that provide high-kcalorie foods in small volumes

d   302,303(A)   53.   Which of the following would **not** be part of a successful program of weight gain in an underweight individual?
   a.   Physical exercise
   b.   Energy-dense foods
   c.   Energy-dense beverages
   d.   Large number of small meals

d   310(K)   54.   Anorexia nervosa is most common in
   a.   male elderly.
   b.   male adolescents.
   c.   female executives.
   d.   female adolescents.

a   310(K)   55.   What term is given to a female athlete who has an eating disorder and develops amenorrhea and osteoporosis?
   a.   Female athlete triad
   b.   Triathlete medical disorder
   c.   High stress tertiary disorder
   d.   Nonadaptable training syndrome

c   310(K)   56.   Approximately how many people in the United States are believed to have eating disorders?
   a.   ½ million
   b.   1 million
   c.   5 million
   d.   9 million

c   311(K)   57.   All of the following are typical characteristics of amenorrhea **except**
   a.   infertility.
   b.   bone mineral loss.
   c.   muscle dysmorphia.
   d.   low blood estrogen.

a   312(K)   58.   Among people with anorexia nervosa, approximately what percentage are males?
   a.   5
   b.   15
   c.   33
   d.   50

a   314(K)   59.   All of the following are characteristics of anorexia nervosa **except**:
   a.   in those who recover, energy intakes return to normal.
   b.   treatment with prescription drugs plays only a limited role.
   c.   it has one of the highest mortality rates among psychiatric disorders.
   d.   only one-half of women who are treated can maintain body weight at a near healthy level.

c   300(K)   60.   Which of the following is a characteristic of people with anorexia nervosa?
   a.   Most are aware of their condition and seek treatment.
   b.   Fewer than 200 women die each year from the disease.
   c.   In those who are treated, many relapse into abnormal eating patterns.
   d.   During initial treatment, metabolism slows and appetite increases but thereafter subsides.

b   314(K)   61.   Approximately what fraction of people treated for anorexia nervosa show reasonable maintenance of their weight gain?
- a.   1/4
- b.   1/2
- c.   4/5
- d.   9/10

d   315(A)   62.   Typical foods chosen by a person with bulimia nervosa during a binge include all of the following **except**
- a.   bread.
- b.   cookies.
- c.   ice cream.
- d.   vegetables.

a   315(K)   63.   What is a cathartic?
- a.   A strong laxative
- b.   An antidiarrheal medication
- c.   An over-the-counter weight loss product
- d.   A medication for the treatment of eating disorders

c   315(K)   64.   Which of the following is characteristic of the eating pattern of people with bulimia nervosa?
- a.   Binge eating is frequently done at buffets.
- b.   Binge eating usually occurs during the daytime.
- c.   Binge eating typically occurs after a period of strict dieting.
- d.   A binge eating episode is usually completed within 20 minutes.

c   316(K)   65.   Diet recommendations for people with bulimia nervosa include all of the following **except**
- a.   avoid skipping meals.
- b.   include fiber-rich foods.
- c.   eat cold foods to stimulate satiety.
- d.   avoid "finger" foods to minimize overeating.

a   316(K)   66.   What is the primary factor that differentiates bulimia nervosa from binge eating?
- a.   Purging is rarely practiced in binge-eating disorder.
- b.   Higher rates of depression are reported in bulimia nervosa.
- c.   More food is consumed at one setting in binge-eating disorders.
- d.   Uncontrollable cravings for high-fat foods are seen only in bulimia nervosa.

MATCHING (Answers can be used only once.)

T	281	01.	A term that describes an increase in fat cell number in obesity
S	281	02.	A term that describes an increase in fat cell size in obesity
L	284	03.	Type of adipose that primarily stores fat
K	284	04.	Type of adipose that primarily produces heat
G	282	05.	Hormone that suppresses appetite
R	280	06.	An enzyme that promotes fat storage
B	301	07.	Percentage of U.S. adults classified as underweight
Q	290	08.	A drug that interferes with serotonin metabolism
H	290	09.	Inhibitor of pancreatic lipase
O	290	10.	A cosmetic surgical procedure
I	289	11.	A fraudulent term to describe lumpy fat
N	288	12.	Inhibitor of taste sensations
E	286	13.	Minimum BMI of a clinically severe obese person
F	279	14.	Percentage of U.S. adults considered overweight
A	292	15.	Recommended rate of weight loss, in pounds per week
D	295	16.	Number of minutes for satiety signal to appear after beginning to eat
C	296	17.	Recommended number of glasses of water to drink on a weight-loss diet
J	283	18.	Hormone that stimulates appetite
M	288	19.	Substance in some herbs that may cause heart attacks and seizures
P	291	20.	Surgical procedure for the severely obese

A.	1	F.	50	K.	Brown fat
B.	5	G.	Leptin	L.	White fat
C.	8	H.	Orlistat	M.	Ephedrine
D.	20	I.	Cellulite	N.	Benzocaine
E.	40	J.	Ghrelin	O.	Liposuction

P.	Gastroplasty
Q.	Sibutramine
R.	Lipoprotein lipase
S.	Hypertrophic obesity
T.	Hyperplastic obesity

ESSAY QUESTIONS

PAGE(S)

280,281	01.	Discuss differences in fat cell metabolism between males and females.
280,281	02.	Explain the role of lipoprotein lipase enzyme in fat cell metabolism.
280-285;219-296;298,299	03.	List the major causes of obesity. Which ones can be controlled by dietary manipulations or behavior modification?
282,283	04.	Discuss the role of genetics in promoting excess weight gain and in discouraging weight loss.
294,295	05.	What are the results of research studies concerning the importance of low fat diets in weight-reduction regimes?
281	06.	Explain the set point theory of obesity.
282-284	07.	Discuss the roles of leptin and ghrelin in the regulation of food intake and energy storage.
284	08.	Contrast the metabolic roles of white adipose tissue and brown adipose tissue.

284   09.   Explain the significance of uncoupling reactions in energy metabolism.

284,285   10.   Explain the factors involved in the promotion of obesity by high-fat diets and food portion sizes.

287   11.   Describe psychological problems encountered by overweight people in their attempts to lose weight.

288   12.   What types of information might be found in a weight-loss consumer "bill of rights"?

287-289   13.   List several factors that help identify inappropriate, unsound, and possibly dangerous commercial weight-loss programs.

287-289   14.   Explain the attraction of unsound weight-loss procedures and plans to obese people.

290   15.   Discuss the use of prescription drugs for the treatment of obesity, including modes of action and adverse side effects.

288,289   16.   Discuss the use of herbal products for weight loss.

290-291   17.   List the approaches for lowering body weight by surgery. What are the adverse side effects of these procedures?

292-296   18.   Describe a good weight-reduction diet in relation to energy content, meal size, carbohydrate and fat levels, and water intake.

292,293   19.   Outline the recommendations for a successful weight-loss diet.

294   20.   Discuss ways in which an increase in the water content of the diet plays an important role in body weight management.

296-298;300   21.   Explain the changes in metabolism consequent to a decrease in energy intake. How are these changes modified by regular physical exercise?

296-298;300   22.   Describe the benefits of regular physical activity as an aid to weight loss dieting.

298,299   23.   Explain the role of behavior modification in weight reduction programs.

302,303   24.   Present a sound diet plan for weight gain in the underweight person.

312-316   25.   List the characteristics of anorexia nervosa and bulimia nervosa. Describe the typical personality traits of individuals with these eating disorders.

316   26.   Discuss the characteristics of binge eating disorder. What is known about its treatment?

CHAPTER 10
THE WATER-SOLUBLE VITAMINS: B VITAMINS AND VITAMIN C

AN PAGE(S)

a   322(K)   01.   Expressions of vitamin quantities in foods and in the body include all of the following **except**
    a.   grams.
    b.   milligrams.
    c.   equivalents.
    d.   micrograms.

c   322(K)   02.   What is a precursor?
    a.   A conditionally essential vitamin
    b.   A sign or symptom of a vitamin deficiency disorder
    c.   A substance that is used to synthesize another compound
    d.   A substance that is recycled through the liver and intestines

b   322(K)   03.   What is meant by the bioavailability of a vitamin in food?
    a.   The total amount available from plant and animal food
    b.   The amount absorbed and subsequently used by the body
    c.   The amount that escapes destruction from food processing
    d.   The number of different chemical forms of the same vitamin

a   322-324(K)   04.   General characteristics of the water-soluble vitamins include all of the following **except**
    a.   they must be consumed daily.
    b.   toxic levels in the body are rarely found.
    c.   they are absorbed directly into the blood.
    d.   excesses are eliminated from the kidneys.

a   322-324(K)   05.   Which of the following is **not** a general characteristic of the fat-soluble vitamins?
    a.   Excesses are eliminated from the kidneys.
    b.   Absorption is via the lymphatic circulation.
    c.   Several of them require protein carriers for transport.
    d.   They can be stored in relatively large amounts in certain body tissues.

b   323,324(A)   06.   Which of the following vitamins would be removed in the production of skim milk?
    a.   Thiamin
    b.   Vitamin A
    c.   Riboflavin
    d.   Vitamin B_{12}

c   323,324(A)   07.   Cooking a food in liberal amounts of water is **least** likely to affect the vitamin content of
    a.   folate.
    b.   thiamin.
    c.   vitamin A.
    d.   riboflavin.

b   323,324(K)   08.   What is the primary excretory route for the water-soluble vitamins?
     a.   Bile
     b.   Kidney
     c.   Intestine
     d.   Perspiration

b   323,324;   09.   When thiamin is consumed in excess of needs, how does the body
    326(A)   treat the excess?
     a.   Not absorbed
     b.   Excreted primarily in the urine
     c.   Excreted primarily in the feces
     d.   Stored in liver, bone, and adipose tissue

d   324,325(K)   10.   What is the primary function of the B vitamins?
     a.   Energy source
     b.   Anticoagulation
     c.   Antibody stabilization
     d.   Coenzyme participation

d   324,325(A)   11.   Which of the following explains why B vitamin deficiencies lead to lack of energy?
     a.   B vitamins are a source of kilocalories.
     b.   Absorption of carbohydrates and fats is decreased.
     c.   Oxygen for energy metabolism cannot be transported to the cells.
     d.   Coenzymes needed for energy metabolism are produced in insufficient amounts.

c   325(K)   12.   Which of the following describes the basic function of a coenzyme?
     a.   Attaches to RNA to assist in the synthesis of an enzyme
     b.   Attaches to cell membranes to assist in uptake of an enzyme
     c.   Attaches to an enzyme and allows a chemical reaction to take place
     d.   Attaches to an enzyme, which allows for transport of the enzyme through the circulation

c   325,326(A)   13.   Which of the following functions has a requirement for thiamin?
     a.   Blood coagulation
     b.   Formation of red blood cells
     c.   Energy release from energy-yielding nutrients
     d.   Formation of epithelial cell mucopolysaccharides

d   325,326(K)   14.   What is the primary chemical reaction in which thiamin participates as its coenzyme?
     a.   Transfers amine groups in the synthesis of amino acids
     b.   Transfers hydrogen atoms in the synthesis of erythrocytes
     c.   Assists in addition of methyl groups to compounds involved in energy metabolism
     d.   Assists in removal of one-carbon units from compounds involved in energy metabolism

b   325(K)   15.   Which of the following is the coenzyme form of thiamin?
     a.   Thiaminacide
     b.   Thiamin pyrophosphate
     c.   Thiamin adenine dinucleotide
     d.   Thiamin flavin mononucleotide

b 326(K) 16. Beriberi results from a deficiency of
           a.   niacin.
           b.   thiamin.
           c.   vitamin C.
           d.   vitamin B12.

b 325-327(K) 17. Which of the following is a property of thiamin nutrition?
           a.   Participates in activation of prothrombin
           b.   Poor sources include seafood and cheeses
           c.   Significant amounts are found in leafy vegetables
           d.   Deficiency results in cheilosis and marked dermatitis

a 326(A) 18. Which of the following diets is most likely to lead to beriberi?
           a.   High intakes of white rice
           b.   Low intakes of whole grains
           c.   High intakes of unrefined rice
           d.   Low intakes of enriched grains

b 326(A) 19. The Wernicke-Korsakoff syndrome, which is often observed in poorly nourished alcohol abusers, is known to respond to supplements of
           a.   folacin.
           b.   thiamin.
           c.   vitamin C.
           d.   vitamin B12.

a 326,327(A) 20. Which of the following provides muscle tissue with the highest concentration of thiamin?
           a.   Pig
           b.   Fish
           c.   Steer
           d.   Chicken

a 326,327(K) 21. Which of the following provides the most thiamin per serving size?
           a.   Ham
           b.   Squash
           c.   Whole milk
           d.   Whole-grain breads

b 326,327(A) 22. Of the following, which is the richest food source of thiamin?
           a.   Milk
           b.   Pork
           c.   Lettuce
           d.   Refined rice

a 326(K) 23. Which of the following is a characteristic of thiamin stability in relation to cooking method?
           a.   Microwaving the food conserves much of the thiamin.
           b.   Prolonged heating of the food has little, if any, effect on the thiamin.
           c.   Boiling the food tends to conserve thiamin by forming a stable, hydrated complex.
           d.   Steaming the food can lead to substantial thiamin loss due to the high heat needed to form the steam.

d   326(A)   24.   Approximately what percentage of alcoholics shows thiamin deficiency?
a.   20
b.   40
c.   60
d.   80

d   327(K)   25.   Which of the following food groups ordinarily contains the highest amount of vitamins when expressed per kcalorie?
a.   Dairy
b.   Meats
c.   Fruits
d.   Vegetables

d   328(K)   26.   Riboflavin in its coenzyme form functions in the transfer of
a.   methyl groups.
b.   1-carbon units.
c.   2-carbon units.
d.   hydrogen atoms.

c   328(K)   27.   Which of the following vitamins is involved substantially in energy transformation reactions?
a.   Biotin
b.   Cobalamin
c.   Riboflavin
d.   Pyridoxine

d   328,329(K) 28.   The coenzyme FAD is formed from what vitamin?
a.   Niacin
b.   Choline
c.   Thiamin
d.   Riboflavin

d   328(K)   29.   Which of the following is indicative of a dietary deficiency of riboflavin?
a.   Beriberi
b.   Diarrhea
c.   Keratomalacia
d.   Inflamed mouth membranes

c   328-330(K) 30.   The signs and symptoms of riboflavin deficiency are known collectively as
a.   pellagra.
b.   antiflavonosis.
c.   ariboflavinosis.
d.   flavin adenine dinucleosis.

c   347(K)   31.   A deficiency of what vitamin produces a characteristic cracking and redness at the corners of the mouth?
a.   Biotin
b.   Niacin
c.   Riboflavin
d.   Ascorbic acid

a   328(A)   32.   Of the following commonly eaten foods, which makes the greatest contribution to riboflavin intake?
a.   Milk
b.   Potatoes
c.   Orange juice
d.   Peanut butter

c   328(A)   33.   Milk and milk products provide liberal amounts of which of the following vitamins?
a.   Folate
b.   Biotin
c.   Riboflavin
d.   Pantothenic acid

d   328(A)   34.   Riboflavin needs are more difficult to meet when the diet is low in
a.   meats.
b.   grains.
c.   vegetables.
d.   dairy foods.

d   328(K)   35.   Riboflavin is most easily destroyed when exposed to
a.   heat.
b.   acid.
c.   alkali.
d.   ultraviolet light.

b   328(A)   36.   What type of container is best for protecting the riboflavin content of milk?
a.   Airtight
b.   Cardboard
c.   Transparent glass
d.   Translucent plastic

a   328,329(K)   37.   Which of the following is a property of riboflavin in nutrition?
a.   Stability to heat is good
b.   Deficiency leads to beriberi
c.   Requirements are proportional to body weight
d.   Significant amounts are found in citrus products

d   330(K)   38.   Which of the following is a property of niacin in nutrition?
a.   It is susceptible to destruction in foods exposed to light.
b.   It participates primarily in reactions involving amino acids.
c.   It is soluble in both water and lipids depending upon its chemical form.
d.   It can be synthesized in the body from the essential amino acid tryptophan.

c   330;329(A)   39.   Which of the following properties is shared by niacin and riboflavin coenzymes?
a.   Unstable to irradiation
b.   Unstable to metal cooking utensils
c.   Acceptance and transfer of hydrogen atoms
d.   Acceptance and transfer of carboxyl groups

a   330,331(A)   40.   Which of the following nutrients functions to prevent the appearance of a bilateral, symmetrical dermatitis, primarily on areas exposed to the sun?
a.   Niacin
b.   Choline
c.   Inositol
d.   Riboflavin

c   330(A)   41.   When the diet contains an adequate amount of protein, what amino acid can be used by the body to synthesize niacin?
a.   Lysine
b.   Valine
c.   Tryptophan
d.   Phenylalanine

a   330(A)   42.   A diet low in protein and in which corn is a principal food has been found to cause a deficiency of what vitamin?
a.   Niacin
b.   Thiamin
c.   Vitamin C
d.   Vitamin B$_{12}$

b   330(K)   43.   What vitamin deficiency disease appeared in people who had subsisted on a diet high in corn and low in protein?
a.   Scurvy
b.   Pellagra
c.   Wet beriberi
d.   Pernicious anemia

d   330,331(K)   44.   Which of the following is **not** among the common signs of pellagra?
a.   Dementia
b.   Diarrhea
c.   Dermatitis
d.   Depression

b   330,331(K)   45.   A general niacin deficiency is known to be manifested in abnormalities of all of the following organs/systems **except**
a.   skin.
b.   skeletal.
c.   nervous system.
d.   gastrointestinal tract.

b   330(A)   46.   Which of the following substances is found in corn and contributes to the development of pellagra?
a.   Avidin
b.   Leucine
c.   Phytates
d.   Phenylalanine

c   330-332(A) 47.   A typical diet of a 50 kg woman provides the RDA level of protein plus 6 mg of
                        niacin. The protein contains an average of 1% tryptophan and 2% tyrosine.
                        Approximately how many niacin equivalents are contributed by the diet?
                        a.   2
                        b.   5
                        c.   13
                        d.   20

a   330,331(A) 48.   What is the term that identifies the characteristic tingling sensations and reddening
                        of the skin after ingesting a pharmacologic dose of nicotinic acid?
                        a.   Niacin flush
                        b.   NAD dermatitis
                        c.   Niacin erythremia
                        d.   Bilateral symmetrical dermatitis

c   330,331(A) 49.   Which of the following overt side effect(s) is likely to appear after a person ingests
                        a high quantity of nicotinic acid?
                        a.   Constipation
                        b.   Mental confusion
                        c.   Painful, tingling, itching sensation
                        d.   Hair loss, bloating, and photophobia

a   331(A)   50.   When taken in large doses, which of the following vitamins is associated with liver
                        injury and peptic ulcers?
                        a.   Niacin
                        b.   Thiamin
                        c.   Vitamin B_6
                        d.   Vitamin B_{12}

d   330,331(K) 51.   Large doses of nicotinic acid are known to result in all of the following **except**
                        a.   liver injury.
                        b.   peptic ulcer disease.
                        c.   dilation of capillaries.
                        d.   disappearance of learning disorders in children.

b   330-332(A) 52.   Approximately how many niacin equivalents would be provided from the protein
                        in the diet of a 130 lb person ingesting the RDA amount of protein?
                        a.   4
                        b.   8
                        c.   12
                        d.   16

b   330,331(K) 53.   Which of the following is a feature of niacin nutrition?
                        a.   Low doses may lead to kidney stones.
                        b.   High doses may lower blood cholesterol.
                        c.   Low doses may lead to heartburn and low blood pressure.
                        d.   High doses may elevate red blood cell count in mildly anemic individuals.

d   331;333(K)   54.   Features of biotin in nutrition include all of the following **except**
a.   it functions in the breakdown of amino acids and fatty acids.
b.   it functions as a carrier of carbon dioxide in energy metabolism.
c.   a deficiency can be induced by ingesting large quantities of raw egg whites.
d.   a deficiency can be induced by ingesting large amounts of thiamin and folic acid which interfere with its absorption.

a   331;333(K)   55.   Among the following compounds that serve as coenzymes in metabolism, which is considered a vitamin for human beings?
a.   Biotin
b.   Inositol
c.   Lipoic acid
d.   Orotic acid

c   333(K)   56.   Which of the following foods contains a protein that decreases bioavailability of biotin?
a.   Aged wine
b.   Aged cheese
c.   Raw egg whites
d.   Raw cauliflower

b   333(K)   57.   A protein that binds with biotin (thus inhibiting absorption) is found in which food?
a.   Aged cheese
b.   Raw egg whites
c.   Whole wheat bread
d.   Unhomogenized milk

d   333(K)   58.   Biotin can be synthesized by
a.   avidin.
b.   the skin.
c.   the liver.
d.   intestinal bacteria.

b   333(K)   59.   Which of the following vitamins is synthesized by intestinal bacteria?
a.   Folate
b.   Biotin
c.   Cyanocobalamin
d.   Pantothenic acid

d   333(K)   60.   What vitamin forms a part of coenzyme A?
a.   Biotin
b.   Folate
c.   Riboflavin
d.   Pantothenic acid

c   334(K)   61.   What vitamin is involved intensively in amino acid metabolism?
a.   Biotin
b.   Vitamin A
c.   Vitamin B6
d.   Riboflavin

b   334,335(A)   62.   Which of the following is **not** a characteristic of vitamin B6 in nutrition?
         a.   It is stored in muscle tissue.
         b.   It is required in amounts proportional to energy expenditure.
         c.   It can lead to irreversible nerve damage when taken in large doses.
         d.   It functions, in part, in the synthesis of glycine and glutamic acid.

d   334,335(K)   63.   All of the following are features of vitamin B6 metabolism **except**
         a.   a deficiency or toxicity leads to depression.
         b.   its destruction and excretion are promoted by alcohol intake.
         c.   it functions primarily as the coenzyme pyridoxal phosphate.
         d.   it enhances physical performance when supplied at a level of l mg/g of dietary protein.

d   335(K)   64.   What vitamin has been taken in large amounts by women in hopes of combating the symptoms of premenstrual syndrome?
         a.   Thiamin
         b.   Inositol
         c.   Cobalamin
         d.   Vitamin B6

a   334,335(K)   65.   Which of the following statements confirms our knowledge of water-soluble vitamin toxicity?
         a.   Toxicity symptoms for vitamin B6 can be severe and irreversible.
         b.   Toxicity symptoms for vitamin C include constipation and hyperactivity.
         c.   Toxicities of the B-vitamins occur almost as often from foods as from supplements.
         d.   Toxicity of niacin has been reported in body builders taking large amounts of amino acid supplements.

c   334(K)   66.   In what major way does alcohol intake affect vitamin B6 metabolism?
         a.   It reduces acetaldehyde formation.
         b.   It increases fecal excretion of the vitamin.
         c.   It dislodges the PLP coenzyme from its enzyme.
         d.   It interferes with synthesis of the PLP coenzyme.

d   335,336(A)   67.   On a per-kcalorie basis, which of the following foods is richest in vitamin B6?
         a.   Meats
         b.   Fruits
         c.   Legumes
         d.   Vegetables

a   335;344(K)   68.   Which of the following is an essential nutrient for human beings?
         a.   Folate
         b.   Inositol
         c.   Methoxatin
         d.   Lipoic acid

b   335-340(K)   69.   All of the following are properties of folate in nutrition **except**
         a.   it is needed for proper functioning of vitamin B12.
         b.   it functions primarily in the transfer of amino groups.
         c.   the coenzyme of folate requires vitamin B12 to function properly.
         d.   it requires enzymes on the intestinal mucosa to enhance its absorption from most foods.

a   336;339(A)   70.   What vitamin is involved mainly with the replacement of red blood cells and digestive tract cells?
  a. Folate
  b. Niacin
  c. Thiamin
  d. Riboflavin

a   336(K)   71.   Which of the following vitamins undergoes significant enterohepatic circulation?
  a. Folate
  b. Niacin
  c. Thiamin
  d. Pyridoxine

b   337(A)   72.   Research has shown that the risk for neural tube defects is lowered by taking supplements of
  a. niacin.
  b. folate.
  c. vitamin C.
  d. vitamin B_{12}.

d   336(K)   73.   Which of the following is a type of neural tube defect?
  a. Scurvy
  b. Beriberi
  c. Pellagra
  d. Spina bifida

a   335;340(A)   74.   Which of the following activities is shared by vitamin B_{12} and folate?
  a. Both are required for nucleic acid synthesis.
  b. Both require intrinsic factors for their release from food proteins.
  c. Both are found in significant amounts in green leafy vegetables.
  d. Both are considered problem nutrients for strict vegetarians.

a   336,337(K)   75.   Which of the following vitamins is usually found in a form that is bound to one or more glutamic acid molecules in food?
  a. Folate
  b. Thiamin
  c. Vitamin B_6
  d. Ascorbic acid

a   336(A)   76.   A person with a disorder that limits absorption of bile is at increased risk for deficiency of
  a. folate.
  b. niacin.
  c. riboflavin.
  d. ascorbic acid.

b   336(A)   77.   What is the most likely explanation for the impaired functioning of the GI tract resulting from folate deficiency?

    a.   Since folate is required for bile synthesis, folate deficiency results in insufficient bile production, thereby promoting fat malabsorption and diarrhea.

    b.   Since folate functions, in large part, in the process of cell renewal, a deficiency slows mucosal cell replacement, thereby resulting in decreased GI functioning.

    c.   The anemia of folate deficiency results in decreased oxygen supply to body tissues, with the intestines being particularly affected because of their high metabolic activity.

    d.   Since folate functions, in part, in the synthesis of pancreatic digestive enzymes, a deficiency leads to decreased enzymatic capacity in the intestines, thereby resulting in malabsorption.

d   336-339(K)   78.   Which of the following is a feature of folate nutrition?

    a.   The coenzyme form is FAD.

    b.   Dairy foods are a poor source of folate except for goat's milk.

    c.   Insufficient folate intake results in deficiency of homocysteine.

    d.   Synthetic folate is 70% more available than naturally occurring food folate.

c   337(K)   79.   Approximately what percentage of dietary folate is bioavailable?

    a.   10

    b.   25

    c.   50

    d.   80

d   337(K)   80.   The percent bioavailability of a folate supplement taken on an empty stomach is

    a.   5.

    b.   25.

    c.   50.

    d.   100.

c   339,340(K)   81.   Which of the following substances is known to adversely affect folate utilization?

    a.   Insulin

    b.   Calcium supplements

    c.   Regular use of antacids

    d.   Vitamin B_{12} supplements

d   340(K)   82.   Which of the following is representative of folate availability in foods?

    a.   Good sources are dairy products and meats.

    b.   Poor sources are fruit juices and vegetable juices.

    c.   Only about 10% of the amount in foods is bioavailable.

    d.   Much of the vitamin is lost during cooking and storage.

b   339K)   83.   Which of the following is known to significantly affect the body's folate status?

    a.   Sedentary lifestyle

    b.   Some anticancer drugs

    c.   Excess protein intake

    d.   Insufficient fiber intake

b   339(A)   84.   Physiological stresses such as blood loss, burns, measles, and cancer are known particularly to increase the risk of deficiency for
    a.   biotin.
    b.   folate.
    c.   riboflavin.
    d.   pantothenic acid.

d   339(K)   85.   Which of the following is associated with a deficiency of folate?
    a.   Hemolysis
    b.   Hypoxemia
    c.   Hemolytic anemia
    d.   Macrocytic anemia

b   339(K)   86.   Folate deficiency has been reported in infants fed
    a.   soy milk.
    b.   goat's milk.
    c.   chicken liver.
    d.   infant formula.

d   340,341(K) 87.   Which of the following foods is highest in folate?
    a.   Meats
    b.   Starches
    c.   Dairy products
    d.   Green leafy vegetables

a   339(K)   88.   Among all the vitamins, which is believed to be most vulnerable to interactions with drugs?
    a.   Folate
    b.   Niacin
    c.   Vitamin B_6
    d.   Vitamin B_{12}

d   340(A)   89.   What is the RDA for folate for a woman weighing 132 pounds?
    a.   180 µg
    b.   220 µg
    c.   242 µg
    d.   400 µg

c   340(K)   90.   Which of the following is required for the absorption of dietary vitamin B_{12}?
    a.   Bile
    b.   Lipase
    c.   Intrinsic factor
    d.   Carboxypeptidase

b   340(K)   91.   What is the function of intrinsic factor in vitamin B_{12} absorption?
    a.   It catalyzes release of the vitamin from its protein-bound form.
    b.   It attaches to the vitamin thereby allowing absorption from the intestines.
    c.   It acts as a storage protein for the vitamin within the intestinal epithelial cells.
    d.   It acts as a cofactor for mucosal enzymes involved in absorption of the vitamin.

c   341,342(A) 92.   The absorption of which of the following vitamins is most affected by the disorder atrophic gastritis?
    a.   Choline
    b.   Vitamin C
    c.   Vitamin B12
    d.   Pantothenic acid

c   340-343(K) 93.   Which of the following is a characteristic of vitamin B12?
    a.   Toxicity symptoms are serious and irreversible.
    b.   Units in food are expressed as cobalamin equivalents.
    c.   It is inactivated when the food is heated in a microwave.
    d.   Bioavailable amounts are found in fermented soy products.

a   342(K)   94.   Which of the following is a property of vitamin B12?
    a.   It is efficiently recycled by the body.
    b.   It is necessary for protection from pinpoint hemorrhages.
    c.   It requires attachment to fatty acids for transport in the circulation.
    d.   It is absorbed from the stomach with the aid of a special binding protein.

c   341,342(A) 95.   What is the most likely reason for the development of a vitamin B12 deficiency?
    a.   Inadequate intake
    b.   Increased excretion
    c.   Inadequate absorption
    d.   Increased losses in food preparation

b   340-342(A) 96.   A similar type of anemia is produced when there is a deficiency of either
    a.   riboflavin or niacin.
    b.   vitamin B12 or folate.
    c.   thiamin or riboflavin.
    d.   vitamin B6 or vitamin B12.

a   342(A)   97.   Which of the following is a common treatment for pernicious anemia caused by inadequate absorption?
    a.   Injection of cobalamin
    b.   Topical administration of liver extract
    c.   Oral supplements of B-vitamin complex
    d.   A diet high in liver and green leafy vegetables

d   341,342(A) 98.   Among the following water-soluble vitamins, a secondary deficiency would most likely be seen for
    a.   biotin.
    b.   thiamin.
    c.   vitamin C.
    d.   vitamin B12.

d   342(A)   99.   If a person refrained from ingesting any of the water-soluble vitamins, deficiency symptoms would appear last for
    a.   folate.
    b.   vitamin C.
    c.   vitamin B1.
    d.   vitamin B12.

b   342(A)   100.   Why are vegetarians at risk of developing vitamin B12 deficiency?
a.   Vegetarian diets inhibit absorption of the vitamin.
b.   Vegetarian diets provide insufficient amounts of the vitamin.
c.   High fiber content of vegetarian diets causes decreased storage by the liver.
d.   High fiber content of vegetarian diets causes increased excretion of the vitamin.

d   342(A)   101.   Normally, the body's storage and re-utilization of vitamin B12 prevents a primary or secondary deficiency from occurring until after about
a.   3 days.
b.   3 weeks.
c.   3 months.
d.   3 years.

d   342(A)   102.   In a person who loses the ability to absorb vitamin B12, approximately what period of time could elapse before deficiency signs develop?
a.   One month
b.   Six months
c.   One year
d.   Three years

b   341,342(K)   103.   Pernicious anemia results from a combination of lack of intrinsic factor and
a.   ariboflavonosis.
b.   atrophic gastritis.
c.   pancreatic vitaminases.
d.   pharmacologic intakes of folate.

a   342,343(A)   104.   Of the following foods, which would be the only source of vitamin B12?
a.   Hot dog
b.   Pecan pie
c.   Cauliflower
d.   Blueberry muffin

a   344(K)   105.   Which of the following is known to perform an essential function in the human body?
a.   Inositol
b.   Orotic acid
c.   Methoxantin
d.   Pangamic acid

b   343,344(K)   106.   Which of the following is classified as a conditionally essential nutrient?
a.   PABA
b.   Choline
c.   Inositol
d.   Ubiquinone

b   344(K)   107.   Which of the following is **not** known to be required in the diet of human beings?
a.   Folic acid
b.   Lipoic acid
c.   Ascorbic acid
d.   Pantothenic acid

a   343,344(K)   108.   Which of the following is probably required in the diet of human beings?
      a.   Choline
      b.   Inositol
      c.   Lipoic acid
      d.   Pangamic acid

b   344(K)   109.   Which of the following is **not** known to be a vitamin for human beings?
      a.   Cobalamin
      b.   Ubiquinone
      c.   Pyridoxine
      d.   Pantothenic acid

c   343(K)   110.   Which of the following vitamins has an RDA?
      a.   Biotin
      b.   Choline
      c.   Cobalamin
      d.   Pantothenic acid

a   345-348;   111.   Which of the following characteristics is shared by vitamins B_6, B_{12}, C and folate?
    351(A)
      a.   Prevention of anemia
      b.   Required for glycolysis
      c.   Required in microgram quantities
      d.   Found in citrus products and legumes

b   334-347(K)   112.   Which of the following is frequently affected by deficiencies of the B vitamins?
      a.   Bones
      b.   Tongue
      c.   Eyesight
      d.   Hair and nails

b   347(A)   113.   Which of the following is an overt sign of a possible B vitamin deficiency?
      a.   Anemia
      b.   Smooth tongue
      c.   Abnormal liver function
      d.   Abnormal heart function

c   350(A)   114.   Which of the following represents the results of well-controlled studies of vitamin C supplementation on the resistance to, and recovery from, colds?
      a.   There was a reduction in the duration of colds by 50% on the average.
      b.   There was only a minor effect on reducing the number and severity of colds.
      c.   There was a significant reduction in the duration of colds in people who consumed at least one gram a day.
      d.   There was a significant reduction in the number of colds only in people who consumed more than three grams per day.

a   350(A)   115.   Why might vitamin C supplements be beneficial in treating the common cold?
      a.   It deactivates histamine.
      b.   It destroys intestinal pathogens.
      c.   It reduces episodes of sneezing.
      d.   It alters hypothalamic control of body temperature.

c 350(K) 116. Which of the following vitamins is known to deactivate histamine, a substance that causes nasal congestion?
   a. Niacin
   b. Vitamin E
   c. Vitamin C
   d. Vitamin B$_{12}$

a 350(A) 117. What is the minimum amount of ascorbic acid that will prevent the appearance of scorbutic symptoms in human beings?
   a. 10 mg
   b. 30 mg
   c. 50 mg
   d. 60 mg

d 351(A) 118. How much vitamin C is needed daily to raise blood ascorbic acid concentrations to a maximum?
   a. 10 mg
   b. 75 mg
   c. 125 mg
   d. 200 mg

c 353(K) 119. In the United States, what is the adult RDA for vitamin C?
   a. 10-20 mg
   b. 50-60 mg
   c. 75-90 mg
   d. 100-135 mg

d 349(K) 120. Which of the following is a general function of vitamin C?
   a. Antiviral agent
   b. Antifungal agent
   c. Anticancer agent
   d. Antioxidant agent

b 349(K) 121. In what capacity does vitamin C function?
   a. Coenzyme for energy release
   b. Cofactor in collagen formation
   c. Cofactor with calcium in blood coagulation
   d. Coenzyme in the formation of red blood cells

c 349(K) 122. The **protein** that requires ascorbic acid for its formation is
   a. keratin.
   b. albumin.
   c. collagen.
   d. hydroxyproline.

a 351(K) 123. Which of the following is an early sign of vitamin C deficiency?
   a. Bleeding gums
   b. Pernicious anemia
   c. Appearance of a cold
   d. Hysteria and depression

d   351;353(K)   124.   Which of the following symptoms is indicative of a deficiency of vitamin C?
  a.   Hair loss
  b.   Muscle spasms
  c.   Bilateral symmetrical dermatitis
  d.   Subcutaneous pinpoint hemorrhages

c   350(K)   125.   What body organ contains the highest amount of vitamin C?
  a.   Liver
  b.   Spleen
  c.   Adrenal glands
  d.   Skeletal muscle

c   352,353(A)   126.   All of the following are consequences of ingesting excess vitamin C supplements **except**
  a.   they frequently cause diarrhea.
  b.   they appear safe at levels up to 300 mg/day.
  c.   they enhance the action of anticlotting medications.
  d.   they interfere with laboratory urine tests for the diagnosis of diabetes.

d   352,353(K)   127.   Which of the following foods provides ample amounts of vitamin C?
  a.   Tofu
  b.   Yogurt
  c.   Legumes
  d.   Broccoli

c   352,353(K)   128.   Which of the following food groups is a rich source of vitamin C?
  a.   Milk group
  b.   Meat group
  c.   Fruit group
  d.   Bread-cereal group

a   353,353(A)   129.   Which of these meals is lacking in vitamin C?
  a.   Roast beef, carrots, noodles, and tea
  b.   Hot dog, cabbage, french fries, and milk
  c.   Roast beef, broccoli, noodles, and coffee
  d.   Spaghetti with tomato sauce, meatball, garlic bread, and red wine

c   352,353(A)   130.   Which of the following would be a very good source of vitamin C for the lacto-ovo-vegetarian?
  a.   Milk
  b.   Eggs
  c.   Broccoli
  d.   Whole-grain bread

a   352,353(K)   131.   What food makes a significant contribution to vitamin C intakes in the U.S. population despite the modest vitamin C concentration?
  a.   Potatoes
  b.   Organ meats
  c.   Breaded fish
  d.   Whole-grain cereals

c   352(A)   132.   What term is used to describe the outcome of a diagnostic test that apparently
                         shows that you have mononucleosis when in reality you do not?
                         a.   True positive
                         b.   True negative
                         c.   False positive
                         d.   False negative

d   352(A)   133.   What term describes the outcome of a diagnostic test that apparently indicates
                         that you do not have an infection when in reality you do?
                         a.   True positive
                         b.   True negative
                         c.   False positive
                         d.   False negative

c   352,353(A) 134.   Which of the following would be the poorest dietary source of vitamin C?
                         a.   Liver
                         b.   Potatoes
                         c.   Whole grains
                         d.   Cruciferous vegetables

d   352(A)   135.   People with the condition known as iron overload are adversely affected from
                         taking supplements of
                         a.   niacin.
                         b.   retinol.
                         c.   cobalamin.
                         d.   ascorbic acid.

c   359,360(A) 136.   Which of the following statements is representative of vitamin supplementation
                         practices?
                         a.   Most people who take supplements consume a poor diet.
                         b.   Most people should take supplements daily because of the great difficulty
                                 in obtaining the needed amounts from food.
                         c.   People who have low energy intakes or are pregnant are at risk for
                                 developing deficiencies and may benefit from supplementation.
                         d.   People should take supplements daily because nutrition surveys in the U.S.
                                 and Canada have detected deficiencies in some population groups.

b   359,360(A) 137.   Groups of people who are at risk for developing marginal deficiencies and may
                         benefit from taking vitamin supplements include all of the following **except**
                         a.   vegans.
                         b.   athletes.
                         c.   food faddists.
                         d.   people with low energy intakes, such as habitual dieters and the elderly.

c   359(K)   138.   Approximately what percentage of the U.S. population takes multi-nutrient
                         supplements regularly?
                         a.   5
                         b.   20
                         c.   50
                         d.   80

c   361(A)   139.   All of the following are known to occur from a mild iron overdose **except**
                       a.   nausea.
                       b.   GI distress.
                       c.   black tongue.
                       d.   black diarrhea.

d   359-363(K) 140.   The known dangers of taking vitamin supplements include all of the following **except**
                       a.   vitamin toxicity.
                       b.   the taker may ignore warning signs of a disease.
                       c.   the taker may feel a false sense of security and consume a poor diet.
                       d.   pathogenic bacterial overgrowth of the large intestines leading to increased risk of infection.

MATCHING (Answers can be used only once.)

J	326	01.	Name of thiamin deficiency disease
A	326	02.	A food unusually rich in thiamin
L	330	03.	Deficiency of this vitamin leads to cracks and redness at corners of the mouth
S	328	04.	Exposure to this leads to destruction of riboflavin
C	328	05.	A food source that supplies a substantial amount of people's riboflavin intake
O	331	06.	Used for synthesis of niacin
B	330	07.	Overconsumption of this food has resulted in pellagra
F	331	08.	High doses are known to lower blood cholesterol
E	333	09.	Deficiency of this vitamin is induced by feeding raw egg whites
T	333	10.	This vitamin is required for synthesis of acetyl-CoA
M	335	11.	Toxicity from this vitamin is known to cause irreversible nerve damage
D	337	12.	Prevention of neural tube defects is related to increased intake of this substance by pregnant women
H	339	13.	One of the first symptoms of folate deficiency
N	340	14.	Required to maintain nerve fiber sheath
R	340	15.	Required for absorption of vitamin B_{12}
G	344	16.	A conditionally essential nutrient
Q	348	17.	The antiscorbutic factor
I	349	18.	Vitamin C is required for the synthesis of this substance
P	352	19.	Excess intake of vitamin C aggravates this disorder
K	353	20.	A concentrated source of vitamin C

A.	Pork		K.	Broccoli
B.	Corn		L.	Riboflavin
C.	Dairy		M.	Vitamin B_6
D.	Folate		N.	Vitamin B_{12}
E.	Biotin		O.	Tryptophan
F.	Niacin		P.	Iron overload
G.	Choline		Q.	Ascorbic acid
H.	Anemia		R.	Intrinsic factor
I.	Collagen		S.	Ultraviolet light
J.	Beriberi		T.	Pantothenic acid

ESSAY QUESTIONS

PAGE(S)

323   01. What steps should be taken by consumers to minimize the loss of vitamins from foods?

326;328,329;331; 02. Discuss the effects of heat and ultraviolet light on vitamin stability.
333;335;340;343;352

323,324;347;352;   03. Under what circumstances can water-soluble vitamins be toxic? Cite
354;360,361   several examples.

337-340   04. Discuss the expected benefits of folate fortification of grain products. What are the possible adverse effects of this practice?

340-343   05. Discuss the interrelationships of folate and vitamin B_{12} in the diagnosis and treatment of large-cell type anemia.

340-342   06. Define intrinsic factor and discuss its relationship to vitamin B_{12} absorption. What other factors are associated with vitamin B_{12} absorption? What is the most common cause of vitamin B_{12} deficiency and how is vitamin B_{12} deficiency treated under this condition?

341-343   07. Why might vegans develop a vitamin B_{12} deficiency? Why might they have a normal vitamin B_{12} status?

324,325;345   08. Discuss the roles of the B vitamins in energy metabolism.

345-347   09. Discuss similarities in the deficiency symptoms of the B vitamins.

345-347   10. What is meant by the expression: "vitamins are like horseshoe nails"?

349,350   11. Explain the modes of action of vitamin C.

350,351   12. Under what conditions and for what reasons would intakes of vitamin C above the RDA be desirable?

350   13. In what ways have vitamin C supplements been shown to affect nasal congestion?

352   14. Describe the hazards of excessive vitamin C intake.

352   15. What is meant by false positive and false negative medical tests as influenced by vitamin supplements?

359-363   16. List several arguments for and against the regular use of vitamin supplements.

360   17. List population groups that have a physiological need for vitamin supplements.

363-364   18. Explain the major aspects of the Dietary Supplement Health and Education Act of 1994.

CHAPTER 11
THE FAT-SOLUBLE VITAMINS: A, D, E AND K

AN PAGE(S)

c   367(A)   01.   Which of the following is **not** among the features of the fat-soluble vitamins?
a.   Require bile for absorption
b.   Found in the fat and oily parts of foods
c.   Transported permanently to the liver and adipose tissue
d.   Pose a greater risk for developing a toxicity than water-soluble vitamins

c   367(K)   02.   What is the major carrier of the fat-soluble vitamins from the intestinal epithelial cell to the circulation?
a.   Albumin
b.   Cholesterol
c.   Chylomicrons
d.   Liposoluble binding proteins

c   367(K)   03.   Which of the following is a property of the fat-soluble vitamins?
a.   Most of them are synthesized by intestinal bacteria
b.   Intestinal transport occurs by way of the portal circulation
c.   Deficiency symptoms may take years to develop on a poor diet
d.   Toxicity risk is higher for vitamins E and K than for other fat soluble vitamins

d   368;380;383(K) 04.   Which of the following is **not** a fat-soluble vitamin?
a.   Retinol
b.   Tocopherol
c.   Phylloquinone
d.   Cyanocobalamin

c   368(K)   05.   How many different forms of vitamin A are active in the body?
a.   1
b.   2
c.   3
d.   5

d   368(K)   06.   All of the following are forms of vitamin A **except**
a.   retinol.
b.   retinal.
c.   retinoic acid.
d.   retinoquinone.

a   369,370(A)   07.   As far as is known, vitamin A does **not** play an important role in which of the following processes?
a.   Blood clotting
b.   Growth of bones and teeth
c.   Synthesis of visual pigment
d.   Maintaining mucous membranes

d   369,370(A) 08.   Which of the following functions of vitamin A accounts for most of the body's need for the vitamin?
a.   Promoting good night vision
b.   Assisting in immune reactions
c.   Promoting the growth of bones
d.   Maintaining mucous membranes

d   370(K)   09.   Which of the following describes the primary function of vitamin A in bone health?
a.   It stimulates uptake of calcium from the intestines.
b.   It promotes synthesis of specific bone proteins involved in the mineralization process.
c.   It inhibits oxidation of bone mucopolysaccharides thereby preserving bone crystal integrity and promoting growth.
d.   It assists enzymes that degrade certain regions of the bone thereby allowing remodeling to occur.

d   371,372(A) 10.   Vitamin A supplements are helpful in treating which of the following conditions?
a.   Acne
b.   Rickets
c.   Osteomalacia
d.   Night blindness

c   368(K)   11.   Which of the following is responsible for transporting vitamin A from the liver to other tissues?
a.   Albumin
b.   Rhodopsin
c.   Retinol-binding protein
d.   Transcarotenoid protein

d   370(K)   12.   Approximately what percent of the body's vitamin A stores are found in the liver?
a.   20
b.   50
c.   70
d.   90

a   370(K)   13.   What tissue contains the majority of the body's store of vitamin A?
a.   Liver
b.   Adipose
c.   Retinal cells
d.   Intestinal mucosal cells

d   371-372(A) 14.   Which of the following features do Retin-A and Accutane share?
a.   They are teratogenic.
b.   They are highly toxic.
c.   They are usually taken orally.
d.   They have chemical structures similar to vitamin A.

d   372(K)   15.   Which of the following is a feature of Accutane?
a.   It is effective in treating rickets.
b.   It is less toxic than pure vitamin A.
c.   It is known to be effective in treating mild but not severe acne.
d.   It is known to cause birth defects when used by pregnant women.

c   369(K)   16.   Which of the following describes an association of vitamin A and vision?
a.   Retinol is the form bound to beta-carotene in the corneal membrane.
b.   Retinoic acid is the form required for synthesis of retinoblasts.
c.   Light causes retinal to shift from a cis to a trans configuration.
d.   Pigment molecules in the retina are composed of a molecule of vitamin A bound to an omega-3 fatty acid.

c   369(K)   17.   Which of the following is the name of the vitamin A compound that is active in the visual response?
a.   Opsin
b.   Keratin
c.   Retinal
d.   Carotene

a   369(K)   18.   Which of the following describes an event in the visual response process?
a.   Light energy strikes the retina and excites pigments to release retinal.
b.   Light energy strikes the cornea and excites pigments to release retinoic acid.
c.   Visual pigments deep in the brain are excited by light transmitted through the retina.
d.   Epithelial cells on the surface of the eye respond to light energy by transmitting opsin molecules along nerve pathways to the brain.

d   368(A)   19.   If the diet contains precursor vitamin A, which of the following tissues can use it to form vitamin A?
a.   Eyes
b.   Kidneys
c.   Adipose cells
d.   Intestinal cells

a   372;380(A)   20.   Which of the following functions is **shared** by beta-carotene and vitamin E?
a.   Inhibition of oxidation
b.   Prevention of keratinization
c.   Prevention of hemolytic anemia
d.   Inhibition of bone calcium loss

d   370(K)   21.   Which of the following substances is converted to vitamin A in the body?
a.   Cholesterol
b.   Chlorophyll
c.   Xanthophyll
d.   Beta-carotene

d   370(K)   22.   Which of the following food substances can be converted to vitamin A in the body?
a.   Tryptophan
b.   Chlorophyll
c.   Xanthophyll
d.   Beta-carotene

c   372(K)   23.   All of the following are characteristics of excess consumption of beta-carotene **except**
a.   overconsumption from **foods** is not harmful.
b.   supplements may destroy the body's vitamin A.
c.   overconsumption from **supplements** is not harmful.
d.   drinking alcohol worsens the adverse effects of supplements.

b   368,369(A) 24.   What are the known effects of raising animals on diets containing retinoic acid as the only source of vitamin A?
a.   Growth is stunted.
b.   Blindness develops.
c.   Retinal synthesis is stimulated.
d.   Retinol synthesis is stimulated.

c   370,371(A) 25.   The effects of vitamin A deficiency are most severe in what population group?
a.   Adults
b.   Elderly
c.   Newborns
d.   Adolescents

d   370,371(K) 26.   If a normal, healthy adult were to begin consuming a vitamin A poor diet, approximately how much time would pass before the first deficiency symptoms would appear?
a.   2 weeks
b.   1 to 2 months
c.   6 months
d.   1 to 2 years

c   370-371(K) 27.   Approximately how many children worldwide have vitamin A deficiency?
a.   1 million
b.   10 million
c.   100 million
d.   500 million

b   371(A)   28.   In Indonesia, people with a disorder termed "chicken eyes" actually suffer from
a.   xerophthalmia.
b.   night blindness.
c.   ocular dystrophy.
d.   intermittent claudication.

b   371(K)   29.   Studies in developing countries have demonstrated that the mortality rate of children with measles can be significantly reduced by providing supplements of
a.   iron.
b.   vitamin A.
c.   folic acid.
d.   phylloquinone.

c   371,372(A) 30.   Which of the following is most likely to occur from a prolonged dietary deficiency of vitamin A?
a.   Osteomalacia
b.   Osteoporosis
c.   Xerophthalmia
d.   Prolonged blood-clotting time

c   372(K)   31.   Keratinization is the result of
a.   toxicity of vitamin A.
b.   toxicity of vitamin D.
c.   deficiency of vitamin A.
d.   deficiency of vitamin D.

c   372(A)   32.   What part of the body is affected most from keratomalacia?
a.   Bone
b.   Liver
c.   Cornea
d.   Immune cells

b   373,374(A) 33.   Which of the following is likely to induce vitamin A toxicity in adults?
a.   Eating beef liver more than once a month
b.   Consuming high-dose vitamin A supplements
c.   Drinking 2 quarts of vitamin A-fortified milk daily
d.   Consuming large amounts of dark green and deep orange vegetables

c   372(A)   34.   Which of the following is the most likely side effect for a person who regularly consumes large quantities of carrots or carrot juice?
a.   Bone pain
b.   Dermatitis
c.   Skin yellowing
d.   Vitamin A toxicity

c   372,373(A) 35.   In which of the following individuals would vitamin A toxicity be most likely to occur?
a.   Adolescent women
b.   Overweight adults
c.   Those taking vitamin A supplements
d.   Those consuming more than 100 g of carrots daily

c   372(A)   36.   To decrease risk for vitamin A toxicity-related birth defects, it is suggested that pregnant women limit vitamin A supplements to less than
a.   5,000 RE.
b.   10,000 RE.
c.   4 times RDA.
d.   10 times RDA.

c   392(K)   37.   Keratinization of lung cells has been reported in smokers taking high-dose supplements of
a.   vitamin C.
b.   vitamin A.
c.   beta-carotene.
d.   alpha-tocopherol.

b   373,374(A) 38.   All of the following are good sources of vitamin A **except**
a.   liver.
b.   pears.
c.   apricots.
d.   sweet potatoes.

b   372,373(K) 39.   Which of the following foods is a very good source of vitamin A?
a.   Corn
b.   Pumpkin pie
c.   Baked potato
d.   Whole-grain bread

a   372,373(A)   40.   Which of the following provides the **least** amount of precursor vitamin A?
      a.   Corn
      b.   Spinach
      c.   Carrots
      d.   Cantaloupe

b   373(K)   41.   Which of the following is a characteristic of vitamin A and foods?
      a.   Fast foods are generally considered good sources of vitamin A.
      b.   A regular intake of chicken liver is known to induce toxicity in children.
      c.   Xanthophylls in certain vegetables can be converted to active vitamin A in the liver.
      d.   Chlorophyll in vegetables can be converted to active vitamin A in the intestinal cells.

d   373(K)   42.   Which of the following is a feature of vitamin A in foods?
      a.   Anthocyanin in beets masks the presence of beta-carotene.
      b.   Margarine made from corn oil is a poor source of vitamin A.
      c.   Most carotenoids can be converted in the body to active vitamin A.
      d.   Chlorophyll in dark green leafy vegetables masks the presence of beta-carotene.

d   373(K)   43.   How many micrograms of dietary beta-carotene are equivalent to 1 retinol activity equivalent?
      a.   2
      b.   4
      c.   8
      d.   12

a   373(K)   44.   **On average**, one retinol activity equivalent is equal to about how many international units?

      a.   3
      b.   5
      c.   8
      d.   10

c   373,374(K)   45.   The adult RDA for vitamin A is approximately
      a.   400 mg.
      b.   1,000 mg.
      c.   800 retinol activity equivalents.
      d.   5,000 retinol activity equivalents.

a   375,376(K)   46.   Which of the following compounds serves as the major precursor for the body's synthesis of vitamin D?
      a.   Cholesterol
      b.   Tryptophan
      c.   Beta-carotene
      d.   Eicosapentanoic acid

d   375(A)   47.   Which of the following can the body use to synthesize vitamin D?
      a.   Bone
      b.   Carotene
      c.   Tryptophan
      d.   Exposure to sunlight

d   378,379(K)   48.   Which of the following is a feature of vitamin D synthesis?
   a.   Tanning lamps and tanning booths do not stimulate vitamin D synthesis.
   b.   Suncreens with sunburn protection factors of 2 and above prevent synthesis of vitamin D.
   c.   The ultraviolet rays of the sun are able to easily pierce heavy clouds and smog to promote vitamin D synthesis.
   d.   Dark skinned people require longer sunlight exposure than light-skinned people to synthesize equivalent amounts of vitamin D.

a   378(A)   49.   Which of the following enables much of the world's population to maintain adequate vitamin D status?
   a.   Outdoor exposure of the skin to sunlight
   b.   Wide availability of low-cost fish products
   c.   Wide availability of food assistance programs
   d.   World Health Organization distribution of vitamin D capsules

c   378(K)   50.   Which of the following is a characteristic of vitamin D nutrition?
   a.   Vitamin D deficiency may be created by a calcium deficiency.
   b.   Only about one-half of the world's population relies on sunlight to maintain adequate vitamin D nutrition.
   c.   Prolonged exposure to sunlight degrades the vitamin D precursor in skin, thus preventing vitamin D toxicity.
   d.   In people living in northern U.S. cities, vitamin D stores from synthesis during the summer are usually sufficient to meet the needs during the winter.

c   376,377(A) 51.   In what tissues must a molecule of vitamin D be chemically altered to yield a compound that is fully active?
   a.   Liver only
   b.   Kidney only
   c.   Liver and kidney
   d.   Liver and intestines

a   375(K)   52.   The major target organs for the action of activated vitamin D include all of the following **except**
   a.   liver.
   b.   bone.
   c.   kidney.
   d.   intestine.

b   375,376(K) 53.   All of the following are other names for vitamin D **except**
   a.   calciferol.
   b.   calcitonin.
   c.   cholecalciferol.
   d.   dihydroxy vitamin D.

d   375,376(K) 54.   What is/are the main function(s) of vitamin D?
   a.   Promotes secretion of calcitonin
   b.   Promotes synthesis of 7-dehydrocholesterol
   c.   Promotes synthesis of carotenoids and controls absorption of fat soluble vitamins
   d.   Promotes calcium and phosphorus absorption and promotes calcium mobilization from bone

d   376-379(K) 55.   All of the following are characteristics of vitamin D nutrition **except**
                        a.   deficient intake may lead to altered bone composition.
                        b.   excessive intake may lead to mineral deposits in the kidneys.
                        c.   fortified milk is the major dietary source in the U.S. population.
                        d.   the requirement is increased in most people who are exposed to the sun.

a   375(K)   56.   Which of the following compounds is known to function as a hormone?
                        a.   Vitamin D
                        b.   Vitamin K
                        c.   Phylloquinone
                        d.   Alpha-tocopherol

a   375(K)   57.   The plant version of vitamin D is known as
                        a.   ergocalciferol.
                        b.   foliocalciferol.
                        c.   cholecalciferol.
                        d.   phyllocalciferol.

c   375(K)   58.   The animal version of vitamin D is known as
                        a.   ergocalciferol.
                        b.   foliocalciferol.
                        c.   cholecalciferol.
                        d.   phyllocalciferol.

b   376(K)   59.   What is the name of the vitamin D-deficiency disease in adults?
                        a.   Rickets
                        b.   Osteomalacia
                        c.   Keratomalacia
                        d.   Hyperkeratosis

c   376(A)   60.   What population group is at highest risk for osteomalacia?
                        a.   Infants
                        b.   Elderly men
                        c.   Adult women
                        d.   Children ages 2-12 years

b   376(A)   61.   In what system would the effects of a vitamin D deficiency be most readily
                        observed?
                        a.   Nervous
                        b.   Skeletal
                        c.   Muscular
                        d.   Circulatory

a   376(K)   62.   Which of the following symptoms would indicate a vitamin D deficiency?
                        a.   Bowed legs
                        b.   Rupture of red blood cells
                        c.   Frequent respiratory infections
                        d.   Abnormally high blood calcium level

a   376(A)   63.   Which of the following conditions or diseases are known to be caused by a deficiency of the same nutrient?
    a.   Osteomalacia and rickets
    b.   Xerophthalmia and breath pentane release
    c.   Kwashiorkor and fibrocystic breast disease
    d.   Hemolytic anemia and large-cell type anemia

c   376(A)   64.   The risk for vitamin D deficiency increases with advancing age for all of the following reasons **except**
    a.   exposure to sunlight is reduced.
    b.   older people decrease milk intake.
    c.   absorption of dietary vitamin D declines.
    d.   the kidneys are less efficient at activating vitamin D.

d   377(A)   65.   Which of the following may result from excessive intakes of vitamin D by adults?
    a.   Increased bone density
    b.   Increased bone calcification
    c.   Deformity of leg bones, ribs, and skull
    d.   Mineral deposits in soft tissues such as the kidney

a   377(A)   66.   Which of the following conditions is known to lead to formation of mineral deposits in the blood vessels and kidney?
    a.   Excessive intake of vitamin D
    b.   Inadequate intake of vitamin D
    c.   Excessive intake of tocopherols
    d.   Inadequate intake of tocopherols

c   377(A)   67.   Which of the following is a feature of vitamin D?
    a.   Toxicity from vitamin D may result from overexposure to the sun.
    b.   Requirements are much higher in the elderly due to degenerative bone diseases.
    c.   Fortification of milk with the vitamin is common in order to provide people with a reliable source.
    d.   Absorption from most food sources is very poor, necessitating the addition of liberal quantities to grain products.

b   377(A)   68.   Which of the following is the most reliable source of vitamin D in the diet?
    a.   Meat
    b.   Fortified milk
    c.   Fruits and vegetables
    d.   Enriched breads and cereals

a   379(K)   69.   What is the Adequate Intake level for vitamin D in individuals around 20 years of age?
    a.   5 μg
    b.   8 μg
    c.   10 μg
    d.   14 μg

a   389(K)   70.   What is a free radical?
                      a.   A molecule that is unstable and highly reactive because it contains
                              unpaired electrons
                      b.   An antioxidant substance that prevents accumulation of cell-damaging
                              oxides
                      c.   A substance in food that interacts with nutrients to decrease their
                              utilization
                      d.   A nutrient in excess of body needs that the body is free to degrade with no
                              consequence

c   380(K)   71.   The main function of vitamin E in the body is to act as a(n)
                      a.   coenzyme.
                      b.   peroxide.
                      c.   antioxidant.
                      d.   free radical.

c   389,390(K) 72.   What is the role of vitamin E in the metabolism of free radicals?
                      a.   Carrier
                      b.   Promoter
                      c.   Eliminator
                      d.   Synthesizer

a   389(K)   73.   Which of the following features do vitamins C and E share?
                      a.   Both function as antioxidants.
                      b.   Both require bile for absorption.
                      c.   Neither participates in protein synthesis.
                      d.   Neither is affected by the processing of foods.

b   380(K)   74.   How is vitamin E thought to play a role in reducing the risk of heart disease?
                      a.   It inhibits dietary absorption of cholesterol.
                      b.   It slows oxidation of low-density lipoproteins.
                      c.   It interferes with cholesterol synthesis by the liver.
                      d.   It speeds removal of blood cholesterol by the liver.

d   380(K)   75.   The major function of vitamin E is to inhibit the destruction of
                      a.   lysosomes.
                      b.   free radicals.
                      c.   mucopolysaccharides.
                      d.   polyunsaturated fatty acids.

c   370;375;   76.   The process of bone remodeling is known to be dependent on all of the fat-soluble
    382(K)   vitamins **except**
                      a.   vitamin A.
                      b.   vitamin K.
                      c.   vitamin E.
                      d.   vitamin D.

a   381,382(K) 77.   Which of the following is a property of the tocopherols?
                      a.   Easily destroyed by air and oxygen
                      b.   Act as precursors for the menaquinones
                      c.   May dissolve from foods into cooking water
                      d.   Absorbed from the intestines into the portal circulation

d   381(K)   78.   Which of the following disorders may result from vitamin E deficiency in people?
                        a.   Rickets
                        b.   Xerophthalmia
                        c.   Muscular dystrophy
                        d.   Erythrocyte hemolysis

c   381(A)   79.   Which of the following is a feature of vitamin E?
                        a.   Functions as a hormone-like substance
                        b.   Toxicity symptoms include bone abnormalities
                        c.   Deficiencies occur from inability to absorb dietary lipids
                        d.   Important food sources include enriched breads and pasta

b   381(A)   80.   What is the reason that vitamin E deficiencies are rarely observed in human beings?
                        a.   The vitamin is not essential.
                        b.   The vitamin is widespread in foods.
                        c.   Most people take vitamin E supplements.
                        d.   The vitamin can be synthesized by the body.

b   381,382(K) 81.   Which of the following is a feature of vitamin E in foods?
                        a.   Vitamin E is fairly stable to heat.
                        b.   Most convenience foods are poor sources of vitamin E.
                        c.   Saturated oils are the major dietary sources of vitamin E.
                        d.   The amount of alpha-tocopherol in foods is underestimated.

c   381,382(K) 82.   Which of the following are major sources of vitamin E in the diet?
                        a.   Meats
                        b.   Citrus fruits
                        c.   Vegetable oils
                        d.   Milk and dairy products

d   381,382(A) 83.   Among the following, which contains the highest concentration of vitamin E?
                        a.   Butter
                        b.   Carrots
                        c.   Milk fat
                        d.   Corn oil

d   381(K)   84.   In comparison with the RDA for vitamin E, about how many fold higher is the
                        Upper Level?
                        a.   2
                        b.   10
                        c.   25
                        d.   65

b   381(A)   85.   Increasing the amount of polyunsaturated fats in the diet increases the need for
                        vitamin
                        a.   A.
                        b.   E.
                        c.   K.
                        d.   D.

d   381(A)   86.   There is some evidence for benefits from vitamin E supplements in all of the
                     following groups **except**
                     a.   premature infants.
                     b.   people with intermittent claudication.
                     c.   women with fibrocystic breast disease.
                     d.   people with problems of sexual impotence.

d   381(A)   87.   Which of the following conditions may benefit from vitamin E therapy?
                     a.   Diabetes
                     b.   Pernicious anemia
                     c.   Muscular dystrophy
                     d.   Intermittent claudication

a   382(K)   88.   In what chief capacity does vitamin K function?
                     a.   Blood clotting
                     b.   Energy metabolism
                     c.   Calcium utilization
                     d.   Epithelial tissue renewal

d   382,383(K) 89.   What is prothrombin?
                     a.   A storage protein for vitamin K
                     b.   A transport protein for vitamin E
                     c.   A protein needed for bone formation
                     d.   A protein needed for blood clot formation

c   382,383(K) 90.   Which of the following is known to require vitamin K for its synthesis?
                     a.   Albumin
                     b.   GI mucosa
                     c.   Prothrombin
                     d.   Mucopolysaccharides

c   382-384(K) 91.   Which of the following is a feature of vitamin K?
                     a.   Deficiencies lead to intravascular clotting.
                     b.   Major dietary sources are whole grains and legumes.
                     c.   No adverse effects have been reported with high intakes.
                     d.   Primary deficiencies are more common than secondary deficiencies.

a   382-384(A) 92.   Knowing the role of vitamin K in the body, in what organ would you expect to find
                     it in large quantities?
                     a.   Liver
                     b.   Pancreas
                     c.   Gallbladder
                     d.   Small intestine

a   385(K)   93.   Which of the following properties do vitamins D and K share?
                     a.   Both are synthesized in the body.
                     b.   Both are required for normal vision.
                     c.   Neither has an effect on bone metabolism.
                     d.   Neither has an effect on erythrocyte function.

a   382(K)   94.   Which of the following is a feature of vitamin K?
       a.   It participates in synthesis of bone proteins.
       b.   Large amounts can be stored in adipose tissue.
       c.   Good food sources are legumes and raw fruits.
       d.   Intestinal bacterial synthesis provides over 90% of the body's need for most people.

b   383(A)   95.   Of the following, which would most readily induce a vitamin K deficiency?
       a.   Achlorhydria
       b.   Antibiotic therapy
       c.   Presence of oxalic acid in food
       d.   Insufficient intake of green leafy vegetables

c   383(K)   96.   What population group has the highest risk for vitamin K deficiency?
       a.   Adults
       b.   Elderly
       c.   Newborns
       d.   Teenagers

d   383(A)   97.   What type of foods should be controlled in individuals taking anticoagulant medicines?
       a.   Cold water fish
       b.   Processed soups
       c.   Enriched breads
       d.   Green leafy vegetables

d   383(K)   98.   The major form of vitamin K in foods is known as
       a.   ergodione.
       b.   menadione.
       c.   tocopherone.
       d.   phylloquinone.

c   383,384(K)   99.   Approximately what percentage of the body's store of vitamin K is derived from GI tract bacterial synthesis?
       a.   Less than 5
       b.   25
       c.   50
       d.   85

d   383,384(A)   100.   All of the following are features of vitamin K in nutrition **except**
       a.   infants frequently require a supplement at birth.
       b.   good food sources are plants of the cabbage family.
       c.   risk of deficiency is increased in people taking antibiotics for prolonged periods.
       d.   gut microflora synthesis supplies sufficient amounts to meet the needs of most healthy adults.

c   383,384(K)   101.   Which of the following vitamins is synthesized by intestinal bacteria?
       a.   A
       b.   E
       c.   K
       d.   D

b   384(K)   102.   What is the adult AI for vitamin K?
                       a.   45-60 ug
                       b.   90-120 ug
                       c.   150-300 ug
                       d.   500-550 ug

c   383(A)   103.   Which vitamin is routinely given as a single dose to newborns?
                       a.   Vitamin A
                       b.   Vitamin E
                       c.   Vitamin K
                       d.   Vitamin B12

b   389(K)   104.   Which of the following is a characteristic of free radicals?
                       a.   They are destroyed by cigarette smoking.
                       b.   They arise from normal metabolic reactions.
                       c.   They typically stop chain reactions associated with the production of
                             peroxides.
                       d.   They are known to accumulate even in the presence of abundant
                             antioxidant nutrients.

a   389(K)   105.   Substances that promote oxidation are usually termed
                       a.   prooxidants.
                       b.   antioxidants.
                       c.   free radical generators.
                       d.   reactive electron oxidants.

MATCHING (Answers can be used only once.)

T	368	01.	Transport protein of vitamin A
F	370	02.	Promotes bone dismantling prior to bone elongation
N	371	03.	Condition that results from severe vitamin A deficiency
C	372	04.	The protein of hair and nails
A	373	05.	Chronic inflammation of skin follicles and oil producing glands
E	373	06.	Pigment in carrots and pumpkins
B	376	07.	Vitamin D deficiency disease in children
I	376	08.	Precursor for vitamin D synthesis
L	376	09.	Vitamin D deficiency disease in adults
M	377	10.	Term denoting high blood calcium
G	381	11.	May be beneficial for treating fibrocystic breast disease
R	381	12.	Vitamin E deficiency disorder in premature infants
K	383	13.	Use of this increases risk for vitamin K deficiency
H	382	14.	Substance that promotes synthesis of prothrombin
J	382	15.	Another term for blood clotting
Q	381	16.	Typical food source of vitamin E
D	381	17.	Type of anemia prevented by vitamin E
O	383	18.	Substance that prevents clotting of the blood
P	383	19.	Catalyzes the conversion of prothrombin to thrombin
S	384	20.	Food source of vitamin K

A. Acne	F. Vitamin A	K. Antibiotics	P. Thromboplastin
B. Rickets	G. Vitamin E	L. Osteomalacia	Q. Vegetable oils
C. Keratin	H. Vitamin K	M. Hypercalcemia	R. Erythrocyte hemolysis
D. Hemolytic	I. Cholesterol	N. Xerophthalmia	S. Green leafy vegetables
E. Carotene	J. Coagulation	O. Anticoagulant	T. Retinol-binding protein

ESSAY QUESTIONS

PAGE(S)

369;375	01.	Explain why vitamin A and vitamin D may function as hormones rather than as vitamins.
369	02.	Explain the mechanism associated with the function of vitamin A in the visual response.
371	03.	Why is the eye especially vulnerable to vitamin A degradation at night?
370-372	04.	Distinguish between the roles of vitamin A in preventing night blindness and permanent blindness.
372	05.	Why are children more likely than others to be affected by vitamin A toxicity?
375,376	06.	Describe how the body can synthesize active vitamin D with the help of sunlight.
375,376	07.	How does vitamin D function to raise blood levels of calcium and phosphorus?
376-379	08.	Compare and contrast the characteristics of the two deficiency diseases osteomalacia and rickets.
380-382	09.	Describe the known functions of vitamin E and false claims of vitamin E supplementation.
380,381	10.	How is vitamin E thought to prevent hemolytic anemia?
381,382	11.	Discuss food sources and stability of vitamin E.
382-384	12.	Discuss the role of vitamin K in bone metabolism.
383	13.	Discuss the conditions under which deficiencies of vitamin K are most likely to occur.
384-385	14.	Compare and contrast the risks for toxicity among the fat-soluble vitamins.
389-391	15.	Explain the relationship of free radicals and degenerative diseases.
391	16.	Discuss the beneficial effects of antioxidant supplements on risk for cancer and heart disease.
391	17.	How are supplements of vitamins C and E thought to benefit individuals who have risk factors for heart disease?
391,392	18.	Discuss the role of antioxidant nutrients in the prevention of degenerative diseases.
391-393	19.	Discuss the pros and cons of taking antioxidant supplements.
391-393	20.	Discuss the potential applications of antioxidant nutrients in disease prevention.
389-392	21.	Discuss the beneficial and adverse effects of free radicals.

391   22.   Discuss the similarities between vitamins C and E in defending against heart
                    disease.

392   23.   Why can antioxidants behave differently in the body depending upon their level
                    of intake?

391-393   24.   Discuss the advantages of increasing the intake of phytochemicals from food
                    rather than from supplements.

CHAPTER 12
WATER AND THE MAJOR MINERALS

AN PAGE(S)

c 395(A) 01. Approximately how much water (lbs) is found in a 134 lb person?
  a. 34
  b. 65
  c. 80
  d. 105

d 395(K) 02. What fraction of lean tissue represents the water content?
  a. 1/10
  b. 1/3
  c. 1/2
  d. 3/4

b 396(K) 03. Which of the following is **not** a function of water in the body?
  a. Lubricant
  b. Source of energy
  c. Maintains protein structure
  d. Participant in chemical reactions

b 395(K) 04. Which of the following contributes most to the weight of the human body?
  a. Iron
  b. Water
  c. Protein
  d. Calcium

d 396(K) 05. Which of the following body structures helps to regulate thirst?
  a. Brain stem
  b. Cerebellum
  c. Optic nerve
  d. Hypothalamus

d 396,397(K) 06. Which of the following is a feature of water?
  a. Not a vital nutrient
  b. Not found in beverages
  c. Oxidized to yield energy
  d. Generated from oxidation of energy nutrients

b 395,396(K) 07. Among the following groups, which has the highest percentage of body water?
  a. Elderly
  b. Children
  c. Obese people
  d. Female adolescents

b 396(K) 08. Where is interstitial water found?
  a. Within cells
  b. Between cells
  c. Within the lungs
  d. Within blood vessels

c   397(K)   09.   The average daily loss of water via the kidneys, lungs, feces, and skin approximates
       a.   0 to 0.5 liter.
       b.   0.5 to 1.5 liters.
       c.   1.5 to 2.5 liters.
       d.   3.0 to 4.0 liters.

c   397(K)   10.   What is the minimum amount of water excreted each day as urine that is needed to carry away the body's waste products?
       a.   100 ml
       b.   250 ml
       c.   500 ml
       d.   1,000 ml

a   396(K)   11.   Which of the following is a feature of water and health?
       a.   Water intoxication is rare but can result in death.
       b.   Water losses from the body are highest through the feces.
       c.   Chronic high intakes increase the risk for bladder cancer.
       d.   Soft water has significant concentrations of magnesium and calcium.

d   397(A)   12.   What is the appropriate water intake for a 65 kg adult with an energy expenditure of 2,500 kcal?
       a.   250 to 500 ml
       b.   650 to 1300 ml
       c.   1,000 ml
       d.   2,500 to 3,250 ml

d   397(K)   13.   Which of the following is a characteristic of caffeine intake and water balance?
       a.   Caffeine inhibits water absorption from the GI tract.
       b.   Caffeine is known to act as a diuretic only when consumed as coffee or tea.
       c.   Regular intake of caffeine promotes an increase in water retention of the interstitial fluid volume.
       d.   Habitual consumers of caffeine lose no more fluid from the body than when ingesting noncaffeinated beverages.

d   397(A)   14.   Approximately how much water is in a loaf of bread?
       a.   2%
       b.   5%
       c.   20%
       d.   35%

b   397(A)   15.   What minimum level of body weight loss as water impairs a person's physical performance?
       a.   1-2%
       b.   3-4%
       c.   5-9%
       d.   10-15%

d   398(K)   16.   Which of the following types of drinking water contains the lowest amount of minerals?
       a.   Soft water
       b.   Hard water
       c.   Natural water
       d.   Distilled water

a   398,399(K)   17.   Which of the following is present in highest concentration in soft water?
    a.   Sodium
    b.   Calcium
    c.   Magnesium
    d.   Phosphorus

c   399(A)   18.   Habitual intake of soft water is most likely to aggravate
    a.   scurvy.
    b.   diabetes.
    c.   hypertension.
    d.   megaloblastic anemia.

c   399(K)   19.   How does antidiuretic hormone function?
    a.   It activates renin.
    b.   It activates angiotension.
    c.   It stimulates water reabsorption by the kidneys.
    d.   It stimulates sodium reabsorption by the kidneys.

d   399(K)   20.   What pituitary hormone regulates kidney retention of water?
    a.   Thyroxine
    b.   Cortisone
    c.   Epinephrine
    d.   Antidiuretic hormone

c   399(A)   21.   What organ provides the major control for homeostasis of body fluids?
    a.   Liver
    b.   Heart
    c.   Kidneys
    d.   Skeletal muscle

a   399,400(A)   22.   Factors that are effective in regulating the body's water balance include all of the following **except**
    a.   adrenaline.
    b.   aldosterone.
    c.   angiotensin.
    d.   antidiuretic hormone.

a   399(A)   23.   What is the function of renin?
    a.   Activates angiotensin
    b.   Activates antidiuretic hormone
    c.   Stimulates the thirst mechanism
    d.   Stimulates water absorption from the GI tract

b   399,400(K)   24.   Aldosterone and renin each function to promote
    a.   electrolyte balance.
    b.   retention of sodium.
    c.   excretion of calcium.
    d.   constriction of blood vessels.

b   400,401(K)   25.   Ions that carry a positive charge are called
    a.   anions.
    b.   cations.
    c.   mineralytes.
    d.   valence ions.

d   400-402(A) 26.   All of the following are properties of electrolytes **except**
                          a.   they attract water.
                          b.   they are charged particles.
                          c.   they carry electrical current.
                          d.   they include fat-soluble as well as water-soluble particles.

a   400,401(A) 27.   Which of the following describes a way to make an electrolyte solution?
                          a.   Dissolve a teaspoon of salt in a glass of water.
                          b.   Vigorously shake a mixture of corn oil and water.
                          c.   Dissolve a pinch of corn starch in a glass of water.
                          d.   Vigorously shake a pinch of table sugar in warm water.

a   402(K)   28.   What is the major extracellular cation?
                          a.   Sodium
                          b.   Sulfate
                          c.   Protein
                          d.   Potassium

d   402(K)   29.   What is the major intracellular cation?
                          a.   Sodium
                          b.   Calcium
                          c.   Phosphate
                          d.   Potassium

d   402(K)   30.   What is the major extracellular anion?
                          a.   Sodium
                          b.   Lactate
                          c.   Sulfate
                          d.   Chloride

c   402(K)   31.   What is the major intracellular anion?
                          a.   Protein
                          b.   Sodium
                          c.   Phosphate
                          d.   Bicarbonate

c   402,403(K) 32.   What is the term for the pressure that develops when two solutions of varying
                        concentrations are separated by a membrane?
                          a.   Hypotension
                          b.   Hypertension
                          c.   Osmotic pressure
                          d.   Hypertonic pressure

b   402,403(K) 33.   What is the force that moves water into a space where a solute is more
                        concentrated?
                          a.   Buffer action
                          b.   Osmotic pressure
                          c.   Permeable selectivity
                          d.   Electrolyte imbalance

b   403(K)   34.   What is the sodium-potassium pump?
   a.   A cell membrane enzyme that uses energy to pump sodium into the cell
   b.   A cell membrane enzyme that uses energy to pump sodium out of the cell
   c.   A mechanism present throughout interstitial fluid for draining sodium from the circulation
   d.   A mechanism present in the kidneys that exchanges sodium with lactic acid in order to regulate organic acid concentration

c   404(K)   35.   What organ is the chief regulator of the body's acid-base balance?
   a.   Skin
   b.   Liver
   c.   Kidneys
   d.   Stomach

a   404(A)   36.   When a person loses fluid by sweating or bleeding, what minerals are lost in greatest quantity?
   a.   Sodium and chloride
   b.   Bicarbonate and sulfate
   c.   Calcium and magnesium
   d.   Potassium and phosphate

d   404(A)   37.   All of the following are typical ingredients in an oral rehydration therapy formula **except**
   a.   salt.
   b.   water.
   c.   sugar.
   d.   protein.

b   404,405(K)   38.   All of the following are common participants in the regulation of body fluid pH **except**
   a.   proteins.
   b.   oxalic acid.
   c.   bicarbonate.
   d.   carbonic acid.

a   404(A)   39.   All of the following play important roles in acid-base balance **except**
   a.   liver.
   b.   lungs.
   c.   kidneys.
   d.   blood buffers.

a   405-406(K)   40.   Which of the following is a general property of the minerals?
   a.   When a food is burned, the ash contains all the minerals.
   b.   Absorption efficiency from foods is similar among the minerals.
   c.   Minerals in food can be degraded by certain processing methods.
   d.   Some minerals in food are destroyed by exposure to ultraviolet light.

a   407(A)   41.   In a normal individual with a daily requirement of 500 mg sodium, what would be the sodium balance after an intake of 10 g of common salt?
   a.   Equilibrium
   b.   Slight positive balance
   c.   Strong positive balance
   d.   Moderate positive balance

c   407(A)   42.   Normally, what is the relationship of the amount of sodium excreted to the amount ingested that day?
- a.   Intake is higher
- b.   Excretion is higher
- c.   Intake and excretion are equal
- d.   Excretion is unrelated to intake

a   407(K)   43.   Which of the following is a feature of sodium nutrition?
- a.   It has no RDA because diets rarely lack sodium.
- b.   It has no RDA because the kidneys are highly efficient at regulating sodium balance.
- c.   The RDA is 3 g, an amount that has been shown to have little or no effect on blood pressure.
- d.   The RDA is only 500 mg because the body possesses an unusually efficient retention mechanism.

c   408(A)   44.   How much sodium is contained in a fast-food deluxe hamburger that lists a salt content of 2.5 g?
- a.   100 mg
- b.   125 mg
- c.   1,000 mg
- d.   2,500 mg

a   408(A)   45.   What is the greatest single source of sodium in the diet?
- a.   Processed foods
- b.   Unprocessed foods
- c.   Natural salt content of foods
- d.   Salt added during cooking and at the table

b   408(A)   46.   What percentage of a person's total sodium intake derives from naturally occurring food sodium?
- a.   0
- b.   10
- c.   50
- d.   80

b   407,408(K)   47.   Which of the following is a feature of sodium and health?
- a.   Salt sensitivity is generally low in African-Americans.
- b.   High sodium intake is known to promote calcium excretion.
- c.   High sodium intake over many years leads to hypertension in most people.
- d.   Sodium alone and sodium in salt have nearly equivalent effects on blood pressure.

b   408,409(K)   48.   Which of the following is a general characteristic of sodium in processed foods?
- a.   Instant chocolate pudding is a low sodium food.
- b.   Salted peanuts contain less sodium than cornflakes on a gram basis.
- c.   Processed foods contribute less than half of the sodium in our diets.
- d.   Dairy products and meats represent major sources of sodium in our diets.

b   409(K)   49.   Hyponatremia refers to low blood concentration of
- a.   renin.
- b.   sodium.
- c.   chloride.
- d.   aldosterone.

b   407(K)   50.   What is another term for hypertension?
- a.   High blood sodium
- b.   High blood pressure
- c.   Excessive mental stress
- d.   Excessive muscular contraction

a   408(K)   51.   Salt-sensitive population groups include all of the following **except**
- a.   Caucasians.
- b.   African-Americans.
- c.   people with obesity.
- d.   people with diabetes.

d   408(K)   52.   The DASH diet plan was devised to prevent
- a.   dehydration.
- b.   constipation.
- c.   osteoporosis.
- d.   hypertension.

b   410(K)   53.   Which of the following is a major function of chloride?
- a.   Participates in wound healing
- b.   Helps maintain gastric acidity
- c.   Acts as principal intracellular electrolyte
- d.   Protects bone structures against degeneration

c   410(K)   54.   All of the following are characteristics of chloride in nutrition **except**
- a.   deficiencies are extremely rare.
- b.   intake is related, in large part, to sodium intake.
- c.   the RDA has recently been set at 10 mg/kg body weight.
- d.   it is necessary for maintaining electrolyte balance of body fluids.

c   411,412(K)   55.   Which of the following is the primary function of potassium?
- a.   Participates in wound healing
- b.   Helps maintain gastric acidity
- c.   Acts as principal intracellular electrolyte
- d.   Protects bone structures against degeneration

b   411(K)   56.   Which of the following is a feature of potassium?
- a.   It is unrelated to blood pressure.
- b.   Liberal intake may correct hypertension.
- c.   Major dietary sources are processed foods.
- d.   Deficiencies are usually the result of deficient intakes.

a   411,412(A)   57.   All of the following are features of potassium in nutrition **except**
- a.   processed foods are a major source.
- b.   high intakes may protect against stroke.
- c.   per serving size, legumes are a rich source.
- d.   per serving size, bananas are a rich source.

a   412(A)   58.   Which of the following is **not** among the common food sources of potassium?
- a.   Cheese
- b.   Potatoes
- c.   Dried fruits
- d.   Orange juice

c   411(K)   59.   What is the cause of most electrolyte imbalances?
   a.   Sodium excess
   b.   Calcium deficiency
   c.   Potassium deficiency
   d.   Magnesium deficiency

d   411,412(K) 60.   Which of the following is **not** a feature of potassium deficiency?
   a.   Prolonged vomiting and dehydration are known to lead to deficiencies.
   b.   Deficiencies occur due to excessive losses rather than to insufficient intakes.
   c.   Chronic use of certain diuretics and laxatives is known to lead to deficiencies.
   d.   Dietary deficiencies are common due to availability of only a few good food sources.

b   411(A)   61.   Which of the following people are at known risk for potassium depletion?
   a.   Athletes who are body-builders
   b.   Those who use diuretics regularly
   c.   Construction workers in cold climates
   d.   Those who consume insufficient amounts of salted foods

b   411(K)   62.   Which of the following is an early symptom of potassium deficiency?
   a.   Extreme thirst
   b.   Muscle weakness
   c.   Profound sweating
   d.   Lowered blood pressure

a   411(A)   63.   Which of the following is a feature of potassium supplements?
   a.   Can cause toxicity
   b.   Should always be taken with diuretics
   c.   Necessary in treatment of low blood pressure
   d.   Absorption of the mineral decreases markedly as intake increases

b   413(A)   64.   Almost all (99%) of the calcium in the body is used to
   a.   provide energy for cells.
   b.   provide rigidity for the bones and teeth.
   c.   regulate the transmission of nerve impulses.
   d.   maintain the blood level of calcium within very narrow limits.

b   413(K)   65.   What is hydroxyapatite?
   a.   Abnormal cellular structures seen in osteoporosis
   b.   The calcium-rich crystalline structure of teeth and bones
   c.   A calcium regulatory hormone secreted from the trabeculae region of bone
   d.   A compound in plant foods that binds to calcium and phosphorus and inhibits absorption

a   413,414(A) 66.   As far as is known, which of the following is **not** a process that directly involves calcium?
   a.   pH regulation
   b.   Blood clotting
   c.   Nerve transmission
   d.   Maintenance of heart beat

c   413,414(K)   67.   Which of the following is a feature of calcium in the body?
                         a.   High blood calcium levels correlate with tetany.
                         b.   Abnormal dietary calcium intakes promote calcium rigor.
                         c.   Higher calcium intakes correlate with lower body fatness.
                         d.   Efficiency of intestinal calcium absorption is similar for children and
                               adults.

c   414;418;   68.   All of the following characteristics are shared by calcium and magnesium **except**
     420-422(A)   a.   both are involved in blood clotting.
                         b.   both are involved in bone formation.
                         c.   both are found in abundance in dairy products.
                         d.   both may result in tetany when blood levels become abnormally low.

b   415(K)   69.   Calcium absorption is facilitated by the presence of
                         a.   fiber.
                         b.   lactose.
                         c.   phytic acid.
                         d.   oxalic acid.

c   415(K)   70.   All of the following are known to enhance calcium absorption from the GI tract
                         except
                         a.   lactose.
                         b.   pregnancy.
                         c.   oxalates.
                         d.   stomach acid.

b   414(A)   71.   How much calcium would be typically absorbed by a normal adult with a calcium
                         intake of 1,000 mg?
                         a.   100 mg
                         b.   250 mg
                         c.   600 mg
                         d.   950 mg

b   415-417(K)   72.   All of the following dietary substances are known to adversely affect calcium
                         balance **except**
                         a.   high fiber diet.
                         b.   lactose in the diet.
                         c.   phytic acid in the diet.
                         d.   phosphorus in the diet at a level 3 times that of calcium.

c   413,414(K)   73.   Which of the following regulates the level of calcium in the blood?
                         a.   Dietary intake of calcium
                         b.   Glucagon and epinephrine
                         c.   Parathormone and calcitonin
                         d.   Dietary intake of phosphorus

c   413-415;   74.   Which of the following represents the **least** likely cause for an abnormal blood
     417,418(A)   calcium level?
                         a.   Diseases of the liver
                         b.   Diseases of the kidney
                         c.   Insufficient dietary intake
                         d.   Altered secretion of parathormone

b   413(K)   75.   What is calmodulin?
          a.   A drug that treats osteoporoses
          b.   A messenger molecule activated by calcium
          c.   A calcium supplement with high bioavailability
          d.   A form of calcium used in fortifying soy products

b   414(A)   76.   Calcium-binding protein acts on the
          a.   kidneys.
          b.   intestines.
          c.   cortical bone.
          d.   trabecular bone.

d   416(K)   77.   Which of the following are good sources of dietary calcium?
          a.   Fruits
          b.   Breads
          c.   Enriched grains
          d.   Certain green vegetables

b   416(K)   78.   Which of the following vegetable greens shows the **lowest** bioavailability of calcium?
          a.   Kale
          b.   Spinach
          c.   Broccoli
          d.   Mustard greens

c   417(K)   79.   Which of the following shows the highest bioavailability for calcium?
          a.   Milk
          b.   Spinach
          c.   Broccoli
          d.   Pinto beans

d   416(A)   80.   On a per kcalorie basis, which of the following are the best sources of calcium?
          a.   Meats
          b.   Fruits
          c.   Breads
          d.   Vegetables

c   415(A)   81.   What is the calcium Adequate Intake for college-age students?
          a.   500 mg
          b.   800 mg
          c.   1000 mg
          d.   1500 mg

b   417,418(K)   82.   Which of the following is a feature of osteoporosis?
          a.   It is most common in men over 45 years of age.
          b.   It has virtually no effect on blood calcium levels.
          c.   It results from short-term deprivation of dietary calcium.
          d.   It causes significant alterations in the blood levels of parathormone and calcitonin.

a   417(K)   83.   At what age do adults normally begin to lose bone mass?
  a.   30-40 yrs
  b.   40-50 yrs
  c.   50-60 yrs
  d.   60-70 yrs

c   417(K)   84.   Approximately how many people in the United States are afflicted with osteoporosis?
  a.   500,000
  b.   5 Million
  c.   25 Million
  d.   50 Million

a   419(K)   85.   Which of the following is a feature of phosphorus?
  a.   Involved in energy exchange
  b.   Activates fat-soluble vitamins
  c.   Ranks lowest among the minerals in amount present in the body
  d.   Ranks highest among the minerals in amount present in the body

d   419(K)   86.   Which of the following is a feature of phosphorus in nutrition?
  a.   Dietary sources include fresh vegetables.
  b.   Absorption is known to be reduced by soft drink consumption.
  c.   Its participation in bone synthesis requires equivalent intake of dietary calcium.
  d.   Dietary deficiencies are virtually unknown.

d   419(K)   87.   Which of the following minerals is involved in the transportation of lipids through the body's lymph and blood systems?
  a.   Iron
  b.   Sodium
  c.   Calcium
  d.   Phosphorus

d   419(A)   88.   Which of the following minerals is **least** likely to be deficient in anyone's diet?
  a.   Iron
  b.   Calcium
  c.   Chromium
  d.   Phosphorus

c   420(K)   89.   Which of the following is a major function of magnesium?
  a.   Transport of oxygen
  b.   Prevention of anemia
  c.   Catalyst in energy metabolism
  d.   Production of thyroid hormone

d   420,421(K) 90.   Magnesium is known to be involved in all of the following **except**
  a.   blood clotting.
  b.   muscle contraction.
  c.   prevention of dental caries.
  d.   production of red blood cells.

a   420(K)   91.   Where is the majority of the body's magnesium found?
  a.   Bones
  b.   Teeth
  c.   Fatty tissue
  d.   Cells of soft tissue

d   420,421(K) 92.   Which of the following is a feature of magnesium in nutrition?
  a.   Toxicity is common in people taking diuretics.
  b.   High intakes interfere with stability of tooth enamel.
  c.   The amounts present in hard water are poorly utilized.
  d.   Average intakes from food are below recommendations.

c   421(A)   93.   The magnesium present in mineral water has a bioavailability of about
  a.   5%.
  b.   25%.
  c.   50%.
  d.   90%.

a   422(K)   94.   Some amino acids can link to each other by bridges made of
  a.   sulfur.
  b.   calcium.
  c.   chloride.
  d.   magnesium.

c   422(A)   95.   All of the following are known to have a high sulfur content **except**
  a.   skin.
  b.   hair.
  c.   teeth.
  d.   nails.

b   422(K)   96.   Sulfur is present in practically all
  a.   vitamins.
  b.   proteins.
  c.   fatty acids.
  d.   carbohydrates.

b   422(K)   97.   What is the major source of dietary sulfur?
  a.   Fats
  b.   Protein
  c.   Mineral salts
  d.   Carbohydrates

b   428,429(K) 98.   Which of the following is a feature of Type I osteoporosis?
  a.   It shows onset after 70 years of age.
  b.   It can be prevented by taking estrogen.
  c.   It leads to formation of the "dowager's hump."
  d.   Its prevalence is similar between males and females.

c   428,429(K) 99.   Which of the following is a function of trabecular bone?
  a.   Synthesis of vitamin D
  b.   Synthesis of calcitonin
  c.   Storage site for calcium
  d.   Storage site for vitamin D

b   430(A)   100.   The strongest predictor for loss of bone density is a person's
a.   sex.
b.   age.
c.   calcium intake.
d.   blood estrogen level.

d   430-433(K) 101.   All of the following are known to have a **high** correlation with risk for osteoporosis
except
a.   being thin.
b.   being female.
c.   having anorexia nervosa.
d.   consuming a high-protein diet.

b   430,431(A) 102.   A person's bone density is highest at around age
a.   18 years.
b.   30 years.
c.   55 years.
d.   70 years.

c   432(K)   103.   Among the following ethnic groups, which has the highest bone density?
a.   Japanese
b.   Caucasian
c.   African-American
d.   South America Hispanic

d   431(A)   104.   What percentage of people with osteoporosis are female?
a.   20
b.   40
c.   60
d.   80

d   431(K)   105.   What component of soy is thought to account for most of its beneficial effects on
bone health?
a.   Fiber
b.   Protein
c.   Calcium
d.   Phytochemicals

a   431(K)   106.   After age, what is the next strongest risk factor for osteoporosis?
a.   Sex
b.   Tobacco use
c.   Calcium intake
d.   Physical activity level

d   432(K)   107.   Which of the following is a feature of physical activity and bone health?
a.   Dancing is not an effective activity for helping maintain bone density.
b.   Weight training improves bone density in young but not older women.
c.   Weight-bearing activities are effective in maintaining bone mass in
adults but not in adolescents.
d.   Working the muscles places stress on bones which stimulates more
trabeculae development.

b   432(K)   108.   Which of the following best explains why Asians from Japan and China show fewer bone fractures than do Caucasians and Hispanic people?
a.   They have denser bones
b.   They have small, compact, hips
c.   They have higher calcium intakes
d.   They use less tobacco and alcohol

d   432(K)   109.   Most drug treatments for osteoporosis work primarily by
a.   stimulating parthormone release.
b.   inhibiting kidney excretion of calcium.
c.   stimulating intestinal calcium absorption.
d.   inhibiting the activities of the bone-degrading cells.

c   433(K)   110.   Which of the following is characteristic of calcium nutrition in teenagers?
a.   The recommended intake is higher for girls than boys.
b.   The recommended intake is 800-1,000 mg for this population group.
c.   The intake of calcium is higher in boys than girls because they eat more food.
d.   The dietary intakes of calcium are similar for girls and boys of this population group.

d   433(K)   111.   All of the following are features of bone health and smoking **except**
a.   smokers have less dense bones than nonsmokers.
b.   bone density appears to recover in former smokers.
c.   smokers have lower blood levels of activated vitamin D.
d.   smokers adapt by increasing their calcium absorption and reducing bone resorption rate.

a   433-434(K) 112.   Which of the following is a feature of calcium supplements?
a.   Common antacids are used as a source of calcium.
b.   The bioavailability of calcium from most supplements is significantly lower than from milk.
c.   There are large differences in the efficiency of calcium absorption from various supplements.
d.   The calcium in supplements made from oyster shell and bone meal is more absorbable than the calcium in calcium citrate and calcium lactate.

c   433,434(A) 113.   Among the following calcium supplements, which is most calcium-dense?
a.   Calcium citrate
b.   Calcium lactate
c.   Calcium carbonate
d.   Calcium gluconate

d   434(A)   114.   Common side effects of taking a high-dose calcium supplement include all of the following **except**
a.   constipation.
b.   excessive gas.
c.   intestinal bloating.
d.   increased iron absorption.

d   434(A)   115.   Among the following calcium supplements, which contains the lowest percentage of calcium?
a.   Calcium citrate
b.   Calcium lactate
c.   Calcium carbonate
d.   Calcium gluconate

b   434(A)   116.   How many mg of calcium is present in a 500 mg tablet of calcium carbonate?
a.   100
b.   200
c.   350
d.   500

a   434(A)   117.   What is most likely to occur when a calcium supplement and an iron supplement are taken simultaneously?
a.   Absorption of iron is reduced.
b.   Absorption of iron is improved.
c.   Excretion of iron in the urine is reduced.
d.   Excretion of iron in the urine is enhanced.

c   434(K)   118.   To minimize the risk of calcium toxicity, total daily intakes should be limited to under
a.   500 mg.
b.   1,000 mg.
c.   2,500 mg.
d.   5,000 mg.

d   433(K)   119.   Calcium supplements most likely to be contaminated with toxic minerals are those made from
a.   oyster shells.
b.   calcium citrate.
c.   calcium carbonate.
d.   powdered animal bones.

MATCHING (Answers can be used only once.)

D	398	01.	Typical amount (in mL) of water lost from lungs every day
M	419	02.	The protein in milk is a good source of this mineral
G	397	03.	Recommended water intake (in mL) for infant expending 1,000 kcal
H	399	04.	Enzyme released by kidneys
O	399	05.	Stimulates retention of sodium by kidneys
R	399	06.	Stimulates retention of water by kidneys
S	401	07.	A cation
T	401	08.	An anion
C	405	09.	Number of times more acidic a substance with pH of 4 is versus a substance with pH of 2
J	406	10.	Most prevalent major mineral in the body
L	406	11.	Least prevalent major mineral in the body
N	415	12.	Substance that inhibits absorption of calcium
Q	413	13.	Crystalline structure of bone
P	413	14.	Hormone that helps regulate calcium balance
A	414	15.	Percentage of dietary calcium absorbed by average adult
F	415	16.	Calcium Adequate Intake for college-age students
B	415	17.	Percentage of dietary calcium absorbed by growing children
K	415	18.	Substance that enhances absorption of calcium
E	416	19.	Amount of calcium, in mg, in 2 cups of milk
I	422	20.	Mineral that accounts for the structure of many proteins

A.	30		K.	Lactose
B.	55		L.	Magnesium
C.	100		M.	Phosphorous
D.	350		N.	Oxalate
E.	600		O.	Aldosterone
F.	1000		P.	Parathormone
G.	1500		Q.	Hydroxyapatite
H.	Renin		R.	Antidiuretic hormone
I.	Sulfur		S.	Potassium in solution
J.	Calcium		T.	Phosphate in solution

ESSAY QUESTIONS

PAGE(S)

396	01.	List 8 different functions for water in the body.
396-399	02.	Discuss the advantages of a liberal daily intake of water.
398-399	03.	Compare and contrast the effects of consuming hard water and soft water.
399,400	04.	Explain the roles of hormones in helping to regulate the body's water balance.
3999-403	05.	In what ways do the GI tract and the kidney function to help maintain fluid and electrolyte balance? How does the body defend itself when faced with conditions that induce excessive water and mineral losses (e.g. sweating; diarrhea)?
3999,400	06.	Describe the role of the kidneys in regulating acid-base balance.
404	07.	Explain the interaction of blood bicarbonate and carbonic acid in the regulation of body pH.

405,406	08.	Contrast the properties of minerals with those of vitamins.
406;415	09.	Identify some of the common substances found in foods that combine with minerals to form complexes the body cannot absorb. In what foods are they found and what minerals are affected?
407,408;411; 413;421	10.	Explain the relationship between dietary sodium and hypertension. What are the roles of calcium, magnesium, and potassium in regulating blood pressure?
402-409	11.	What are the major sources of sodium in the diet of the U.S. population? Describe ways in which consumers can lower intakes of salt in their diets.
414	12.	Define calcium rigor and calcium tetany. What role does dietary intake of calcium play in these disorders?
413-415	13.	Explain the functions of parathormone, calcitonin, and vitamin D in the regulation of calcium metabolism.
415-417	14.	List 5 nonmilk sources of calcium.
417	15.	Explain how cooking techniques may improve calcium extraction from ethnic foods.
420	16.	Discuss the importance of the dietary calcium-to-phosphorus ratio and bone health.
428-433	17.	Discuss major risk factors in the development of osteoporosis. What population groups are most at risk? What dietary measures are advocated for high risk groups?
428,429	18.	Compare and contrast trabecular bone and cortical bone formation and function.
428-430	19.	Discuss the contributions of cortical bone and trabecular bone development of osteoporosis.
428-430	20.	Explain the difference between type I and type II osteoporosis.
429-431	21.	What dietary and metabolic factors are associated with poor calcium balance in older adults?
431,432	22.	Discuss the role of male and female hormones in calcium balance and bone loss.
432,433	23.	Discuss the role of physical activity in reducing the risk for osteoporosis.
433	24.	Discuss the role of nutrients other than calcium in the support of bone health.
433	25.	Discuss the roles of alcohol and smoking in development of osteoporosis.
433,434	26.	A. Discuss bioavailability of the various calcium supplements. B. How can you easily test a supplement pill's ability to dissolve?
433,434	27.	Explain the risks associated with taking calcium supplements.

CHAPTER 13
THE TRACE MINERALS

AN   PAGE(S)

a   437,438(K)   01.   Which of the following is a characteristic of the trace minerals?
   a. The amounts found in foods are not predictable.
   b. A deficiency sign common to many trace minerals is dermatitis.
   c. Deficiencies are more difficult to recognize in children than in adults.
   d. The amount of all trace minerals in the average person totals approximately 100 grams.

b   442(K)   02.   Which of the following is a feature of iron nutrition?
   a. Most people absorb about 50-60% of dietary iron.
   b. Most women do not eat enough iron-containing foods.
   c. Iron plays an important role in the synthesis of thyroxine.
   d. Iron deficiency represents the second most common mineral deficiency in the United States.

d   439(K)   03.   What is the ionic state of ferrous iron?
   a. -2
   b. -1
   c. +1
   d. +2

a   439(K)   04.   What is the ionic state of ferric iron?
   a. +3
   b. +2
   c. -2
   d. -3

d   439(K)   05.   What iron-containing compound carries oxygen in the bloodstream?
   a. Ferritin
   b. Myoglobin
   c. Transferrin
   d. Hemoglobin

b   439(K)   06.   What is the oxygen carrying protein of muscle cells?
   a. Transferrin
   b. Myoglobin
   c. Hemoglobin
   d. Cytochrome

d   440,441(K)   07.   All of the following are body proteins directly involved in iron metabolism **except**
   a. ferritin.
   b. transferrin.
   c. hemosiderin.
   d. metallothionein.

b   441(K)   08.   Which of the following is a feature of iron absorption?
- a.   It is lower in people with iron toxicity.
- b.   It is higher in people with severe iron deficiency.
- c.   It is lower when iron is in the form of heme rather than non-heme.
- d.   It is higher in adults than children due to more mature intestinal function.

b   440(A)   09.   Among the following, which does **not** contain the MFP factor?
- a.   Tuna
- b.   Spinach
- c.   Hamburger
- d.   Chicken leg

a   440,441(K)   10.   What is the function of MFP factor?
- a.   Enhances iron absorption
- b.   Acts as iron enrichment nutrient
- c.   Simulates metallothionein synthesis
- d.   Acts as chelating agent for iron toxicity treatment

d   440,441(K)   11.   All of the following factors are known to **enhance** the absorption of iron **except**
- a.   MFP factor.
- b.   stomach acid.
- c.   ascorbic acid.
- d.   calcium from milk.

b   440;445(K)   12.   When calculating the amount of iron that can be absorbed from a meal, all of the following factors are of major importance **except**
- a.   MFP factor content.
- b.   EDTA content.
- c.   phytate content.
- d.   vitamin C content.

d   445;440(K)   13.   Which of the following nutrients enhances iron absorption from the intestinal tract?
- a.   Biotin
- b.   Calcium
- c.   Vitamin D
- d.   Vitamin C

c   445;440(K)   14.   Which of the following is known to enhance iron absorption?
- a.   Tea
- b.   Coffee
- c.   Foods containing vitamin C
- d.   Foods containing vitamin E

c   445;440(A)   15.   When eaten in the same meal, which of the following foods enhances the absorption of iron in legumes?
- a.   Nuts
- b.   Fiber
- c.   Oranges
- d.   Whole-grain breads

b   441(K)   16.   Under normal circumstances, what is the average percentage of dietary iron that is absorbed?
- a.   10
- b.   18
- c.   33
- d.   60

a   440(A)   17.   Iron bioavailability from complete meals is known to be affected significantly by each of the following substances **except**
- a.   caffeine.
- b.   phytates.
- c.   Vitamin C.
- d.   MFP factor.

c   440(K)   18.   All of the following are known to **reduce** the absorption of iron **except**
- a.   tea.
- b.   coffee.
- c.   sugars.
- d.   phytates.

b   440(K)   19.   All of the following are known to reduce the absorption of iron **except**
- a.   phytates.
- b.   MFP factor.
- c.   tannic acid in tea.
- d.   EDTA in food additives.

b   440;445(A)   20.   Absorption of iron from supplements is improved by taking them with
- a.   tea.
- b.   meat.
- c.   milk.
- d.   whole grain bread.

c   446(A)   21.   Which of the following has been shown to improve absorption of iron from iron supplements?
- a.   Taking then with milk
- b.   Taking them with orange juice
- c.   Taking them on an empty stomach rather than with meals
- d.   Taking them in the form of the ferric salt rather than the ferrous salt

b   446(A)   22.   Why is taking vitamin C ineffective at enhancing iron-absorption from standard iron supplements?
- a.   The iron in the supplement is in a chelated form.
- b.   The iron in the supplement is already in the ferrous form.
- c.   The iron in the supplement binds irreversibly with vitamin C.
- d.   The iron supplement already contains MFP to enhance absorption.

c   447(A)   23.   Which of the following is a common side effect from taking iron supplements?
- a.   Itching
- b.   Diarrhea
- c.   Constipation
- d.   Black tongue

a   441(K)   24.   Which of the following compounds provides a major storage reservoir for iron?
      a.   Ferritin
      b.   Myoglobin
      c.   Transferrin
      d.   Hemoglobin

b   440(K)   25.   Which of the following is a characteristic of iron transport?
      a.   Albumin is the major iron transport protein in the blood.
      b.   Transferrin in the blood carries iron to the bone marrow.
      c.   Hemochromatosis results from inability to absorb and transport iron.
      d.   Ferritin functions by transporting iron from the spleen to the bone marrow.

b   440(K)   26.   Which of the following is a protein that carries iron through the circulation to the tissues?
      a.   Albumin
      b.   Transferrin
      c.   Hemosiderin
      d.   Metallothionein

a   441,442(K)   27.   Which of the following is a characteristic of iron utilization?
      a.   Most of the body's iron is recycled.
      b.   The chief storage site for iron is the intestinal epithelium.
      c.   Iron is absorbed better from supplements than from foods.
      d.   Iron from nonheme food sources is absorbed better than from heme food sources.

b   440(K)   28.   What fraction of the total iron content of a normal diet is heme iron?
      a.   1/100
      b.   1/10
      c.   1/3
      d.   1/2

d   440(K)   29.   What percentage of the iron in meat is nonheme iron?
      a.   0
      b.   20
      c.   40
      d.   60

c   445,446(A)   30.   Which of the following foods provides iron in the most absorbable form?
      a.   Rice
      b.   Spinach
      c.   Hamburger
      d.   Orange juice

c   445(A)   31.   Approximately how much iron would be provided by a balanced diet supplying 2000 kcalories?
      a.   3 mg
      b.   6 mg
      c.   12 mg
      d.   30 mg

b   445(K)   32.   In the United States, iron is currently added to which of the following foods?
      a.   Milk and cheese
      b.   Breads and cereals
      c.   Peanut butter and jellies
      d.   Orange juice and tomato juice

a   446(A)   33.   Which of the following would represent a source of possible iron contamination?
      a.   An iron frypan
      b.   An iron chelate
      c.   A ferric iron supplement
      d.   A ferrous iron supplement

a   446(A)   34.   Which of the following is a common example of iron contamination in the diet?
      a.   Using an iron skillet to scramble eggs can triple their iron content.
      b.   Cooking acidic foods in a copper pot can extract chelate iron from the pot.
      c.   Simmering acidic foods in glass dishes leads to leaching of iron salts from the glass.
      d.   Cooking leafy vegetables in a galvanized pot leads to a six-fold increase in iron content.

c   445;447(K)   35.   What is the RDA for iron for females 19-50 years old?
      a.   8 mg
      b.   10 mg
      c.   18 mg
      d.   32 mg

b   445(A)   36.   Approximately how much higher is the RDA for iron for a vegetarian woman of childbearing age compared with her nonvegetarian counterpart?
      a.   33%
      b.   75%
      c.   150%
      d.   200%

c   445(A)   37.   If a normal, healthy young adult woman loses an average of 2 mg/day of iron from the body, approximately what minimum amount (mg/day) should she consume from the diet to prevent negative iron balance?
      a.   2
      b.   5
      c.   11
      d.   19

b   441,442(A)   38.   Taking into account the intestinal absorption efficiency of iron, approximately how much dietary iron must be consumed to account for the iron lost by donating a pint of blood?
      a.   5 mg
      b.   15 mg
      c.   50 mg
      d.   100 mg

c   441(K)   39.   What is the average lifespan of red blood cells?
      a.   Two weeks
      b.   One month
      c.   Four months
      d.   Six months

a   441(A)   40.   How would the body respond typically to loss of blood from hemorrhage?
    a.   More transferrin is produced to allow absorption and transport of more iron.
    b.   The average life of the red blood cell is increased in order to allow better tissue oxygenation.
    c.   Less iron storage proteins are produced which increases the amount of iron available for synthesis of new red blood cells.
    d.   The liver and muscles release their supply of stored red blood cells which compensates, in part, for the decrease in red blood cell concentration of the circulation.

b   442,443(A) 41.   What is the major cause of iron deficiency?
    a.   Blood loss
    b.   Poor nutrition
    c.   Hereditary defect
    d.   Parasitic infections of the GI tract

a   442(A)   42.   Iron deficiency in children is likely to result from a diet that overemphasizes
    a.   milk.
    b.   cereals.
    c.   vegetables.
    d.   dried beans.

c   443(K)   43.   What type of anemia results from iron deficiency?
    a.   Hemolytic
    b.   Megaloblastic
    c.   Hypochromic microcytic
    d.   Hyperchromic macrocytic

b   443(K)   44.   Which of the following is descriptive of iron deficiency and behavior?
    a.   The practice of pica may enhance iron absorption.
    b.   Changes in behavior precede the appearance of anemia.
    c.   The practice of pica may delay the onset of iron-induced behavioral changes.
    d.   Adults are more resistant to iron-induced behavioral changes than children.

d   443;447(A) 45.   Which of the following symptoms would ordinarily **not** be found in individuals with iron-deficiency anemia?
    a.   Fatigue
    b.   Headaches
    c.   Concave nails
    d.   Diminished sense of smell

c   442(K)   46.   Approximately how many of the world's population are thought to be affected by iron deficiency?
    a.   1 million
    b.   100 million
    c.   1.2 billion
    d.   3.5 billion

d   442;444(A)   47.   Which of the following population groups is **least** susceptible to iron deficiency anemia?
    a.   Older infants
    b.   Children 2-10 years of age
    c.   Women of childbearing age
    d.   Men 20-45 years of age

c   445(A)   48.   Which of the following individuals would most likely need an iron supplement?
    a.   One-year-old
    b.   Elderly female
    c.   Pregnant female
    d.   Adolescent female

a   442(K)   49.   Which of the following represents the order of the stages of iron deficiency?
    a.   Iron stores decline - iron transport diminishes - hemoglobin synthesis falls
    b.   Hemoglobin synthesis falls - iron transport diminishes - iron stores decline
    c.   Iron transport diminishes - hemoglobin synthesis falls - iron stores decline
    d.   Iron transport diminishes - iron stores decline - hemoglobin synthesis falls

a   442(A)   50.   Which of the following is found in the first stage of iron deficiency?
    a.   Iron stores decline as assessed by serum ferritin.
    b.   Hemoglobin levels fall, as assessed by complete blood count.
    c.   Red blood cell count falls, as assessed by hematocrit count.
    d.   Hemoglobin synthesis declines, as assessed by erythrocyte protoporphyrin.

c   442,443(K)   51.   Which of the following is a characteristic of iron deficiency?
    a.   Blood erythrocyte protoporphyrin levels decline as anemia worsens.
    b.   Iron supplements are not as effective at treating anemia as is proper nutrition.
    c.   People with anemia generally become fatigued only when they exert themselves.
    d.   The concave nails of iron-deficiency anemia result from abnormal ferritin levels.

c   442,443(A)   52.   The most common tests to diagnose iron deficiency include all of the following measures **except**
    a.   size of red blood cells.
    b.   number of red blood cells.
    c.   DNA content of red blood cells.
    d.   hemoglobin content of red blood cells.

b   442,443(A)   53.   Low levels of blood hemoglobin most likely indicate a deficiency of
    a.   zinc.
    b.   iron.
    c.   copper.
    d.   manganese.

c   442(K)   54.   Why are hemoglobin and hematocrit tests of limited usefulness in the assessment of iron status?
       a.   They are expensive to perform.
       b.   They are notoriously inaccurate.
       c.   They are late indicators of iron deficiency.
       d.   The range of normal value is usually wide.

b   442(K)   55.   What is erythrocyte protoporphyrin?
       a.   Iron chelating drug
       b.   Hemoglobin precursor
       c.   Indicator of iron toxicity
       d.   Inherited iron deficiency disease

c   442(K)   56.   The erythrocyte protoporphyrin level is used as an indicator of
       a.   late iron toxicity.
       b.   early iron toxicity.
       c.   late iron deficiency.
       d.   early iron deficiency.

d   445(A)   57.   Which of the following is the most effective and least costly strategy for preventing an iron deficiency?
       a.   Consume iron supplements at a level 2-3 times the RDA.
       b.   Switch to iron cooking utensils and eat 4 servings of red meat daily.
       c.   Eat small amounts of citrus products and increase intake of low fat milk.
       d.   Eat small quantities of meat, fish, and poultry frequently together with liberal amounts of vegetables and legumes.

b   445(A)   58.   A child diagnosed with iron-deficiency anemia would most likely benefit from increasing the consumption of
       a.   milk.
       b.   red meat.
       c.   fresh fruits.
       d.   yellow vegetables.

a   443(K)   59.   What is the name given to the ingestion of nonnutritive substances?
       a.   Pica
       b.   Goiter
       c.   Tetany
       d.   Hemosiderosis

c   444(K)   60.   Iron overload is also known as
       a.   ferrocyanosis.
       b.   hemoglobinemia.
       c.   hemochromatosis.
       d.   metalloferrothionosis.

b   444(K)   61.   Common terms that describe the body's accumulation of excess iron include all of the following **except**
       a.   iron overload.
       b.   hemosiderosis.
       c.   hemoglobinemia.
       d.   hemochromatosis.

b   444(K)   62.   The most common cause of iron overload is
                 a.   an injury to the GI tract.
                 b.   a genetic predisposition.
                 c.   excessive use of iron cookware.
                 d.   excessive use of iron supplements.

b   441(K)   63.   Which of the following is known as an iron-overload protein?
                 a.   Transferrin
                 b.   Hemosiderin
                 c.   Marrowferritin
                 d.   Metallothionein

c   444(A)   64.   Which of the following foods should be especially limited in the diet of individuals with hemochromatosis?
                 a.   Dairy products
                 b.   Fluoridated water
                 c.   Iron-fortified cereals
                 d.   Carbonated beverages

b   444(A)   65.   Why are people with iron overload at increased risk for infections?
                 a.   Excess tissue iron destroys vitamin C.
                 b.   Iron-rich blood favors growth of bacteria.
                 c.   Iron-rich blood impairs the immune system.
                 d.   Excess tissue iron interferes with antibiotic function.

c   444(A)   66.   Which of the following disorders is positively correlated with the presence of high blood iron?
                 a.   Dermatitis
                 b.   Diverticulosis
                 c.   Heart disease
                 d.   Neural tube defects

a   444(K)   67.   Which of the following describes one aspect of iron toxicity?
                 a.   Among men in the United States, it is twice as common as iron-deficiency anemia.
                 b.   In adults, the consumption of alcohol is somewhat protective against absorption of excess iron.
                 c.   In most people with this disorder, infections are rare because bacteria are killed by excess iron in the blood.
                 d.   It is usually caused by a virus that attacks the intestinal mucosal cells leading to unregulated and excessive iron absorption.

c   444;447(K)   68.   Signs of iron **toxicity** include all of the following **except**
                 a.   apathy.
                 b.   fatigue.
                 c.   hypochromic anemia.
                 d.   increases in infections.

a   448(K)   69.   Which of the following is a feature of zinc in nutrition?
                 a.   Pancreatic enzymes are rich in zinc.
                 b.   The body's primary excretory route is urine.
                 c.   Good food sources are whole grain products.
                 d.   Toxicity symptoms include constipation and low body temperature.

d   447;451(A)   70.   Zinc is known to play an important role in all of the following functions **except**
a.   wound healing.
b.   synthesis of retinal.
c.   production of sperm.
d.   oxidation of polyunsaturated fatty acids.

a   447(K)   71.   An enzyme in which zinc or copper is an integral part of its structure is classified as a(n)
a.   metalloenzyme.
b.   oxidoreductase.
c.   cytochromidase.
d.   metallothionase.

a   448(K)   72.   Which of the following is known to regulate the absorption of zinc?
a.   Metallothionein in the intestinal cells
b.   Zinc-releasing enzymes in the intestinal mucosa
c.   Pancreatic juice containing zinc-absorption enhancers
d.   Bile acids which form a complex with zinc to promote its absorption

d   449(K)   73.   What dietary ratio of iron to zinc inhibits zinc absorption?
a.   0.5 to 1
b.   1 to 1
c.   Less than 2 to 1
d.   Greater than 2 to 1

c   449(A)   74.   Which of the following would be the minimum amount of dietary iron known to impair zinc absorption in an individual with a zinc intake of 15 mg?
a.   5 mg
b.   15 mg
c.   30 mg
d.   60 mg

d   448(K)   75.   Which of the following is a major binding protein for zinc?
a.   Ligand
b.   Ferritin
c.   Hemosiderin
d.   Metallothionein

c   440;448,449(K) 76.   All of the following characteristics are shared by iron and zinc **except**
a.   absorption is inhibited by fiber.
b.   absorption is inhibited by cow's milk.
c.   transport in the blood is primarily by albumin.
d.   absorption rises with increased needs of the body.

b   440;449(A)   77.   Which of the following characteristics is shared by zinc and iron?
a.   Good food sources include dairy products.
b.   Proteins in the blood are needed for their transport.
c.   Severe deficiencies lead to delay in the onset of puberty.
d.   Doses of 10 times the RDA are known to cause death in children.

d   448(A)   78.   Which of the following characteristics are shared by iron and zinc?
    a.   Neither functions in the maintenance of blood glucose.
    b.   Neither is circulated from the pancreas to the intestines and back to the pancreas.
    c.   Both are absorbed into intestinal mucosal cells and bound to metallothionein for transport first to the liver.
    d.   Both are absorbed into intestinal epithelial cells but may then be lost by normal villus cell renewal processes.

a   449(K)   79   What is the chief transport substance for zinc in the circulation?
    a.   Albumin
    b.   Metallothionein
    c.   Carbonic anhydrase
    d.   High-density lipoproteins

b   448(K)   80.   Which of the following minerals undergoes enteropancreatic circulation during normal metabolism?
    a.   Iron
    b.   Zinc
    c.   Copper
    d.   Fluoride

d   449(K)   81.   Which of the following represents the most reliable dietary source of zinc?
    a.   Milk
    b.   Fiber
    c.   Fruits
    d.   Meat and whole-grain cereals

c   449;451(A)   82.   Zinc is highest in foods that also contain a high amount of
    a.   fat.
    b.   fiber.
    c.   protein.
    d.   carbohydrate.

c   448(K)   83.   What is the bioavailability of dietary zinc?
    a.   2-5%
    b.   5-10%
    c.   15-40%
    d.   50-60%

b   449;451(K)   84.   Deficiency of which of the following minerals is associated with retarded growth and sexual development in children?
    a.   Iron
    b.   Zinc
    c.   Iodine
    d.   Chromium

b   449;451(K)   85.   Conditions associated with zinc deficiency include all of the following **except**
    a.   altered taste.
    b.   kidney failure.
    c.   abnormal night vision.
    d.   poor healing of wounds.

a   449;451(K)   86.   All of the following are recognized symptoms of zinc deficiency **except**
                         a.   anemia.
                         b.   altered taste acuity.
                         c.   impaired dark vision.
                         d.   increased susceptibility to infection.

a   449(K)   87.   Which of the following conditions is known to lead to copper deficiency?
                         a.   Excess zinc
                         b.   Excess protein
                         c.   Insufficient iodine
                         d.   Insufficient calcium

b   449;451(K)   88.   All of the following are known to result from excessive zinc intake **except**
                         a.   inhibition of iron absorption.
                         b.   galvanized liver and kidneys.
                         c.   inhibition of copper absorption.
                         d.   decreases in high-density lipoproteins.

c   449(A)   89.   Which of the following is a known side effect of prolonged ingestion of excessive
                         amounts of zinc supplements?
                         a.   Iron toxicity due to increased ferritin synthesis
                         b.   Zinc salt deposits in soft tissues such as the heart and kidneys
                         c.   Copper deficiency due to interference with copper absorption
                         d.   Mineral binding protein deficiency due to a decrease in metallothionein
                                 production

c   450(A)   90.   Under which of the following conditions are certain supplements of zinc reported
                         to be beneficial?
                         a.   In the treatment of colds
                         b.   In the treatment of Menkes' syndrome
                         c.   In the treatment of toxicity from certain other metals
                         d.   In the treatment of slow growth syndrome in U.S. children

b   450(K)   91.   What formulation of zinc has been found effective in treating the symptoms of the
                         common cold?
                         a.   Zinc chelator
                         b.   Zinc gluconate
                         c.   Zinc plus ferrous iron
                         d.   Zinc plus copper salt

c   450 (K)   92.   Commercially available zinc-containing lozenges are advertised to be effective
                         against
                         a.   fatigue.
                         b.   vitamin A toxicity.
                         c.   the common cold.
                         d.   slowing of the BMR.

c   451(K)   93.   What mineral is critical to the synthesis of thyroxin?
                         a.   Iron
                         b.   Copper
                         c.   Iodine
                         d.   Magnesium

a   451(K)   94.   One of the thyroid gland hormones is called
  a.   thyroxine.
  b.   goitrogen.
  c.   thiostimulating hormone.
  d.   tissue stimulating hormone.

c   451(K)   95.   What is the primary function of the thyroid hormones?
  a.   Precursors for hemoglobin synthesis
  b.   Counteract a deficiency of goitrogens
  c.   Control the rate of oxygen use by cells
  d.   Regulate acetylcholine concentrations in the central nervous system

b   451(K)   96.   Which of the following is a feature of iodine in nutrition?
  a.   Excessive intakes shrink the thyroid gland.
  b.   Processed foods in the United States do not use iodized salt.
  c.   Iodization of salt is mandatory in the United States but not in Canada.
  d.   Worldwide, the prevalence of iodine deficiency and iodine toxicity are approximately the same.

b   452(A)   97.   Which of the following is the richest source of iodine?
  a.   Corn
  b.   Seafood
  c.   Orange juice
  d.   Cruciferous vegetables

d   452(A)   98.   If cow's milk is found to contain unusually high levels of iodine, what is the most likely explanation?
  a.   Storage of milk in galvanized tanks
  b.   Grazing of cows on high iodine soils
  c.   Addition of fortified salt at the milk processing plant
  d.   Exposure of cows to iodide-containing medications and disinfectants

b   452(A)   99.   Which of the following would be the most appropriate food source of iodide for a person who lives inland?
  a.   Fresh water fish
  b.   Iodized table salt
  c.   Locally grown produce
  d.   Plants of the cabbage family

b   452(A)   100.   Approximately how much iodized salt must be consumed to meet but not exceed the RDA for iodine?
  a.   1 mg
  b.   ½ teaspoon
  c.   1 teaspoon
  d.   1 tablespoon

a   451(K)   101.   The most common cause of iodine deficiency is
  a.   insufficient intake of iodine from foods.
  b.   overconsumption of other trace elements.
  c.   overconsumption of anti-thyroid substances.
  d.   pituitary deficiencies of thyroid-stimulating hormone.

c   451(A)   102.   What is the response of the pituitary gland of a person who is deficient in iodine?
                        a.   Increase in its size to trap more iodine
                        b.   Increase in its size to trap more thyroxine
                        c.   Increased release of thyroid-stimulating hormone
                        d.   Decreased release of thyroid-stimulating hormone

b   451(K)   103.   Which of the following may result from iodine deficiency?
                        a.   Gout
                        b.   Goiter
                        c.   Anemia
                        d.   Hypertension

c   451(A)   104.   A woman with a severe iodine deficiency during pregnancy may have a child who
                        develops
                        a.   anemia.
                        b.   rickets.
                        c.   cretinism.
                        d.   allergies.

a   451(A)   105.   What nutrient deficiency during pregnancy may give rise to a child with cretinism?
                        a.   Iodine
                        b.   Copper
                        c.   Chromium
                        d.   Molybdenum

c   451(K)   106.   What is a goitrogen?
                        a.   One of the hormones produced by the thyroid gland
                        b.   A substance that enhances absorption of dietary iodide
                        c.   A substance that interferes with the functioning of the thyroid gland
                        d.   A compound used to supplement salt as a way to increase iodide intake

b   451(A)   107.   A person ingesting large amounts of thyroid antagonist substances is at high risk of
                        developing
                        a.   cretinsm.
                        b.   simple goiter.
                        c.   high blood T3 levels.
                        d.   high blood thyroxin levels.

c   451(A)   108.   Which of the following foods are known to contain goitrogens?
                        a.   Shellfish
                        b.   Whole grains
                        c.   Cauliflower and broccoli
                        d.   Strawberries and raspberries

d   451(K)   109.   Which of the following fruits are known to contain substances that inhibit the
                        functioning of the thyroid gland?
                        a.   Raw apples
                        b.   Lemons and limes
                        c.   Avocados and mangos
                        d.   Peaches and strawberries

d   451(K)   110.   Which of the following is a prominent feature of mild iodine deficiency in children?
    a.   Demineralization
    b.   Growth retardation
    c.   Discoloration of teeth
    d.   Poor performance in school

c   451(K)   111.   Which of the following is a feature of iodide utilization?
    a.   Ingestion of plants of the cabbage family stimulates iodide uptake.
    b.   It is an integral part of pituitary thyroid stimulating hormone.
    c.   A deficiency or a toxicity leads to enlargement of the thyroid gland.
    d.   The amount in foods is unrelated to the amount of iodine present in the soil.

d   452(A)   112.   Which of the following would most likely result from an excessive intake of iodine?
    a.   Diarrhea
    b.   Skin rashes
    c.   Dehydration
    d.   Thyroid gland enlargement

b   453(K)   113.   Which of the following is an important function of selenium?
    a.   Helps blood to clot
    b.   Inhibits the formation of free radicals
    c.   Stabilizes the alcohol content of beer
    d.   Acts as a cross-linking agent in collagen

b   453(A)   114.   Which of the following nutrients has functions similar to those of vitamin E?
    a.   Iron
    b.   Selenium
    c.   Chromium
    d.   Molybdenum

c   453(K)   115.   What trace element is part of the enzyme glutathione peroxidose?
    a.   Iron
    b.   Zinc
    c.   Selenium
    d.   Chromium

b   453(K)   116.   Which of the following is a property of selenium in nutrition?
    a.   It participates in the functioning of insulin.
    b.   Severe deficiency is associated with heart disease in China.
    c.   Significant food sources include dairy and unprocessed vegetables.
    d.   It has no RDA but the estimated safe and adequate dietary intake is only 2-3 μg/day.

b   453(K)   117.   Keshan disease results from a deficiency of
    a.   copper.
    b.   selenium.
    c.   manganese.
    d.   molybdenum.

c 454(K) 118. The rare genetic disorders Menkes disease and Wilson's disease result from abnormal utilization of
    a. iron.
    b. zinc.
    c. copper.
    d. manganese.

c 454(A) 119. All of the following are characteristics of copper in nutrition **except**
    a. deficiency is rare.
    b. legumes are a rich source.
    c. absorption from foods is poor.
    d. absorption is reduced from taking zinc supplements.

b 454(A) 120. Which of the following minerals is a cofactor in the formation of hemoglobin?
    a. Iodine
    b. Copper
    c. Sodium
    d. Calcium

b 454(K) 121. Which of the following minerals functions primarily in reactions that consume oxygen?
    a. Zinc
    b. Copper
    c. Chromium
    d. Molybdenum

b 454(K) 122. Which of the following is a feature of copper nutrition?
    a. Absorption efficiency is similar to that of iron.
    b. It is involved in collagen synthesis and wound healing.
    c. Soft water may provide significant amounts in the diet.
    d. Deficiency is common in children of Middle East countries.

b 454(A) 123. Which of the following meats would be the best source of copper?
    a. Chicken
    b. Shellfish
    c. Beefsteak
    d. Hamburger

b 455(K) 124. Characteristics of manganese in nutrition include all of the following **except**
    a. good sources are plant foods.
    b. deficiencies are seen primarily in the elderly.
    c. absorption is inhibited by calcium supplements.
    d. toxicity is more common from environmental contamination than from the diet.

c 455(A) 125. Which of the following represents the most likely cause of manganese toxicity?
    a. Consumption of supplements
    b. Increased absorption due to genetic defect
    c. Inhalation of dust contaminated with manganese
    d. Consumption of foods grown on manganese-rich soils

d   455(K)   126.   What is the primary mechanism associated with the role of fluoride in prevention of dental caries?
    a.   Fluoride increases calcium absorption which increases crystal formation of teeth.
    b.   Decay is inhibited due to neutralization of organic acids produced by bacteria on the teeth.
    c.   Decay is reduced due to the inhibitory effects of fluoride on growth of bacteria on the teeth.
    d.   Fluoride becomes incorporated into the crystalline structure of teeth making them less susceptible to decay.

b   455(A)   127.   Which of the following mechanisms explains why fluoride is effective in controlling tooth decay?
    a.   It helps regulate calcium levels in saliva.
    b.   It helps form decay-resistant fluorapatite.
    c.   It inhibits growth of decay-producing bacteria.
    d.   It changes the pH of the mouth, inhibiting bacterial growth.

a   456(K)   128.   What is the most reliable source of dietary fluoride?
    a.   Public water
    b.   Dark green vegetables
    c.   Milk and milk products
    d.   Meats and whole-grain cereals

a   454;456(A) 129.   Which of the following characteristics are shared by copper and fluoride?
    a.   Both may be obtained from drinking tap water.
    b.   Both serve as cofactors for a number of enzymes.
    c.   Neither is involved in the integrity of bones and teeth.
    d.   Neither is known to be toxic at intakes of 10 times the estimated safe and adequate dietary intake.

d   456(K)   130.   Which of the following does **not** have an RDA?
    a.   Iron
    b.   Zinc
    c.   Iodine
    d.   Fluoride

a   456(A)   131.   What is the optimal fluoride concentrated in community water supplies?
    a.   1 ppm
    b.   2 ppm
    c.   2.5 ppm
    d.   4 ppm

c   455,456(K) 132.   Which of the following is a feature of fluoride in nutrition?
    a.   Most bottled waters are fluoridated.
    b.   A severe deficiency is known as fluorosis.
    c.   A deficiency causes the most widespread health problem in the United States.
    d.   Fluorapatite refers to an increase in the desire to eat fluoride-rich foods.

a   455,456(K)   133.   Fluoride deficiency is best known to lead to
        a.   dental decay.
        b.   osteoporosis.
        c.   discoloration of teeth.
        d.   nutritional muscular dystrophy.

a   456(K)   134.   Which of the following is known to cause discolored enamel of the teeth?
        a.   Excessive fluoride in the water
        b.   Insufficient fluoride in the water
        c.   Excessive intake of simple sugars
        d.   Inability of the body to absorb fluoride

c   456,457(K)   135.   One of the chief functions of chromium is participation in the metabolism of
        a.   iron.
        b.   proteins.
        c.   carbohydrates.
        d.   metallothionein.

c   456(K)   136.   As far as is known, what hormone is dependent upon chromium for optimal activity?
        a.   Renin
        b.   Gastrin
        c.   Insulin
        d.   Antidiurectic hormone

c   456,457(K)   137.   Which of the following is a characteristic of chromium in nutrition?
        a.   A deficiency leads to hypothyroidism.
        b.   Supplements are known to be helpful.
        c.   Whole grains represent an excellent source.
        d.   In the body, it enhances the action of ceruloplasmin.

b   456,457(K)   138.   Chromium deficiency is characterized by
        a.   hypertension.
        b.   hyperglycemia.
        c.   enlargement of the liver.
        d.   enlargement of the thyroid gland.

b   457(K)   139.   Which of the following is a characteristic of the mineral molybdenum?
        a.   Enhances the activity of insulin
        b.   Deficiency symptoms in animals and people are unknown
        c.   Unusually poor food sources are legumes and cereal grains
        d.   Toxicity symptoms in human beings include damage to red blood cells

b   458(K)   140.   What mineral is part of vitamin B12?
        a.   Copper
        b.   Cobalt
        c.   Nickel
        d.   Vanadium

c 458(K) 141. Which of the following trace minerals is known to be essential in bone development?
 a. Tin
 b. Cobalt
 c. Silicon
 d. Barium

b 458(A) 142. Evidence to date in animals and/or human beings suggests that normal bone metabolism requires all of the following trace minerals **except**
 a. boron.
 b. silver.
 c. silicon.
 d. nickel.

a 458(K) 143. All of the following are considered heavy metals **except**
 a. iron.
 b. lead.
 c. mercury.
 d. cadmium.

d 458(A) 144. In the body, lead is known to significantly interfere with utilization of all of the following minerals **except**
 a. iron.
 b. zinc.
 c. calcium.
 d. selenium.

c 465(K) 145. What term designates foods that contain nonnutrient substances which may provide health benefits beyond basic nutrition?
 a. Health foods
 b. Organic foods
 c. Functional foods
 d. Disease preventative foods

b 466(K) 146. Which of the following is a rich source of phytoestrogens?
 a. Potatoes
 b. Soybeans
 c. Cold-water fish
 d. Green leafy vegetables

b 466(K) 147. Lycopene is classified as a(n)
 a. lignan.
 b. carotenoid.
 c. phytoestrogen.
 d. enzyme cofactor.

d 468(A) 148. The unique nature of a probiotic is its content of
 a. saponins.
 b. phytonutrients.
 c. lycopene and lutein.
 d. live microorganisms.

a   468(K)   149.   Which of the following is most descriptive of the term probiotics?
  a.   Living microbes in foods
  b.   Concentrated phytonutrients
  c.   Vitamins and essential trace elements
  d.   Vitamin supplements that include biotin

MATCHING (Answers can be used only once.)

H	439	01.	Iron storage protein
N	440	02.	Enhances absorption of nonheme iron
E	440	03.	Form of iron found only in animal flesh
J	440	04.	Form of iron found in both plant and animal foods
M	439	05.	Oxygen-carrying protein in muscle
P	440	06.	Substance in coffee and tea that reduces iron absorption
C	443	07.	Craving for non-food substances
B	444	08.	Toxicity from this mineral is twice as prevalent as deficiency in men
S	444	09.	Condition characterized by large deposits of iron protein in body tissues
T	448	10.	Zinc binding protein of intestine
D	449	11.	A deficiency of this element retards growth and arrests sexual maturation
O	439	12.	Iron-containing protein in erythrocytes
F	451	13.	Iodine deficiency disease
R	452	14.	Major dietary source of iodine
I	453	15.	Disease associated with severe selenium deficiency
Q	455	16.	Stabilized form of tooth crystal
K	456	17.	Deficiency leads to hyperglycemia
L	456	18.	Condition associated with discoloration of tooth enamel
A	456	19.	Significant dietary source of fluoride
G	458	20.	Mineral that forms integral part of vitamin B_{12}

A.	Tea	K.	Chromium
B.	Iron	L.	Fluorosis
C.	Pica	M.	Myoglobin
D.	Zinc	N.	MFP Factor
E.	Heme	O.	Hemoglobin
F.	Goiter	P.	Tannic acid
G.	Cobalt	Q.	Fluorapatite
H.	Ferritin	R.	Fortified salt
I.	Keshan	S.	Hemosiderosis
J.	Nonheme	T.	Metallothionein

ESSAY QUESTIONS

PAGE(S)

437,438   01.   Make several general statements about trace elements in nutrition, including common food sources, deficiencies, toxicities, and interactions.

438-457   02.   Choose any 3 trace elements and discuss their major functions, deficiency symptoms, toxicity symptoms, and food sources.

440-442;448,449   03.   Compare and contrast the absorption, transport, and recycling of iron and zinc.

440,441;445-447   04.   What factors are known to reduce or enhance iron absorption?

440,441;445-447   05.   Discuss factors that influence the bioavailability of dietary iron. What are good sources of bioavailable iron? What factors interfere with iron absorption?

440,441;445   06.   Explain the difference between heme and nonheme iron. How can the efficiency of absorption be increased for both types of iron?

442,443   07.   In the proper sequence, describe the three stages in the development of iron deficiency.

444,445   08.   Discuss the pros and cons of increasing the iron level of enriched bread in the United States.

444   09.   Explain how iron is thought to modify the risks for heart disease and for cancer.

444   10.   A.   What signs and symptoms of iron deficiency are shared with iron overload?
           B.   What tests are used to assess for iron overload?

448,449   11.   What are the signs and symptoms of zinc deficiency? Which ones have similarities to other nutrient deficiencies?

451,452   12.   What factors account for the above average intake of iodine by many people in the U.S. population?

451,452   13.   What are the effects of iodine deficiency and iodine excess? What population groups show iodine abnormalities?

452   14.   Discuss iodine availability and sources of iodine in the U.S. diet.

453   15.   Discuss the essential nature of selenium. Where and why are deficiencies observed in the world?

454   16.   Explain how a deficiency of copper can lead to "iron deficiency" anemia.

455,456   17.   Discuss the essential nature of fluoride. What level in the diet is considered optimal? What are the effects of excess fluoride intake and how does toxicity usually occur?

456,457   18.   Discuss the essential nature of chromium, and list good food sources of chromium. Why are chromium supplements promoted by the supplements industry?

458   19.   Discuss the effects of lead exposure on health and human performance.

465-470   20.   What is the meaning and significance of functional foods? Give several examples of potential functional foods and their proposed uses.

465-469   21.   Discuss the potential consequences of adding phytochemicals to foods.

467   22.   Discuss the health benefits and food sources of flavonoids.

468   23.   Discuss the meaning and significance of probiotics in foods.

CHAPTER 14
FITNESS: PHYSICAL ACTIVITY, NUTRIENTS, AND BODY ADAPTATIONS

AN PAGE(S)

d   481,482(K)   01.   According to the American College of Sports Medicine, which of the following would meet the exercise schedule to maintain an appropriate level of fitness?
   a.   2 hours of aerobic exercise daily
   b.   1 hour of strength training 4 times a week
   c.   5 minutes of aerobic exercise 2 times a week
   d.   20 minutes of any continuous activity using large muscle groups 3 times a week

b   481,482(K)   02.   To help maintain a desirable Body Mass Index, the DRI Committee recommends a level of moderately intense exercise at a frequency of at least
   a.   20 minutes/day.
   b.   60 minutes/day.
   c.   2 hours/week.
   d.   5 hours/week.

c   479(K)   03.   All of the following are acceptable definitions of the term fitness **except**
   a.   the ability of the body to resist stress.
   b.   the ability of the body to perform physical activity without undue stress.
   c.   the ability to maintain a normal body composition and remain free of injury while performing strenuous physical tasks.
   d.   the ability to meet normal physical and emotional demands while maintaining an energy reserve sufficient to overcome an immediate challenge.

a   480(K)   04.   Which of the following is generally **not** associated with a regular program of physical fitness?
   a.   Lowering of bone density
   b.   Lowering of blood pressure
   c.   Lowering of blood cholesterol
   d.   Lowering of resting pulse rate

b   480(K)   05.   What percentage of U.S. adults live a completely sedentary lifestyle?
   a.   5
   b.   25
   c.   45
   d.   60

c   480,481(K)   06.   The components of fitness include all of the following **except**
   a.   strength.
   b.   flexibility.
   c.   bone fragility.
   d.   cardiovascular endurance.

b   483(A)   07.   A muscle that increases size in response to use is an example of
   a.   atrophy.
   b.   hypertrophy.
   c.   muscular endurance.
   d.   muscle engorgement.

c   483(A)   08.   Athletes can safely add muscle tissue by
    a.   tripling protein intake.
    b.   taking hormones duplicating those of puberty.
    c.   putting a demand on muscles by making them work harder.
    d.   relying on protein for muscle fuel and decreasing intake of carbohydrates.

a   483(K)   09.   What is muscle atrophy?
    a.   Loss of muscle size and strength
    b.   Muscle cramps arising from insufficient warm-up
    c.   Muscle spasms resulting from too rapid progressive overloading
    d.   Alterations in heart muscle contractions when first initiating a fitness program

c   478,479(K) 10.   Two definitive indicators of the physical fitness of older adults are strength and
    a.   VO₂ max.
    b.   jumping ability.
    c.   walking endurance.
    d.   resting heart rate below 70.

c   483(K)   11.   All of the following are strategies comprising the progressive overload principle **except**
    a.   duration.
    b.   intensity.
    c.   flexibility.
    d.   frequency.

a   484(A)   12.   A person engaging in exercise at a moderate level should walk at a speed of one mile per
    a.   quarter hour.
    b.   half hour.
    c.   hour.
    d.   hour and a half.

d   484(A)   13.   In weight training, muscle endurance can best be emphasized by combining a
    a.   low number of repetitions with heavy weight.
    b.   low number of repetitions with lighter weight.
    c.   high number of repetitions with heavy weight.
    d.   high number of repetitions with lighter weight.

a   484(A)   14.   In weight training, muscle strength can best be emphasized by combining a
    a.   low number of repetitions with heavy weight.
    b.   low number of repetitions with lighter weight.
    c.   high number of repetitions with heavy weight.
    d.   high number of repetitions with lighter weight.

a   485(K)   15.   Which of the following is **not** derived directly from cardiorespiratory conditioning?
    a.   Increased flexibility
    b.   Slowed resting pulse
    c.   Increased breathing efficiency
    d.   Increased blood volume and oxygen delivery

d   485(K)   16.   The effect of regular exercise on heart and lung function is known as
      a.   muscle fitness.
      b.   muscle endurance.
      c.   cardiopulmonary adaptation.
      d.   cardiorespiratory conditioning.

d   485(A)   17.   With cardiorespiratory conditioning muscle cells show all of the following changes **except**
      a.   they hold more myoglobin.
      b.   they become stronger in the lungs.
      c.   they hold more fat oxidizing enzymes.
      d.   they draw less oxygen due to increased efficiency of aerobic metabolism.

a   485(K)   18.   For maximum benefits, cardiorespiratory endurance episodes should be sustained for at least
      a.   20 minutes.
      b.   40 minutes.
      c.   1 hour.
      d.   2 hour.

b   485(K)   19.   What is VO_2 max?
      a.   An individual's maximum velocity on a test treadmill
      b.   An individual's maximum rate of oxygen consumption
      c.   An individual's maximum intake of oxygen while at rest
      d.   An individual's maximum intake of air at 70% physical exhaustion

a   487(K)   20.   What substance contains the chemical energy that drives immediate muscle contraction?
      a.   ATP
      b.   NAD
      c.   Glucose
      d.   Fatty acids

d   487(K)   21.   What high-energy compound acts as a reservoir of energy for the maintenance of a steady supply of ATP?
      a.   Glycerol
      b.   Glycogen
      c.   Fatty acids
      d.   Phosphocreatine

b   487(K)   22.   During physical performance, what is the role of creatine phosphate?
      a.   Removal of lactic acid
      b.   Transfer of energy to make ATP
      c.   Removal of nitrogen waste products
      d.   Transfer of phosphate to muscle fiber

b   487(A)   23.   A person who suddenly begins sprinting will exhaust the muscle's supply of creatine phosphate in about
      a.   1 second.
      b.   10 seconds.
      c.   1 minute.
      d.   10 minutes.

a   487,488(A)   24.   If muscle work is anaerobic, which of the following **cannot** serve as fuel?
     a.   Fat
     b.   Protein
     c.   Carbohydrate

b   488,489(A)   25.   A tissue deprived of an oxygen supply during exercise would have an accumulation of
     a.   ATP.
     b.   lactic acid.
     c.   glucose-1-phosphate.
     d.   TCA cycle intermediates.

a   488,489(A)   26.   Which of the following is a common product of anaerobic metabolism?
     a.   Lactic acid
     b.   Phytic acid
     c.   Phosphoric acid
     d.   Hydrochloric acid

a   489(K)   27.   What is the name of the biochemical pathway describing the conversion of lactic acid to glucose?
     a.   Cori cycle
     b.   Krebs cycle
     c.   Beta-oxidation
     d.   Reverse glycolysis

a   488(A)   28.   What is the usual fate of muscle glycogen during exercise?
     a.   Utilized as a fuel within the muscle cells only
     b.   Released into the bloodstream to provide fuel for brain cells
     c.   Released into the bloodstream to replenish liver glycogen as needed
     d.   Utilized to support lung and heart function under conditions of intense physical performance

c   488(A)   29.   What dietary nutrients are most effective at raising muscle glycogen concentrations?
     a.   Fats
     b.   Proteins
     c.   Carbohydrates
     d.   Chromium and iron

a   488(K)   30.   What is the predominant fuel used by muscle cells during low or moderate intensity activity?
     a.   Fat
     b.   Protein
     c.   Glycogen
     d.   Blood glucose

d   487,488(A)   31.   Which of the following activities depletes glycogen most quickly?
     a.   Hiking
     b.   Jogging
     c.   Walking
     d.   Quarter-mile run

c   488,489(A) 32. Which of the following substances increases in muscles during increasing exercise intensity?
- a. ATP
- b. Glycogen
- c. Lactic acid
- d. Phosphocreatine

b   488(K) 33. How much time is usually needed in vigorous activity to cause depletion of glycogen reserves?
- a. 1 hour
- b. 2 hours
- c. 3 hours
- d. 4 hours

b   489(K) 34. What is the Cori cycle?
- a. The coordinated muscle contraction sequence of slow-twitch and fast-twitch fibers
- b. A process in the liver that regenerates glucose from lactic acid released by muscles
- c. An exercise machine that allows development of both aerobic and anaerobic capacities
- d. A group of enzymatic reactions to accelerate muscle glycogen repletion in the trained athlete

d   489(K) 35. During the first 20 minutes of moderate exercise, the body uses about
- a. 50% of the available fat.
- b. 10% of the available water.
- c. 90% of the available protein.
- d. 20% of the available glycogen.

c   489(A) 36. When a marathon runner experiences the phenomenon known as "hitting the wall," what nutrient is most likely depleted?
- a. Water
- b. Protein
- c. Glucose
- d. Fatty acids

c   489-491(A) 37. Which of the following is **least** likely to affect the size of the body's glycogen stores?
- a. Exercise regimen
- b. Fat content of the diet
- c. Type of supplements taken
- d. Carbohydrate content of the diet

c   488(A) 38. Which of the following diets promotes superior physical performance in athletes?
- a. High fat diet
- b. High protein diet
- c. High carbohydrate diet
- d. Normal mixed diet with vitamin supplements

b   488(K)   39.   Which of the following is a property of conditioned muscles?
           a.   They can store more glycogen.
           b.   They are more efficient at converting fat to glucose.
           c.   They contain less mitochondria due to increased glucose utilization.
           d.   They rely less on fat breakdown and more on glucose oxidation for energy.

d   490(A)   40.   What type of meal and time of its ingestion promote the most rapid repletion of
                 glycogen stores after physical activity?
           a.   Mixed meal taken within 4 hours
           b.   Mixed meal taken within 30 minutes
           c.   High-carbohydrate meal taken within 2½ hours
           d.   High-carbohydrate meal taken within 15 minutes

c   491(A)   41.   During a physical activity, what hormone signals the fat cells to begin releasing
                 their fatty acids?
           a.   Leptin
           b.   Glucagon
           c.   Epinephrine
           d.   Neuropeptide-y

c   491,492(K) 42.   What cellular organelles are responsible for producing ATP aerobically?
           a.   Ribosomes
           b.   Golgi bodies
           c.   Mitochondria
           d.   Cell membranes

c   491,492(A) 43.   Which of the following describes fat utilization during physical activity?
           a.   Fat that is stored closest to the exercising muscle is oxidized first.
           b.   Fat oxidization makes more of a contribution as the intensity of the exercise
                 increases.
           c.   Fat oxidation may continue at an above normal rate for some time after
                 cessation of physical activity.
           d.   Fat is burned in higher quantities during short high-intensity exercises than
                 prolonged low-intensity exercises.

c   491(K)   44.   For optimal performance of endurance athletes, sports nutritionists recommend
                 approximately how much dietary fat energy?
           a.   5-10%
           b.   10-15%
           c.   20-30%
           d.   35-45%

b   491(A)   45.   Which of the following is an effect of physical fitness on fat metabolism?
           a.   Fatty acid release from adipose cells directly into muscle cells becomes
                 more efficient.
           b.   Fatty acid concentrations in the blood rise significantly after the first 20
                 minutes of physical activity.
           c.   Fatty acid energy release requires less oxygen on a per-kcal basis than does
                 the use of glucose.
           d.   Fat utilization slows down and liver glucose release rises in response to
                 adaptation of the body's hormonal profile.

b   492(A)   46.   Which of the following is an effect of exercise on protein metabolism?
a.   Protein use as a fuel is lowest in endurance athletes.
b.   Protein synthesis is inhibited during exercise and for some time thereafter.
c.   Protein use during physical performance is generally not related to carbohydrate content of the diet.
d.   Protein synthesis is increased slightly during exercise but diminishes by a like amount to remain in balance.

a   492(K)   47.   Which of the following is a feature of protein nutrition in physical activity?
a.   Protein is not a major fuel for physical activity.
b.   Protein contributes 30% more to total fuel used versus that in the resting state.
c.   Body protein synthesis rates are increased about 10% during the physical activity.
d.   Body protein synthesis rates are increased about 30% for several hours after the physical activity.

d   492,493(A) 48.   Which of the following is **not** known to modify the body's use of protein?
a.   Diet
b.   The degree of training
c.   Exercise intensity and duration
d.   Vitamin supplements above the RDA

b   492,493(A) 49.   Which of the following is a role for diet in physical activity?
a.   Diets high in fat lead to a fall in amino acid utilization for fuel.
b.   Diets lacking in carbohydrates lead to increased amino acid utilization for fuel.
c.   Deficiencies of vitamins have no effect on performance provided that all other nutrients are adequate.
d.   Deficiencies of minerals have no effect on performance provided that all other nutrients are adequate.

d   492(A)   50.   In the immediate postexercise period, what type of diet enhances muscle protein synthesis?
a.   Protein alone
b.   Carbohydrate alone
c.   Carbohydrate plus fat
d.   Carbohydrate plus protein

c   493(A)   51.   For female endurance athletes, about how much more protein above the RDA is recommended by recognized health organizations?
a.   10-20%
b.   25-35%
c.   50-100%
d.   100-150%

b   493(A)   52.   According to several recognized health organizations, about how many grams of protein per day are recommended for a male, 70 kg strength athlete?
a.   56
b.   112
c.   140
d.   168

c   493(A)   53.   Which of the following describes the role of protein in the diet of competitive athletes?
a.   The need for protein per kg body weight is higher in females than male athletes.
b.   The need for protein is best met by increasing the level to 20-25% of total energy content of the diet.
c.   The need for protein in weight lifters and marathon runners may be up to 75-100% higher than the RDA.
d.   The need for protein in most athletes generally could **not** be obtained from diets meeting energy requirements but containing only 10% of the energy as protein.

c   493(A)   54.   According to several recognized health organizations, about how many grams of protein per day are recommended for a female, 50 kg marathon runner?
a.   40-45
b.   50-64
c.   66-88
d.   120-154

d   494,495(K)   55.   Which of the following represents current knowledge of the role of vitamin and mineral supplements in physical performance?
a.   When taken right before an event, they have been shown to benefit performance.
b.   Moderate amounts have been shown to improve the performance of most elite athletes.
c.   Except perhaps for iron, they are needed in high amounts to meet the needs of athletes exposed to hot and humid weather conditions.
d.   Except perhaps for iron and vitamin E, supplements are not recommended since there is no difference in the RDA of physically active people compared with sedentary people.

a   494,495(A)   56.   What nutrient is important in transport of oxygen in blood and in muscle tissue and energy transformation reactions?
a.   Iron
b.   Calcium
c.   Thiamin
d.   Vitamin C

b   495(K)   57.   Which of the following is a characteristic of sports anemia?
a.   It requires a prolonged treatment period.
b.   It is a temporary condition requiring no treatment.
c.   It responds to treatment only with high doses of iron.
d.   It is due primarily to increased iron loss via perspiration.

a   495(K)   58.   Which of the following is a feature of sports anemia?
a.   It is not a true iron deficiency anemia.
b.   It is usually corrected by iron supplementation.
c.   It is found primarily in over-conditioned athletes.
d.   It is associated with reduced cardiorespiratory fitness.

d   494,495(K)   59.   Which of the following is a known feature of iron nutrition in athletes?
a.   Iron in sweat represents the major route of iron loss from the body.
b.   Iron deficiency affects a higher percentage of male athletes than female athletes.
c.   Sports anemia is successfully treated by increasing dietary iron to levels 2-3 times the RDA.
d.   Iron losses in runners occur when blood cells are squashed by the impact of the foot on a hard surface.

b   495(A)   60.   The change in a person's red blood cell count that occurs from running on a hard surface is termed
a.   hyphemoglobinemia.
b.   exertional hemolysis.
c.   sports hypochronemia.
d.   iron-deficient adaptive syndrome.

a   496(K)   61.   Physical performance is noticeably affected when body water loss first reaches
a.   1-2%.
b.   5-10%.
c.   15-20%.
d.   25-30%.

c   496(A)   62.   The appearance of euphoria in a person engaged in outdoor sports activities may be an early sign of
a.   heat stroke.
b.   dehydration.
c.   hypothermia.
d.   exertional distress.

d   496(A)   63.   A person engaged in an endurance event has lost two liters of body water by sweating. What would be the approximate energy loss from the evaporation of the sweat?
a.   100 kcal
b.   500 kcal
c.   850 kcal
d.   1200 kcal

a   496(K)   64.   All of the following are characteristics of heat stroke **except**
a.   it is rarely fatal.
b.   it is due, in part, to dehydration.
c.   it is caused by heat buildup in the body.
d.   its symptoms include headache, nausea, and mental changes.

b   496(A)   65.   A person engaged in physically active work in hot humid weather and who wears a rubber suit to promote weight loss is at high risk of experiencing
a.   ketosis.
b.   heat stroke.
c.   hypothermia.
d.   overhydration.

b   496(K)   66.   What nutrient becomes depleted most rapidly during physical exercise?
  a.   Iron
  b.   Water
  c.   Glucose
  d.   Glycogen

a   496,497(A) 67.   In the endurance athlete, the first priority of nutrient repletion should be
  a.   fluids.
  b.   protein.
  c.   glycogen.
  d.   electrolytes.

b   496(K)   68.   Which of the following are common early symptoms of hypothermia in athletes?
  a.   Headache and nausea
  b.   Euphoria and shivering
  c.   Confusion and delirium
  d.   Dizziness and clumsiness

c   496(K)   69.   Which of the following is a feature of water metabolism during exercise?
  a.   The maximum loss of fluid per hour of exercise is about 0.5 liters.
  b.   In cold weather, the need for water falls dramatically because the body does not sweat.
  c.   Sweat losses can exceed the capacity of the GI tract to absorb water resulting in some degree of dehydration.
  d.   Heavy sweating leads to a marked rise in the thirst sensation to stimulate water intake which delays the onset of dehydration.

b   497,498(K) 70.   All of the following are valid reasons for consuming sports drinks by most physically active people **except**
  a.   they may provide a psychological advantage.
  b.   they are better than water at preventing sodium depletion.
  c.   they contain a source of fuel which may enhance performance in endurance events.
  d.   they have a good taste which encourages their consumption and ensures adequate hydration.

c   496-498(A) 71.   Which of the following would be the best choice for physically active people who need to rehydrate?
  a.   "Sweat" replacers
  b.   Salt tablets and tap water
  c.   Diluted juice or cool water
  d.   Water warmed to body temperature

a   496(K)   72.   What is the recommended amount of water to meet the needs of athletes?
  a.   1-1½ mL per kcal expended
  b.   5-7 mL per kcal expended
  c.   1,000 mL per hour of activity
  d.   1,500 mL per hour of activity

a   496(A)   73.   What would be the minimum amount of body water loss necessary to bring about a reduction in work capacity of an average 165 pound individual?
   a.   1½ liters
   b.   3½ liters
   c.   6 liters
   d.   10 liters

a   496(K)   74.   The first sign of dehydration is typically
   a.   fatigue.
   b.   dizziness.
   c.   intense thirst.
   d.   intense sweating.

d   499(A)   75.   How can water loss from the body be quickly estimated at the end of a physical activity?
   a.   Multiply body weight (kg) by 1%, which equals the number of liters water loss.
   b.   Multiply duration of activity (minutes) by body weight (kg), which equals ml of water loss.
   c.   Subtract air temperature (°F) from body weight (lbs), then multiply by 5 to obtain mL water loss.
   d.   Take the difference in body weight (lbs) before and after the event and multiply by 2 for the number of cups of water loss.

c   497,498(K)   76.   All of the following are characteristics of electrolyte metabolism in sports **except**
   a.   the trained athlete actually loses fewer electrolytes than the untrained person.
   b.   replenishment of lost electrolytes in most athletes can be accomplished by ingesting a regular diet.
   c.   sweating leads to significant losses of calcium, sulfur, and chromium which can be replaced by including milk and whole grains in the diet.
   d.   salt tablet supplements to replace electrolyte losses of sweat are known to cause fluid retention in the GI tract, irritation of the stomach, and vomiting.

b   497(K)   77.   Hyponatremia refers to low blood levels of
   a.   water.
   b.   sodium.
   c.   glucose.
   d.   potassium.

d   497(K)   78.   All of the following are features of sodium in endurance athletes **except**
   a.   they need to replace sodium during the event.
   b.   they should eat pretzels during the second half of the event.
   c.   they are susceptible to hyponatremia if they refrain from adequate sodium intake during the event.
   d.   they can easily replace sodium loss by consuming conventional sports drinks during the event.

a   498(K)   79.   What is the principal reason that intake of alcohol is not beneficial to athletic performance?
   a.   It is not metabolized in muscle.
   b.   It inhibits glycogen breakdown.
   c.   It inhibits creatine-phosphate synthesis.
   d.   It interferes with ATP synthesis in the liver.

c   498(K)   80.   Which of the following is a benefit of glucose polymer sports drinks as compared with sugar containing drinks?
a.   They supply more energy per gram of carbohydrate.
b.   They require less digestion and therefore are absorbed faster into the circulation.
c.   They attract less water in the GI tract and thus allow more water to remain in the circulation.
d.   They are absorbed much more slowly and therefore provide a more even carbohydrate load to the body.

a   505;508(A) 81.   Which of the following describes an effect of caffeine use in the athlete?
a.   It induces fluid losses.
b.   It enhances performance for almost all athletes.
c.   It raises blood pH to counteract the buildup of lactic acid.
d.   It promotes absorption of electrolytes from the intestinal tract.

c   489(A)   82.   The optimal carbohydrate concentration of sports drinks for the endurance athlete is
a.   1-2%.
b.   5%.
c.   6-10%.
d.   15-20%.

b   497(A)   83.   What is the minimum amount of fluid that an athlete should drink for each pound of body weight lost during an activity?
a.   ¼ liter
b.   ½ liter
c.   1 liter
d.   2 liters

c   499(A)   84.   Which of the following should be a component of a healthy diet for athletes?
a.   Salt tablets
b.   Protein powders
c.   Nutrient dense foods
d.   Vitamin and mineral supplements

c   499(A)   85.   The recommended amount of dietary carbohydrate for an athlete training for a marathon is
a.   2 g/kg body weight.
b.   4 g/kg body weight.
c.   8 g/kg body weight.
d.   12 g/kg body weight.

c   495(A)   86.   What should be the composition of the last (pregame) meal before an athletic event?
a.   High-protein, providing 30 kcal per kg body weight
b.   Vegetable and fruit juices, providing 100 to 200 kcal
c.   High-carbohydrate, low-fiber, providing 300 to 800 kcal
d.   High-fiber, providing 200 to 300 kcal and liberal amounts of fluid which is beneficially retained by the fiber in the GI tract

d   495(A)   87.   What is the recommended composition of the postgame meal of the athlete?
                a.   Low-protein
                b.   High-protein
                c.   Low-carbohydrate
                d.   High-carbohydrate

d   495(K)   88.   Why should fiber-rich foods be avoided in an athlete's pregame meal?
                a.   The fiber delays absorption of fat.
                b.   The fiber interferes with glycolysis.
                c.   The meal crowds out more energy-dense foods.
                d.   The fiber retains water in the GI tract that would otherwise be absorbed.

c   505;507(K) 89.   What is the source of whey protein sold as supplements to body builders?
                a.   An alkaline extract of brewer's yeast
                b.   An acid extract of soybean processing
                c.   A waste product of cheese manufacturing
                d.   A complementary protein composed of animal and legume extracts

a   505;507(A) 90.   Research results of carnitine supplementation as an ergogenic aid showed that it
                a.   produced diarrhea in half of the subjects.
                b.   enhanced carbohydrate oxidation rate but not fat oxidation.
                c.   raised muscle carnitine concentration but did not improve performance.
                d.   promoted retention of amino acids but did not lead to increased muscle mass.

a   494(K)   91.   Which of the following is a feature of specific ergogenic acids?
                a.   Vitamin E in high doses seems to protect against exercise-induced oxidative stress.
                b.   Branched-chain amino acid supplementation appears to lower blood ammonia levels.
                c.   Carnitine supplementation appears to increase the concentration of muscle carnitine.
                d.   Chromium supplementation (as chromium picolinate) appears to enhance fat oxidation in most athletes.

b   506(A)   92.   An athlete who believes in soda loading as a means of improving performance would, right before the event, consume
                a.   caffeine tablets.
                b.   sodium bicarbonate.
                c.   a carbonated beverage.
                d.   a lactose containing beverage.

d   509(K)   93.   Which of the following ergogenic aids increases the risk for acromegaly?
                a.   HMB
                b.   Creatine
                c.   Octacosanol
                d.   Growth hormone

a   505;509(K) 94.   What type of chemicals are DHEA and androstendione?
                a.   Hormones
                b.   Estrogens
                c.   Phytonutrients
                d.   Herbal extracts

a   505;509,510(K) 95.   Which of the following is a characteristic of human growth hormone use in athletes?
- a.   Excessive use shortens life span.
- b.   Low cost accounts for some of its popularity.
- c.   Excessive use leads to shrinking of internal organs.
- d.   Laboratory tests can differentiate between the naturally occurring form and the drug form of growth hormone.

b   507(A)   96.   Which of the following is a known risk from ingesting large doses of the branched-chain amino acids in athletes?
- a.   Diarrhea
- b.   Elevated plasma ammonia levels
- c.   Slightly enhanced physical performance in endurance events
- d.   More rapid replacement of muscle creatine-phosphate levels

a   508(K)   97.   Which of the following is a characteristic of oxygenated water use in athletes?
- a.   The oxygen in the water is without benefit.
- b.   Regular use reduces risk for sports anemia.
- c.   The water's oxygen can more easily traverse the GI tract.
- d.   It increases blood oxygen levels but only for about 15 minutes.

MATCHING (Answers can be used only once.)

H	479	01.	The body's ability to deal with stress
O	482	02.	The capacity of the joints to move with less chance of injury
Q	483	03.	Increase in muscle size and strength
G	487	04.	Required for aerobic metabolism
L	487	05.	Used as precursor to form a high-energy compound in muscle cells
P	489	06.	A chief substance of the Cori cycle
M	489	07.	Depletion of this substance leads runners to experience "hitting the wall"
D	499	08.	Recommended amount of carbohydrate as percentage of total energy intake of endurance athletes
K	488	09.	Substance in muscle that serves as a source of energy and water
C	491	10.	Number of minutes after starting a physical activity for blood fatty acid concentrations to rise
E	493	11.	Recommended protein intake (g per day) for a 70 kg male competitive body builder
T	495	12.	Transient condition of low blood hemoglobin in athletes
S	496	13.	Early symptoms of this disorder include nausea and stumbling
F	496	14.	Number of kcalories expended from evaporation of one liter of sweat
R	496	15.	Early symptoms of this disorder are shivering and euphoria
N	496	16.	The replacement of fluids during physical activities
A	496	17.	Water intake recommendation for physically active people, in mL/kcal expended
J	505	18.	Stimulant that promotes urine losses during exercise
I	498	19.	Depressant that promotes urine losses
B	499	20.	Recommended carbohydrate intake, in g/kg body weight, of athletes in heavy training

A.	1	F.	600	K.	Glycogen	P.	Lactic acid
B.	8	G.	Oxygen	L.	Creatine	Q.	Hypertrophy
C.	20	H.	Fitness	M.	Glucose	R.	Hypothermia
D.	70	I.	Alcohol	N.	Hydration	S.	Hyperthermia
E.	112	J.	Caffeine	O.	Flexibility	T.	Sports anemia

ESSAY QUESTIONS

PAGE(S)

480-482	01.	Discuss the physiological and psychological benefits of being physically fit.
482,483	02.	Explain the recommended training procedure (i.e., overload principle) for mastering the components of fitness.
482-485	03.	Explain the meaning and significance of cardiorespiratory endurance.
483	04.	Define the progressive overload principle as it applies to physical fitness.
488-493	05.	Discuss the use of protein, fat, and carbohydrate as fuels during low, moderate, and intense exercise.
489-491	06.	Explain the training technique of glycogen loading. What are its advantages and disadvantages?
491,492	07.	Describe three factors that influence fat use during physical activity.
491,492	08.	Discuss the pros and cons of high-fat diets for athletic performance.
494,495	09.	Discuss the effects of athletic training on iron nutrition.
494,495	10.	Compare and contrast the characteristics of sports anemia, exertional hemolysis, and iron-deficiency anemia..
496-498	11.	Discuss the need for water in maintaining physical performance. What are the symptoms of dehydration? What are the recommendations for ensuring that the body is well hydrated prior to an athletic event?
497-498	12.	Discuss the importance of sodium nutrition for the athlete.
498-499	13.	Why are alcoholic beverages considered poor sources of energy, water, and electrolytes for athletes?
499-501	14.	Describe an appropriate diet for physically active people.
494	15.	Under what circumstances might supplemental vitamin E be of benefit for physically active people?
505-510	16.	Discuss the use of 6 substances promoted as aids to enhance athletic performance.
505-508	17.	Discuss the use and abuse of caffeine, carnitine, and creatine as ergogenic substances.
508-510	18.	Describe the hazards of using anabolic steroids and human growth hormone as ways of improving physical performance.

CHAPTER 15
LIFE CYCLE NUTRITION: PREGNANCY AND LACTATION

AN. PAGE(S)

a   508(K)   01.   What is the placenta?
- a.   An organ from which the infant receives nourishment
- b.   A muscular organ within which the infant develops before birth
- c.   The developing infant from the eighth week after conception until birth
- d.   The developing infant during its second through eighth week after conception

c   508(K)   02.   What organ of the pregnant woman is central to the exchange of nutrients for waste products with the fetus?
- a.   Uterus
- b.   Vagina
- c.   Placenta
- d.   Amniotic sac

c   508(K)   03.   What organ functions to prepare the mother's breasts for lactation?
- a.   Uterus
- b.   Ovaries
- c.   Placenta
- d.   Amniotic sac

d   508(K)   04.   What connects the umbilical cord to the placenta?
- a.   Uterus
- b.   Placenta
- c.   Caesareas
- d.   Belly button

c   508(K)   05.   A newly fertilized egg is known as a(n)
- a.   fetus.
- b.   ovum.
- c.   zygote.
- d.   embryo.

b   508(K)   06.   What is the name given to the human organism two to eight weeks after fertilization and the stage at which the digestive system is formed?
- a.   Fetus
- b.   Embryo
- c.   Ectoderm
- d.   Mesoderm

a   510(K)   07.   What is the term given to the developing infant from the eighth week after conception until birth?
- a.   Fetus
- b.   Ovum
- c.   Zygote
- d.   Embryo

a   510(K)   08.   At what stage of pregnancy does an embryo show a beating heart and a complete central nervous system?
- a.   8 weeks
- b.   12 weeks
- c.   20 weeks
- d.   29 weeks

d   510(K)   09.   During development of the fetus, what organ(s) are the first to reach maturity?
- a.   Heart and lungs
- b.   Liver and kidneys
- c.   Gastrointestinal tract
- d.   Central nervous system and brain

d   510(K)   10.   Gestation is generally divided into equal periods of
- a.   4 weeks, called quarters.
- b.   9 weeks, called quartiles.
- c.   4 months, called semesters.
- d.   3 months, called trimesters.

c   510(A)   11.   All of the following statements are specific to the critical periods of cell division **except**
- a.   malnutrition during pregnancy can affect fetal cell division.
- b.   malnutrition during critical periods can have irreversible effects.
- c.   high-nutrient-density food fed after the critical period can remedy a growth deficit.
- d.   whatever nutrients are needed during a critical period must be supplied at that time.

b   510(K)   12.   What term is given to the time period during which irreversible damage to the fetus may occur from specific events such as malnutrition or exposure to toxins?
- a.   First trimester
- b.   Critical period
- c.   Fertility period
- d.   Conceptual period

a   511(K)   13.   Which of the following is a characteristic of neural tube defects?
- a.   They are found in about 1,000 newborns in the United States each year.
- b.   They include common disorders such as liver and kidney disease.
- c.   They can be prevented by supplementation of the pregnant woman's diet with vitamin B_{12}.
- d.   They can be prevented by supplementation of the pregnant woman's diet with vitamins A and E.

b   511(K)   14.   Among the following, which is **not** known to represent a significant risk factor of a pregnancy being affected by a neural tube defect?
- a.   Maternal obesity
- b.   Age at time of pregnancy
- c.   Low socioeconomic status
- d.   Exposure to hot-tub use in pregnancy

d 510,511(K) 15. The neural tube forms the early parts of the
- a. umbilical cord.
- b. liver and pancreas.
- c. gastrointestinal tract.
- d. brain and spinal cord.

a 511(A) 16. An infant born with incomplete closure of the spinal cord has
- a. spina bifida.
- b. macrosomia.
- c. anencephaly.
- d. neural tube seizure.

b 511(K) 17. The most common forms of neural tube defects are spina bifida and
- a. macrosomia.
- b. anencephaly.
- c. preeclampsia.
- d. cesarean section.

c 511(A) 18. What organ is most affected in anencephaly?
- a. Liver
- b. Heart
- c. Brain
- d. Pancreas

b 512(K) 19. Which of the following nutrients taken as a prenatal supplement has been found to be associated with a lower incidence of neural tube defects?
- a. Iron
- b. Folate
- c. Calcium
- d. Cobalamin

d 512(K) 20. Studies report that folate supplements for women may lower the incidence of neural tube defects of infants when the vitamin is taken during the
- a. last trimester of pregnancy.
- b. second trimester of pregnancy.
- c. second and third trimesters of pregnancy.
- d. month before conception through the first trimester of pregnancy.

b 512(A) 21. What is the percentage increase in the folate RDA during pregnancy?
- a. 25
- b. 50
- c. 75
- d. 100

c 513(A) 22. The process by which maternal nutrient intake affects the child's development of diseases later in life is known as
- a. retrogenetics.
- b. reverse genetics.
- c. fetal programming.
- d. postpartum degenerative expression.

b 514(K) 23. What is macrosomia?
    a. A neural tube defect
    b. A high-birthweight infant
    c. Excessive weight gain of the mother
    d. Abnormal cravings for carbohydrate during pregnancy

b 514(A) 24. Which of the following increases the risk of macrosomia?
    a. Folate deficiency
    b. Prepregnancy obesity
    c. Postpregnancy infection
    d. Gestational oxygen deprivation

b 514(A) 25. Which of the following describes an infant born during the 36th week of pregnancy?
    a. Term
    b. Preterm
    c. Post term
    d. Caesarean

c 514(A) 26. Which of the following describes an infant born during the 43rd week of pregnancy?
    a. Term
    b. Preterm
    c. Post term
    d. Caesarean

a 514(K) 27. What is the most reliable indicator of an infant's future health status?
    a. Infant's birthweight
    b. Mother's weight before pregnancy
    c. Mother's weight gain during pregnancy
    d. Mother's nutrition status prior to pregnancy

c 514,515(K) 28. What is the recommended range of weight gain during pregnancy for a normal-weight woman?
    a. 10-18 lbs
    b. 19-24 lbs
    c. 25-35 lbs
    d. 38-44 lbs

b 515(K) 29. What is the minimum recommended weight gain for the obese pregnant woman?
    a. 10 lbs
    b. 15 lbs
    c. 25 lbs
    d. 35 lbs

b 515(K) 30. In pregnancy, a large weight gain over a short time is usually an indication of
    a. excessive fat deposition.
    b. excessive fluid retention.
    c. abnormal fetal development.
    d. normal pregnancy only if it occurs during the second trimester.

a   517(A)   31.   Edema in a pregnant woman who does not have high blood pressure or protein in the urine is
   a.   expected and normal.
   b.   a sign of dietary deficiencies.
   c.   very rare and life threatening.
   d.   a warning signal of a difficult labor.

c   516(A)   32.   The component of weight gain during pregnancy that is similar to the average weight of the infant at birth is the
   a.   placenta.
   b.   amniotic sac fluid.
   c.   maternal fat stores.
   d.   uterus and supporting muscles.

b   516(K)   33.   Which of the following is a characteristic of body weight changes associated with pregnancy?
   a.   Weight gain is generally steady throughout pregnancy for normal-weight women.
   b.   Most women are unable to lose all of the weight that was gained during pregnancy.
   c.   Sudden, large, weight gain in pregnancy may signal the development of hypotension.
   d.   Overweight pregnant women should gain as much weight as underweight pregnant women.

c   517;518;   34.   Adaptational responses in the woman who becomes pregnant include all of the following **except**
     520,521(K)
   a.   a 50% increase in blood volume.
   b.   an increase in calcium absorption.
   c.   an increase in serum albumin concentration.
   d.   an increase in iron absorption.

c   517(K)   35.   All of the following are normal body responses to pregnancy **except**
   a.   breast size increases.
   b.   blood volume increases.
   c.   body water level decreases.
   d.   joints become more flexible.

a   516,517(K) 36.   To maintain physical fitness during pregnancy, all of the following activities are considered acceptable **except**
   a.   saunas.
   b.   swimming.
   c.   playing singles tennis.
   d.   45-minute balanced exercise sessions 3 times/week.

c   518(K)   37.   What is the recommended **increase** in energy intake for the third trimester of pregnancy?
   a.   200 kcal/day
   b.   300 kcal/day
   c.   450 kcal/day
   d.   440 kcal/day

d   518(A)   38.   Over the course of the **entire** pregnancy, approximately how much **extra** energy
                      does the average pregnant woman need to consume?
                      a.   10,500 kcal
                      b.   26,000 kcal
                      c.   49,000 kcal
                      d.   72,000 kcal

d   518(K)   39.   Which of the following statements characterizes energy needs during pregnancy?
                      a.   The need is proportionally greater than for most other nutrients.
                      b.   The increased needs are similar at the beginning and end of pregnancy.
                      c.   The needs increase by similar amounts in teenagers and 30 year-old
                            women.
                      d.   The increased need is equivalent to the amount supplied by about 5 extra
                            slices of bread per day.

b   518(A)   40.   In the United States, what is the minimum daily amount of protein that should be
                      consumed by a 135-pound woman during pregnancy?
                      a.   49 g
                      b.   74 g
                      c.   108 g
                      d.   135 g

Examine the following menu for a pregnant woman.

Breakfast	Lunch	Supper
• 2 scrambled eggs • 1 crushed wheat English muffin • 1 cup orange juice	• 2 pieces (4 oz) fried chicken • 2 wheat rolls w/butter • ½ cup mashed potatoes and gravy • Iced tea	• 3 oz pork chop • 1 ear corn on the cob • Lettuce and tomato salad with 2 tbsp dressing • 1 slice bread

b   518-521(A) 41.   According to the recommended food intake for pregnancy, which of the following
                       food groups is the only one that is provided in sufficient amounts by this menu?
                       a.   Milk
                       b.   Meats
                       c.   Vegetables
                       d.   Bread/cereal

b   518(A)   42.   Which of the following nutrients are required in higher amounts during pregnancy
                      due to their roles in the synthesis of red blood cells?
                      a.   Protein and chromium
                      b.   Folate and vitamin B_{12}
                      c.   Calcium and vitamin A
                      d.   Vitamin E and vitamin C

a   518;520,521(K) 43. Of the following nutrient needs, which is considered the most difficult to meet
                         during pregnancy?
                         a.   Iron
                         b.   Protein
                         c.   Vitamin D
                         d.   Vitamin B_6

c   520(K)   44.   All of the following reflect a state of iron nutrition in pregnancy **except**
    a.   the mineral is conserved during this period.
    b.   absorption of the mineral increases due to higher blood transferrin.
    c.   most women enter pregnancy with adequate stores of the mineral.
    d.   stores of the mineral are transferred to the fetus even with low dietary intake.

c   520,521(K)   45.   During pregnancy, which of the following nutrients show a dramatic increase in absorption?
    a.   Salt and sugar
    b.   Protein and fat
    c.   Calcium and iron
    d.   Thiamin and ascorbic acid

a   520,521(A)   46.   Why is routine vitamin D supplementation during pregnancy **not** recommended?
    a.   It may be toxic to the fetus.
    b.   It inhibits absorption of vitamin A.
    c.   Self-synthesis rate of vitamin D increases markedly in pregnancy.
    d.   Pregnancy leads to increased absorption efficiency of calcium and therefore extra vitamin D is not needed.

b   518;520(K)   47.   All of the following are features of zinc nutrition in pregnancy **except**
    a.   typical intakes are lower than the recommended amount.
    b.   supplements are effective in preventing neural tube defects.
    c.   the mineral is needed for nucleic acid synthesis and thus cell development.
    d.   a secondary deficiency may develop when iron supplements are taken.

b   521(K)   48.   Which of the following is a feature of calcium nutrition in pregnancy?
    a.   The AI increases by over 100%.
    b.   Intestinal absorption increases by over 100%.
    c.   Supplements are needed for most women due to the increased needs.
    d.   Transfer of calcium from maternal stores to the fetus increases rapidly at the beginning of the second trimester.

b   521(K)   49.   Which of the following is a feature of calcium nutrition in pregnancy?
    a.   Calcium intakes usually meet the recommendations.
    b.   The AI for calcium is the same as in nonpregnancy.
    c.   Calcium absorption efficiency is the same as in nonpregnancy.
    d.   Calcification of the fetal skeleton begins during the 14th week of pregnancy.

c   521(K)   50.   Since repeated pregnancies occurring within short time frames lead to depletion of the mother's nutrient reserves, what is the optimal interval **between** pregnancies?
    a.   ½ year
    b.   1 year
    c.   1 ½-2 years
    d.   3-4 years

d   522(K)   51.   Which of the following statements reflects current knowledge of food choices in pregnancy?
a.   A craving for pickles is a strong indicator that the body needs salt.
b.   A craving for milk is a strong indicator that the body needs calcium and/or phosphorus.
c.   Careful and appropriate selection of foods can meet all nutrient needs for most women.
d.   Cravings and aversions to certain foods are probably the result of altered taste and smell sensitivities induced by hormones.

a   522(K)   52.   What is the most likely reason for a pregnant woman to crave pickles?
a.   A change in hormones
b.   A hypoglycemic episode
c.   A physiologic need for fluid
d.   A physiologic need for sodium

d   524,525(K)   53.   What is WIC?
a.   A serious neural tube defect
b.   The World Intervention and Conception program of the United Nations
c.   An environmental contaminant that may interfere with breast milk production
d.   A food and nutrition services program for pregnant women, children, and infants

d   522(K)   54.   The common problems of pregnancy include all of the following **except**
a.   nausea.
b.   heartburn.
c.   constipation.
d.   low blood pressure.

d   522(A)   55.   To help alleviate pregnancy-related nausea, all of the following actions are recommended **except**
a.   eat dry toast or dry crackers.
b.   avoid milk when feeling nauseated.
c.   avoid orange juice when feeling nauseated.
d.   eat large, infrequent meals so as to limit contact time with food.

a   522(K)   56.   Which of the following is one of the recommendations to treat pregnancy-associated heartburn?
a.   Eat many small meals
b.   Drink fluids only with meals
c.   Exercise within 30 minutes after eating
d.   Lie down within 15 minutes after eating

a   522(K)   57.   A craving for non-food substances is known as
a.   pica.
b.   bulimia.
c.   toxemia.
d.   hyperemesis.

a   523,524(K)   58.   Risks from malnutrition in women or men before conception include all of the
following **except**
    a.   it usually results in macrosomia.
    b.   it may lead to cessation of menstruation.
    c.   it may result in a poorly developed placenta.
    d.   it results in more complications during pregnancy in both overweight and
underweight women.

c   523(K)   59.   Which of the following is the standard classification for a low-birthweight infant?
    a.   3½ lbs or less
    b.   4 lbs or less
    c.   5½ lbs or less
    d.   6½ lbs or less

a   524(K)   60.   Which of the following is the standard classification for a very-low-birthweight
infant?
    a.   3 ½ lbs or less
    b.   4 ½ lbs or less
    c.   5 ½ lbs or less
    d.   6 ½ lbs or less

b   525(K)   61.   What is gestational diabetes?
    a.   A severe form of type 1 diabetes in newborns
    b.   Abnormal blood glucose maintenance during pregnancy
    c.   Reactive hypoglycemia expressed during the third trimester of
pregnancy
    d.   A temporary loss of insulin secretion during the first trimester of
pregnancy

c   525(K)   62.   Which of the following is a characteristic of gestational diabetes?
    a.   It predicts risk of diabetes for the infant.
    b.   It occurs in over one-half of normal weight women.
    c.   It leads to adult-onset diabetes in about a third of the women.
    d.   It occurs more often in women with a history of having premature births.

b   525(K)   63.   All of the following are features of gestational diabetes **except**
    a.   Asian ancestry is a risk factor.
    b.   infant birthweights are typically low.
    c.   it usually develops during the second half of pregnancy.
    d.   the most common consequences include labor and delivery complications.

a   525(A)   64.   Approximately how many women who do not have diabetes before pregnancy
develop type 2 diabetes after pregnancy?
    a.   1 in 50
    b.   1 in 150
    c.   1 in 300
    d.   1 in 1,000

a   526(K)   65.   What is the name of the condition characterized by high blood pressure, edema,
and protein in the urine of a pregnant woman?
    a.   Preeclampsia
    b.   Gestational diabetes
    c.   Teratogenic hypertension
    d.   Pregnancy-induced blood pressure crisis

b   526(K)   66.   Preeclampsia typically develops during the
- a.   first half of pregnancy.
- b.   second half of pregnancy.
- c.   first month after delivery.
- d.   first trimester of pregnancy.

b   526(K)   67.   All of the following are features of preeclampsia **except**
- a.   edema.
- b.   diabetes.
- c.   proteinuria.
- d.   high blood pressure.

a   526(K)   68.   Which of the following is a distinguishing characteristic of eclampsia?
- a.   Convulsions by the mother
- b.   Convulsions by the newborn
- c.   Low blood pressure in the mother
- d.   Low blood pressure in the newborn

b   526(K)   69.   What is the approximate percentage of babies born to teenagers in the United States?
- a.   2
- b.   5
- c.   12
- d.   25

a   526,527(K)   70.   Which of the following is a characteristic associated with adolescent pregnancy?
- a.   The recommended weight gain is approximately 35 lbs.
- b.   The incidence of stillbirths and preterm births is 5-10% lower compared with adult women.
- c.   The incidence of pregnancy-induced hypertension is 5-10% lower compared with older women.
- d.   The time in labor is usually shorter than for older women because there are fewer overweight teenagers.

d   527(K)   71.   What is the risk of giving birth to a child with Down syndrome for a woman who is 40 years old compared with a 20-year-old?
- a.   One-half as much
- b.   About the same
- c.   25 times higher
- d.   100 times higher

a   527(K)   72.   All of the following are features of older pregnant women in comparison with younger pregnant women **except**
- a.   maternal mortality rates are lower.
- b.   fetal mortality rates are twice as high.
- c.   cesarean delivery is twice as common.
- d.   complications that arise typically reflect chronic conditions such as diabetes and hypertension.

d   527(K)   73.   What term best describes a factor that causes abnormal fetal development and birth defects?
    a.   Toxigenic
    b.   Mutagenic
    c.   Neonagenic
    d.   Teratogenic

a   527,528(K)   74.   Which of the following recommendations for pregnant women and alcohol intake has been issued by the U.S. Surgeon General?
    a.   They should drink absolutely no alcohol.
    b.   They should refrain from drinking hard liquor only.
    c.   They are permitted to ingest no more than 2 drinks per day.
    d.   They are permitted to ingest small amounts of alcohol during the first 3 months but none thereafter.

c   527-530(A)   75.   With few exceptions, all of the following substances or practices should be totally eliminated during pregnancy **except**
    a.   cigarette smoking.
    b.   weight-loss dieting.
    c.   artificial sweeteners.
    d.   alcohol consumption.

d   528(K)   76.   Relationships between the use of tobacco products and complications of pregnancy include all of the following **except**
    a.   smoking during pregnancy increases the risk of vaginal bleeding.
    b.   chewing tobacco during pregnancy leads to lower birthweight infants.
    c.   smoking during pregnancy increases the risk of sudden infant death syndrome.
    d.   taking zinc supplements prevents the development of pregnancy-induced hypertension in smokers.

b   528(K)   77.   All of the following are effects of tobacco use in pregnancy **except**
    a.   an increased risk for fetal death.
    b.   an increased risk for macrosomia.
    c.   an increased risk for vaginal bleeding.
    d.   an association with SIDS and cigarette smoking during pregnancy.

d   529(K)   78.   What are the known effects of heavy caffeine use on human pregnancy?
    a.   It may worsen edema.
    b.   It may increase the risk of birth defects.
    c.   It may increase the risk of stillborn infants.
    d.   It may increase the risk of spontaneous abortion.

b   529(K)   79.   Which of the following is a feature of heavy metal intake and pregnancy?
    a.   Mercury but not lead can easily cross the placenta.
    b.   The adverse effects from intake of lead can be reduced by liberal intakes of calcium.
    c.   Pregnant women are advised to limit consumption of shark and swordfish to no more than once per week.
    d.   Pregnant women are advised to avoid shellfish around the critical period but may resume normal intake thereafter.

c   531(k)   80.   Which of the following is a function of prolactin?
  a.   Acts to reverse the effects of certain mutagens
  b.   Acts to reverse the effects of certain teratogens
  c.   Acts on mammary glands to stimulate milk release
  d.   Acts on mammary glands to promote milk production

a   531(K)   81.   What causes the "let-down reflex"?

  a.   Oxytocin
  b.   Estrongen
  c.   Prepartum amenorhea
  d.   Postpartum amenorrhea

c   532,533(K) 82.   In general, what are the chief consequences of nutritional deprivation in the lactating mother?
  a.   Cessation of lactation
  b.   Reduced quality of milk
  c.   Reduced quantity of milk
  d.   Reduced quality and quantity of milk

c   532(A)   83.   The number of extra kcal/day needed to produce a normal supply of milk during the first 6 months of lactation is approximately
  a.   100.
  b.   250.
  c.   500.
  d.   1,000.

a   533-534(K) 84.   Which of the following is a characteristic of alcohol and lactation?
  a.   Alcohol easily enters breast milk.
  b.   Alcohol actually stimulates lactation.
  c.   Infants drink slightly more breast milk when the mother consumes up to 1 drink per day.
  d.   The small amounts of alcohol that are secreted along with breast milk stimulate infant digestion.

c   533(K)   85.   Which of the following reflects one of the effects of alcohol intake on lactation?
  a.   It does not pass into the milk.
  b.   It mildly stimulates milk production.
  c.   It hinders the infant's ability to breastfeed.
  d.   It passes into the milk but is degraded by enzymes in breast tissue.

b   533,534(K) 86.   Which of the following is an effect of alcohol intake in the mother who breastfeeds?
  a.   It stimulates lactation.
  b.   It hinders breastfeeding.
  c.   It first appears in the milk approximately 12 hours after ingestion.
  d.   It passes into the milk and stimulates the infant's acceptance.

b   533(K)   87.   Which of the following statements describes an association between nutrient intake and lactation?
  a.   Milk production is increased by higher fluid intake.
  b.   Ingestion of garlic may lead to an off-flavor of the milk.
  c.   Inadequate protein intake lowers the protein concentration of the milk.
  d.   The energy RDA for milk production calls for an **additional** 1,000 kcal/day.

d   533(K)   88.   Which of the following describes the findings from studies of lactating women who exercised intensely compared with sedentary lactating women?
- a. They had similar energy intakes.
- b. Their milk was more nutrient-dense.
- c. They had a slightly greater amount of body fat.
- d. Their milk contained more lactic acid which alters taste.

c   533,534(A) 89.   Under which of the following circumstances would it still be acceptable for a mother to breastfeed?
- a. She has abused alcohol.
- b. She has a drug addiction.
- c. She has an ordinary cold.
- d. She has a communicable disease.

b   535;519,520(K) 90.   What is the benefit of postpartum amenorrhea?
- a. It stimulates milk production.
- b. It conserves iron in the mother.
- c. It stimulates the let-down reflex.
- d. It stimulates the suckling reflex in the infant.

c   539(K)   91.   A less severe form of fetal alcohol syndrome is known by all of the following terms **except**
- a. fetal alcohol effects.
- b. prenatal alcohol exposure.
- c. fetal subdevelopment syndrome.
- d. alcohol-related neurodevelopmental disorder.

a   539,540(K) 92.   According to many experts, what **minimum** level of alcohol intake increases the risk of giving birth to an infant with fetal alcohol syndrome?
- a. 1 drink/day
- b. 2 drinks/day
- c. 4 drinks/day
- d. 7 drinks/week

a   540,541(K) 93.   Which of the following statements describes a relationship between alcohol intake and fetal development?
- a. Birth defects are most severe when the woman drinks around the time of conception.
- b. Infants born with fetal alcohol syndrome typically show immediate signs of brain impairment.
- c. Eating well and maintaining adequate nutrient stores will prevent alcohol-induced placenta damage.
- d. Toxicity to the fetus begins to occur when fetal blood alcohol levels rise above maternal blood alcohol levels.

b   540(K)   94.   In what period of pregnancy would most damage occur from alcohol consumption?
- a. Before conception
- b. First trimester
- c. Second trimester
- d. Third trimester

MATCHING (Answers can be used only once.)

K	508	01.	A newly fertilized ovum
L	508	02.	Developing infant from 2 to 8 weeks after conception
O	508	03.	Fluid in which the fetus floats
D	510	04.	Number of days after conception during which the neural tube is highly vulnerable to nutrient deficiency
J	512	05.	Adequate intakes of this nutrient within the first 30 days of conception are especially important to lower risk of birth defects
A	511	06.	Percentage of U.S. newborns with a neural tube defect
P	514	07.	Most reliable indicator of an infant's health
G	514	08.	An infant born prior to this number of weeks of pregnancy is classified as preterm
F	514	09.	Upper limit for the recommended number of pounds that a pregnant woman of normal weight should gain
C	516	10.	Approximate weight, in pounds, of average newborn baby
E	518	11.	Number of grams of extra protein per day recommended for the pregnant woman
H	520	12.	Dietary supplements of this nutrient are recommended for the last 6 months of pregnancy
S	522	13.	A recommended practice to prevent or relieve heartburn
T	522	14.	A recommended practice to prevent or alleviate constipation
I	522	15.	A craving for non-food substances
Q	526	16.	A condition characterized by high blood pressure and protein in the urine
N	526	17.	A condition characterized by convulsions
B	526	18.	Percentage of U.S. babies born to teenagers
M	539	19.	Excess intake of this substance in pregnancy is known to result in mental retardation of the child
R	531	20.	A practice that may reduce risk of breast cancer

A.	0.3		K.	Zygote
B.	5		L.	Embryo
C.	7		M.	Alcohol
D.	17-30		N.	Eclampsia
E.	25		O.	Amniotic
F.	35		P.	Birthweight
G.	38		Q.	Preeclampsia
H.	Iron		R.	Breastfeeding
I.	Pica		S.	Eat small, frequent meals
J.	Folate		T.	Drink at least 8 glasses of liquid a day

ESSAY QUESTIONS

PAGE(S)

508-510   01.   Describe the three major stages of fetal growth and development.

512   02.   What is the U.S. government's rationale for requiring the fortification of grain products with folate?

513   03.   Discuss the association between maternal nutrition and the risk for development of chronic diseases in her child.

513   04.   Discuss the influence of prenatal malnutrition on the appearance of degenerative diseases in later life of the child.

227

514	05.	Discuss the consequences of being overweight or obese at the time of pregnancy.
514-516	06.	Compare the recommended weight gains for pregnancy in women who, at conception, are normal weight, underweight, overweight, or obese.
516,517	07.	What are several benefits of exercise specifically for the pregnant woman? What types of exercise should be avoided and why?
518-521	08.	What nutrients are needed in larger amounts during pregnancy and what physical changes account for the increased needs?
522	09.	What steps can be taken to minimize the development and discomfort of nausea, heartburn, and constipation during pregnancy?
523,524	10.	List the complications experienced by low-birthweight infants.
524,525	11.	Discuss 6 factors and conditions that lead to high-risk pregnancies
524	12.	Describe the consequences of malnutrition on conception and early pregnancy.
526	13.	Describe the condition known as preeclampsia. What are its risk factors and what is known about its prevention?
525	14.	Define gestational diabetes and list risk factors. How is it managed?
525,526	15.	Explain the development of pregnancy-induced hypertension and the consequences if it is not properly managed.
526,527	16.	Describe the risks associated with adolescent pregnancy.
527	17.	Describe the risks associated with pregnancy of older women.
527-530	18.	What practices should be avoided during pregnancy and why?
528	19.	Discuss the effects of tobacco use in the pregnant woman and its effects on health of the newborn.
531	20.	List the benefits of breastfeeding for the infant and for the mother.
531-533	21.	Explain the energy needs for breastfeeding in light of the mother's desire to lose the extra weight from pregnancy.
533	22.	Give examples of associations between maternal food choices and breastmilk flavor.
528	23.	Discuss the effects of maternal tobacco use on breastfeeding.
539-541	24.	Discuss the consequences of maternal alcohol intake on fetal development.
539-541	25.	Describe the physical and mental abnormalities associated with fetal alcohol syndrome.
539,540	26.	Describe distinguishing facial characteristics associated with fetal alcohol syndrome.
539	27.	Compare and contrast the features of prenatal alcohol exposure with fetal alcohol syndrome.

CHAPTER 16
LIFE CYCLE NUTRITION: INFANCY, CHILDHOOD, AND ADOLESCENCE

AN. PAGE(S)

c   537(A)   01.   To maintain optimal blood glucose concentrations of school-age children, how often should they eat?
a.   Every hour
b.   Every 2 hours
c.   Every 4 hours
d.   Every 5 hours

a   544(K)   02.   Which of the following is a feature of energy metabolism in infancy?
a.   Infants fed fat-free milk are at risk for protein overload.
b.   Most of the energy in breast milk is derived from lactose.
c.   The brain of an infant uses less glucose than that of an adult.
d.   Infants require about 25% more energy than adults when expressed per kg body weight.

c   544(A)   03.   What would be a normal body weight after 1 year for a healthy infant with a birthweight of 8 lbs?
a.   12 lbs
b.   16 lbs
c.   24 lbs
d.   35 lbs

a   544(A)   04.   Infants showing symptoms of acidosis, dehydration, diarrhea, elevated blood ammonia and urea, and fever may be reacting to the nutritional problem of
a.   protein overload.
b.   milk protein intolerance.
c.   carbohydrate intolerance.
d.   insufficient protein and energy.

d   544(A)   05.   The recommended amounts of vitamins and minerals for infants are based on
a.   The average amounts present in body tissues of thriving infants.
b.   The adult RDA scaled down to infants on a per kg body weight basis.
c.   The older child's RDA scaled down to the infant on a per kg body weight basis.
d.   The average amounts ingested by thriving infants breastfed by well-nourished mothers.

a   544(K)   06.   What is the approximate energy requirement of infants, in kcal/kg body weight?
a.   25
b.   35
c.   75
d.   100

a   544,545(A) 07.   When expressed per kilogram body weight, the nutrient needs of infants are markedly higher than those of adults for all of the following nutrients **except**
a.   iron.
b.   iodine.
c.   vitamin C.
d.   vitamin D.

d   545(K)   08.   According to the American Academy of Pediatrics and the Canadian Pediatric Society, breastfeeding of full-term infants is
- a.   optional.
- b.   mildly recommended.
- c.   moderately recommended.
- d.   strongly recommended.

b   546(A)   09.   What is the chief reason that breast-fed infants usually need to eat more frequently than formula-fed infants?
- a.   Breast milk contains less fat.
- b.   Breast milk is digested faster.
- c.   Breast milk is less nutrient dense.
- d.   The amount of milk consumed per feeding episode is lower in breast-fed infants.

c   547(A)   10.   For optimal breast-feeding benefits, it is recommended that the infant be encouraged to suckle on each breast for about
- a.   1-2 minutes.
- b.   5 minutes.
- c.   10-15 minutes.
- d.   30 minutes.

d   547(K)   11.   Which of the following is a feature of infant development and nutrition?
- a.   It is generally easier to overfeed a breast-fed infant than a formula-fed infant.
- b.   Breast-fed infants are at high risk of iron deficiency for the first 6 months of life.
- c.   For optimal development, infants should be transitioned to formula after one year of breast-feeding.
- d.   Breast-fed infants generally score higher on tests of mental development than do formula-fed infants.

c   547(K)   12.   Which of the following is a finding of the importance of fatty acid intake of preterm infants fed formulas?
- a.   Formulas enriched with oleic acid led to reduced atherogenic plaque by age five in comparison to standard formulas.
- b.   Formulas enriched with omega-3 fatty acids led to increased brain cell number in comparison to standard formulas.
- c.   Formulas enriched with docosohexanoic acid and arachidonic acid resulted in improved visual acuity in comparison to standard formulas.
- d.   Formulas enriched with equal amounts of omega-3, omega-6, and omega-9 fatty acids led to lower prevalence of obesity after two years in comparison with standard formulas.

d   547(K)   13.   What is the chief protein in human breast milk?
- a.   casein
- b.   lactose
- c.   albumin
- d.   alpha-lactalbumin

b   547(K)   14.   Breast milk as the sole source of nutrition, up to the first 6 months in healthy
                      infants, is satisfactory for all nutrients **except**
                      a.   sodium.
                      b.   vitamin D.
                      c.   iron and folate.
                      d.   zinc and vitamin A.

d   547(K)   15.   Nutrient characteristics of human breast milk include all of the following **except**
                      a.   the sodium content is low.
                      b.   the zinc is highly bioavailable.
                      c.   the iron is highly bioavailable.
                      d.   the vitamin D content meets optimal growth requirements.

d   547,548(K) 16.   Which of the following vitamin-mineral supplements need **not** be prescribed for an
                      infant breastfed beyond 6 months of age?
                      a.   Iron
                      b.   Fluoride
                      c.   Vitamin D
                      d.   Vitamin E

d   548(K)   17.   What is colostrum?
                      a.   Clot in the bloodstream
                      b.   Major protein in breast milk
                      c.   Hormone that promotes milk production
                      d.   Milk-like substance secreted right after delivery

b   547-549(K) 18.   Which of the following is an advantage of breastfeeding compared with formula
                      feeding?
                      a.   There is no limit to the supply.
                      b.   It provides immunological protection.
                      c.   The mother can be sure the baby is getting enough milk.
                      d.   It is the only way to develop a true loving relationship with the baby.

b   548(K)   19.   Which of the following is associated with bifidus factors?
                      a.   Increased iron absorption
                      b.   Increased bacterial growth
                      c.   Decreased allergy protection
                      d.   Decreased hormone production

b   548(K)   20.   What is the factor in breast milk that binds iron and prevents it from supporting the
                      growth of the infant's intestinal bacteria?
                      a.   Colostrum
                      b.   Lactoferrin
                      c.   Lactalbumin
                      d.   Bifidus factor

c   548(K)   21.   What is lactadherin?
                      a.   An iron-binding protein in breast milk
                      b.   A vitamin D-binding protein in breast milk
                      c.   A breast milk protein that inactivates a GI virus that causes diarrhea
                      d.   A protein supplement to infant formulas that simulates the digestibility
                              properties of alpha-lactalbumin

a   549,550(A)   22.   In comparison with cow's milk, breast milk contains
   a.   less protein and calcium.
   b.   less lactose and vitamin C.
   c.   more fat and less carbohydrate.
   d.   more energy and less vitamin E.

b   549(A)   23.   Which of the following sources of nutrition for infants is **least** likely to become contaminated with microorganisms?
   a.   Soy formula
   b.   Breast milk
   c.   Iron-fortified formula
   d.   Liquid concentrate formula

b   547(K)   24.   To gradually replace breast milk with infant formula or other foods appropriate to an infant's diet is to
   a.   feed.
   b.   wean.
   c.   nurse.
   d.   breastfeed.

a   549(K)   25.   Features of infant formulas include all of the following **except**
   a.   they contain antibodies.
   b.   they breed bacteria in bottles left at room temperature.
   c.   they typically contain over twice the amount of iron compared with breast milk.
   d.   they contain fat and carbohydrate at concentrations resembling those in breast milk.

b   550(A)   26.   What type of formula is available for infants with milk allergy?
   a.   Egg
   b.   Soy
   c.   Meat
   d.   Peanut

c   549(K)   27.   Which of the following is a common source of lead poisoning in infants?
   a.   Maternal passage of lead to fetus
   b.   Baby bottles made from lead crystal
   c.   Contaminated water used to make infant formula
   d.   Preparation of infant formula in galvanized containers

c   549(A)   28.   What is the most realistic advice for reducing lead exposure content of tap water used to prepare infant formula?
   a.   Whenever possible boil the water to vaporize the lead and thus decrease the amount remaining in the water.
   b.   Since upon sitting overnight the lead in hot water pipes settles out, draw the drinking water from this source first.
   c.   Since the first water drawn from the tap each day is highest in lead, let the water run a few minutes before using it.
   d.   Add a small amount of citrus juice to the water to provide citric acid to complex with the lead and inhibit its absorption.

b   550(A)   29.   Goat's milk is inappropriate for infants due to its low content of
    a.   iron.
    b.   folate.
    c.   protein.
    d.   calcium.

b   550(A)   30.   An infant diagnosed with "goat's milk anemia" is most likely deficient in
    a.   iron.
    b.   folate.
    c.   vitamin B_6.
    d.   vitamin B_{12}.

b   551(K)   31.   During the first year of life, cow's milk is considered an inappropriate food due to all of the following **except**
    a.   it is too low in iron.
    b.   it is too low in sodium.
    c.   it is too high in protein.
    d.   it is too low in vitamin C.

a   551(K)   32.   Which of the following should **not** be used to feed an infant?
    a.   Whole milk
    b.   Ready-to-feed formula
    c.   Liquid concentrate formula appropriately diluted
    d.   Powdered formula or evaporated milk formula appropriately reconstituted

c   550(K)   33.   Which of the following defines nursing bottle tooth decay?
    a.   Caries development resulting from frequent use of non-sterile bottles and nipples
    b.   Bacterial attack of teeth due to severe tooth misalignment from sucking on oversized bottle nipples
    c.   Marked tooth decay of an infant due to prolonged exposure to carbohydrate-rich fluids from a bottle
    d.   Tooth decay resulting from constant exposure to food due to inability of the infant to swallow in normal fashion

d   550(K)   34.   What term defines the condition of infant tooth deterioration resulting from chronic exposure to carbohydrate-rich fluids from a bottle?
    a.   Juice bottle erosion
    b.   Suckling enamelosis
    c.   Formula-induced gingivitis
    d.   Nursing bottle tooth decay

b   550(K)   35.   Approximately what percentage of infants are born prematurely?
    a.   4
    b.   11
    c.   20
    d.   33

c   550(K)   36.   Which of the following feeding practices is recommended for preterm infants?
            a.   They should be fed exclusively on breast milk.
            b.   They should be fed on breast milk enriched in a 1 to 1 ratio with cow's milk.
            c.   They should be fed preterm breast milk, occasionally fortified with specific nutrients.
            d.   They should be fed only on special formula because breast milk nutrient content is too low.

c   551(K)   37.   What is beikost?
            a.   An oral rehydration solution
            b.   A term that describes a type of malnutrition in infants
            c.   A term that describes any nonmilk food offered to an infant
            d.   A fermented milk product used as a substitute for breastmilk

c   551(A)   38.   Which of the following represents a good age to introduce solid foods to infants?
            a.   Two weeks
            b.   Two months
            c.   Five months
            d.   One year

c   551(K)   39.   At what age does the normal infant first develop the ability to swallow solid food?
            a.   3-5 weeks
            b.   26-32 weeks
            c.   4-6 months
            d.   9-12 months

a   551,552(K)   40.   What adverse side effect is most likely to develop in infants who are deprived of solid foods for the entire first year of life?
            a.   Delayed growth
            b.   Impaired speech
            c.   Mental dysfunction
            d.   Impaired eye coordination

b   551(K)   41.   Why should new foods be introduced to an infant one at a time?
            a.   It prevents overfeeding
            b.   Any allergic reactions can be detected
            c.   Immunological protection hasn't been developed
            d.   The swallowing reflex is not under voluntary control

c   551(K)   42.   What should be the first cereal introduced to the infant?
            a.   Oat
            b.   Corn
            c.   Rice
            d.   Wheat

d   551(A)   43.   Of the following cereals, which is **most** likely to result in an allergic reaction upon first feeding?
            a.   Oat
            b.   Rice
            c.   Corn
            d.   Wheat

c   551(K)   44.   Low-fat or nonfat milk should not be given routinely to a child until after the age of
           a.   two weeks.
           b.   three months.
           c.   two years.
           d.   six years.

a   552(K)   45.   Which of the following nutrients need to be supplied first by solid foods in a baby's diet?
           a.   Vitamin C and iron
           b.   Vitamin A and zinc
           c.   Vitamin B_{12} and fluoride
           d.   Vitamin E and magnesium

c   553(K)   46.   Infants should not be given canned vegetables due to excessive amounts of
           a.   tin.
           b.   fiber.
           c.   sodium.
           d.   botulinum spores.

b   553(A)   47.   Infants fed honey or corn syrup are at increased risk for
           a.   obesity.
           b.   botulism.
           c.   osteopenia.
           d.   type 1 diabetes.

c   553(A)   48.   What should be the parent's response when a one-year-old child wants to clumsily spoon-feed himself?
           a.   Punish the child
           b.   Let the child eat with his fingers instead
           c.   Let the child try to feed himself so that he will learn
           d.   Gently take the spoon back and feed the child with it

b   553(K)   49.   Which of the following is the primary factor in the development of milk anemia?
           a.   Impaired absorption of iron
           b.   Excessive intake of cow's milk
           c.   Low iron content of breast milk
           d.   Insufficient intake of whole cow's milk

a   553(A)   50.   A child who drinks a lot of milk at the expense of other foods is at high risk of showing signs of
           a.   anemia.
           b.   rickets.
           c.   hyperkeratosis.
           d.   ariboflavinosis.

b   553(A)   51.   The consumption of milk by children should not exceed 4 cups per day in order to lower the risk for
           a.   solute overload.
           b.   iron deficiency.
           c.   vitamin A toxicity.
           d.   vitamin D toxicity.

a   553(K)   52.   Young children who drink more than 2 to 3 ½ cups of milk a day are most likely at increased risk for deficiency of
    a.   iron.
    b.   folate.
    c.   vitamin A.
    d.   vitamin C.

d   555(K)   53.   Which of the following is associated with energy metabolism of the preschool child?
    a.   Food intake is remarkably similar from meal to meal.
    b.   Overweight individuals have appetites similar to normal weight individuals.
    c.   Energy needs per kg body weight increase from 1 year of age to 5 years of age.
    d.   A 1-year-old who needs 800 kcal/day would require only about 1600 kcal at 6 years of age.

c   555(K)   54.   Approximately how many kcal per day does an average 6-year-old need to obtain?
    a.   500
    b.   800
    c.   1600
    d.   2400

c   555(A)   55.   How much more total energy does a normal 10-year-old need vs. a 1-year-old?
    a.   25%
    b.   50%
    c.   150%
    d.   200%

c   555(A)   56.   A reasonable fiber intake for a 5-year-old would be
    a.   2 grams.
    b.   5 grams.
    c.   Age plus 5 grams.
    d.   Age plus 10 grams.

d   555(K)   57.   Which of the following is a characteristic of fat in the diet of children?
    a.   The recommended daily fat intake up to age 12 is age plus 20 g.
    b.   There is an RDA for total fat for children beginning at 3 years of age.
    c.   Low-fat diets usually provide sufficient amounts of the micronutrients.
    d.   Fat intakes below 30% of total energy do not impair growth provided that total energy intake is adequate.

a   557(K)   58.   Which of the following is characteristic of children who regularly eat breakfast or skip breakfast?
    a.   Breakfast-skippers actually show lower scores on IQ tests than those who eat breakfast.
    b.   Attention spans are similar but a significant number of breakfast-skippers show hyperglycemia.
    c.   Breakfast-skippers initially show decreased mental performance but with time they adapt and show almost identical achievements.
    d.   Breakfast-skippers who change to eating breakfast show a temporary improvement in mental concentration but also a moderate degree of hypoglycemia.

a   555(A)   59.   The most prevalent nutrient deficiency among U.S. and Canadian children is for
a.   iron.
b.   protein.
c.   calcium.
d.   vitamin C.

c   558(K)   60.   All of the following are features of iron nutrition in children **except**
a.   anemia makes children more disruptive.
b.   iron deficiency may be mistaken for lead poisoning.
c.   the brain appears to be less sensitive to iron-deficiency than the rest of the body.
d.   children who had iron-deficiency anemia as infants do not show normal school performance even after iron status improved.

c   558(K)   61.   Which of the following is a feature of iron nutrition in the very young?
a.   Iron deficiency is most prevalent in children aged 2 to 3 years old.
b.   The supply of stored iron becomes depleted after the birthweight triples.
c.   Infants with iron-deficiency anemia demonstrate abnormal motor development.
d.   Serum ferritin concentrations fall in infants who start drinking whole milk at 3 months of age but not at 6 months of age.

a   558(K)   62.   Which of the following is a characteristic of iron deficiency in children?
a.   It affects brain function before anemia sets in.
b.   It rarely develops in those with high intakes of milk.
c.   It is the primary factor in tension-fatigue syndrome.
d.   Mild deficiency enhances mental performance by lowering physical activity level thereby leading to increased attention span.

c   558(A)   63.   Which of the following is the most likely reason that teachers promote the consumption of midmorning snacks for children?
a.   It provides an opportunity to learn about nutrition.
b.   It meets federally mandated school nutrition guidelines.
c.   It provides carbohydrate for maintenance of blood glucose and brain function.
d.   It helps decrease the symptoms of attention-deficit-hyperactivity disorder in 5% of school-age children.

a   560(K)   64.   What is the prevalence of hyperactivity in children?
a.   3-5%
b.   8-12%
c.   15-20%
d.   25-35%

d   559,560(K)   65.   All of the following are characteristics of hyperactivity in children **except**
a.   it impairs learning ability.
b.   it occurs in approximately 5% of young, school-age individuals.
c.   it is managed, in part, by prescribing stimulant drugs when necessary.
d.   it responds favorably to dietary manipulations such as limiting sugar intake.

d   559,560(K)   66.   What is the term given to the child who is hyperactive with severe and impulsive behavior?
a.   Food hypersensitivity
b.   Fetal alcohol syndrome
c.   Caffeine hypersensitivity
d.   Attention-deficit/hyperactivity disorder

c   558,559(A)   67.   All of the following are common signs of mild lead toxicity **except**
a.   diarrhea.
b.   lethargy.
c.   dermatitis.
d.   irritability.

a   558(K)   68.   Which of the following is a characteristic of lead exposure and health?
a.   Absorption of lead is higher on an empty stomach.
b.   Lead toxicity is most prevalent in children around the time of puberty.
c.   Lead-induced anemia is similar to the anemia of vitamin B_{12} deficiency.
d.   The symptoms of lead toxicity can be reversed by adding iron to the diet.

b   562(K)   69.   An adverse reaction to food that does **not** signal the body to form antibodies is termed a
a.   food allergy.
b.   food intolerance.
c.   mild food challenge.
d.   transient food episode.

a   561(A)   70.   A child who develops antibodies to a certain food is said to have a
a.   food allergy.
b.   food intolerance.
c.   specific inducible episode.
d.   transient immune suppression.

b   561,562(K)   71.   Which of the following is a characteristic of a food allergy?
a.   It always elicits symptoms in the person.
b.   It always involves the production of antibodies.
c.   It usually shows up immediately after exposure to the allergic food.
d.   It is usually elicited from very small, simple molecules as well as large, complex molecules.

a   561(A)   72.   Which of the following foods are most often the cause of allergies?
a.   Eggs, peanuts, and milk
b.   Bananas, juice, and cola
c.   Apples, noodles, and rice
d.   Pears, oatmeal, and chocolate

b   561(A)   73.   What food is responsible for the most life-threatening allergic reactions in people?
a.   Eggs
b.   Peanuts
c.   Shellfish
d.   Cow's milk

a 561(K) 74. A life-threatening whole-body allergic reaction is known as
  a. anaphylactic shock.
  b. hyperhistamine response.
  c. hyporespiratory syndrome.
  d. wheezing food intolerance.

b 563,564(A) 75. Which of the following is a feature of nutrition and behavior in children?
  a. Hyperactivity responds favorably to a low sugar diet.
  b. Television commercials featuring snack foods have been found to affect children's food preferences.
  c. The adverse effects from caffeine intake typically first appear only after drinking 6 cans of cola in one day.
  d. Most children are able to control their intake of cola beverages since they are more sensitive to the stimulating effects of caffeine.

b 564(K) 76. Which of the following two conditions are associated with television's influence?
  a. Anorexia and nutrient deficiencies
  b. Obesity and high blood cholesterol
  c. Drug abuse and teenage pregnancy
  d. Hyperactivity and lower body weight

d 563,564(K) 77. What is the most likely explanation for the increased prevalence of obesity in children over the past 30 years?
  a. Genetics
  b. They sleep more hours
  c. They consume more kcalories
  d. They are less active physically

a 564(K) 78. What is the leading cause of high blood pressure in children?
  a. Obesity
  b. High sodium intake
  c. Insufficient calcium intake
  d. Insufficient potassium intake

d 564(A) 79. Why is it **not** recommended that overweight children go on a diet?
  a. It can lead to a lowering of self-esteem.
  b. Children's school performance can deteriorate.
  c. Most children are unable to learn new food habits.
  d. Diet restriction can interfere with growth and development.

c 565(K) 80. To lower the risk of obesity in children, which of the following practices should parents institute for their children?
  a. Serve them smaller portions.
  b. Serve them 3 meals a day without dessert.
  c. Teach them to take appropriate food portions.
  d. Serve them more beverages and less solid food.

b   566,567(A)   81.   Which of the following is an effective strategy for dealing with obesity in a child?
- a.   Encourage the individual to eat quickly and then leave the table.
- b.   Teach the individual to take small portions first and then second helpings if desired.
- c.   Institute new eating habits such as teaching the individual to clean the food plate.
- d.   Take control and strongly encourage the individual to lose weight by dieting and regular exercise.

a   566,567(K)   82.   Even in preschoolers whose habits are being established, existing dietary attitudes are relatively resistant to change. How should wise parents react?
- a.   Be patient and persistent.
- b.   Impose their own eating habits on the children.
- c.   Wait until the children start school to initiate changes.
- d.   Exert continuous pressure to initiate good food habits.

a   565,566(K)   83.   Which of the following steps should be undertaken by the parent or guardian to ensure that young people eat well?
- a.   Control the availability of food.
- b.   Control the consumption of food.
- c.   Prohibit eating except at mealtime.
- d.   Provide an emotional climate that discourages snacking.

d   566,567(K)   84.   Which of the following practices is **not** among the recommendations to help children develop an interest in vegetables?
- a.   Serve vegetables warm, not hot.
- b.   Serve vegetables separately on the plate.
- c.   Serve vegetables undercooked and crunchy.
- d.   Serve vegetables with the promise that after they are eaten, dessert will follow.

d   566,567(K)   85.   Which of the following is **not** among the recommended methods for introducing new foods to children?
- a.   Offer foods one at a time.
- b.   Offer foods in small amounts.
- c.   Create a pleasant eating atmosphere.
- d.   Present new foods at the end of the meal.

c   567(K)   86.   If a child is reluctant to try a new food, it is best to
- a.   send the child to his/her room.
- b.   withhold dessert until all food on the plate is eaten.
- c.   quietly remove it and present it again at another time.
- d.   encourage other family members to coax the child to eat it.

c   567(K)   87.   When children are allowed to eat freely from a variety of foods, they usually select foods that are high in
- a.   iron.
- b.   fiber.
- c.   sugar.
- d.   protein.

a   567,568(A)   88.   The single most effective way to teach nutrition to children is by
        a.   example.
        b.   punishment.
        c.   singling out only hazardous nutrition practices for attention.
        d.   explaining the importance of eating new foods as a prerequisite for dessert.

c   569(K)   89.   What minimum fraction of the RDA for children 10-12 years of age should be provided by public school lunches?
        a.   1/8
        b.   1/4
        c.   1/3
        d.   ½

a   569(K)   90.   Which of the following is a feature of public school food programs?
        a.   They must meet the Dietary Guidelines over a week's menus.
        b.   They allow for low fat menus while still meeting the needs for iron.
        c.   They ensure a lunch period is long enough to consume the entire meal.
        d.   They are overwhelmingly preferred over the foods obtained by students through on-site vending machines and snack bars.

d   571(K)   91.   The adolescent growth spurt
        a.   affects the brain primarily.
        b.   decreases total nutrient needs.
        c.   affects every organ except the brain.
        d.   begins and ends earlier in girls than in boys.

c   571(K)   92.   What is the approximate time period of the adolescent growth spurt?
        a.   6 months
        b.   1 year
        c.   2 ½ years
        d.   6 years

a   571(K)   93.   Which of the following is a characteristic of the adolescent period?
        a.   Obesity occurs more often in African-American females.
        b.   Appetite for red meat increases in females to meet iron needs.
        c.   More nutrient-dense foods are needed by males because of their faster development.
        d.   The risk for calcium insufficiency is greatest in males due to their high intake of soft drinks.

a   572(A)   94.   Approximately what fraction of an average teenager's daily energy intake is derived from snacks?
        a.   1/4
        b.   1/3
        c.   1/2
        d.   2/3

b   573(A)   95.   About how many meals each week are eaten outside the home by adolescents?
        a.   3
        b.   7
        c.   12
        d.   15

d   573(K)   96.   Which of the following is a feature of beverage intake in adolescents?
a.   Juice intake is spread throughout the day.
b.   Milk intake occurs primarily between meals.
c.   Males are more likely to drink less milk than are females.
d.   Four standard colas a day provides enough caffeine to alter behavior.

b   573(K)   97.   Approximately how much caffeine is delivered by a typical cola beverage?
a.   5 mg
b.   50 mg
c.   100 mg
d.   500 mg

c   573(K)   98.   What is considered to be the minimum pharmacologically active dose of caffeine?
a.   5 mg
b.   100 mg
c.   200 mg
d.   500 mg

b   574(K)   99.   Approximately what percentage of high school seniors admit having used cocaine at least once?
a.   2
b.   9
c.   15
d.   22

a   573,574(K)   100.   Which of the following is a characteristic of marijuana use?
a.   Appetite for sweet foods is increased.
b.   Regular use leads to excessive weight gain.
c.   Smoking it dulls the sense of taste and smell.
d.   The active ingredient is cleared from the body within 24 hours.

c   574(K)   101.   Which of the following is a characteristic of use of the drug ecstasy?
a.   Its primary action is on the liver.
b.   It leads to low body temperature.
c.   Using it regularly leads to weight loss.
d.   Its potency is increased when taken with caffeinated beverages.

b   574,575(K)   102.   Associations between cigarette smoking and nutrition include all of the following **except**
a.   smokers have blunted hunger sensations.
b.   smokers have higher intakes of carotene-rich foods.
c.   smokers have lower body weights than nonsmokers.
d.   smokers degrade vitamin C faster than nonsmokers.

c   574(A)   103.   A cigarette smoker who is planning to quit should expect a weight gain in the first year of about
a.   2 lbs.
b.   5 lbs.
c.   10 lbs.
d.   18 lbs.

a   575(K)   104.   Which of the following is a characteristic of tobacco use and adolescents?
   a.   Smokers require more vitamin C to maintain body stores.
   b.   The prevalence of smokeless tobacco use in high school is one in 100 students.
   c.   Supplements of beta-carotene are recommended for tobacco users in this population group.
   d.   The risk of mouth cancer is slightly lower for users of smokeless tobacco compared with smokers.

c   582,583(K)   105.   The association of cholesterol to the health of children is described by all of the following **except**
   a.   cholesterol intake should be limited beginning at 2 years of age.
   b.   blood cholesterol levels in children are good predictors of their adult levels.
   c.   there appears to be only a very weak correlation between obesity in children and their blood cholesterol levels.
   d.   serum cholesterol is higher in children viewing television for 2 hours per day compared with more active individuals.

a   582,583(K)   106.   All of the following are characteristics of blood cholesterol in children **except**
   a.   acceptable total cholesterol levels are up to 240 mg/d.
   b.   cholesterol levels at birth are similar in all populations.
   c.   childhood obesity and high cholesterol levels show a strong association.
   d.   children with high cholesterol levels usually have parents with high cholesterol levels.

MATCHING (Answers can be used only once.)

B   544   01.   Expected weight, in pounds, of an infant with a birthweight of seven pounds who reaches one year of age
E   544   02.   Typical daily energy need, in kcalories per kg body weight, of an infant
O   547   03.   Nutrient that is low in human milk but adequate in infant formulas
L   547   04.   Essential fatty acid in breast milk
T   547   05.   Chief protein in human breast milk
F   547   06.   Chief protein in cow's milk
P   548   07.   Substance in breast milk that deprives intestinal bacteria of iron
K   549   08.   Process whereby breast milk is gradually replaced by formula or semi-solid foods
Q   548   09.   A breast milk protein that fights virus-induced diarrhea
N   548   10.   Pre-milk substance from the breast, containing antibodies
S   548   11.   Substance in breast milk that promotes growth of beneficial bacteria in the intestines
G   550   12.   Low content of this nutrient makes goat's milk inappropriate for infants
R   558   13.   Deficiency of this nutrient in children shows symptoms similar to mild lead toxicity
I   551   14.   Another term for supplemental or weaning foods
H   553   15.   Possible source of infant botulism
A   561   16.   Approximate percentage of young children with food allergies
D   563   17.   Percent chance of becoming an obese adult for an obese teen with one obese parent
J   571   18.   Period in life when an individual becomes physically capable of reproduction
C   574   19.   Percentage of teenagers who drink alcohol regularly
M   561   20.   Substance given to prevent anaphylactic shock in people with food allergies

A.   5   K.   Weaning
B.   21   L.   Linoleic
C.   50   M.   Epinephrine
D.   80   N.   Colostrum
E.   100   O.   Vitamin D
F.   Casein   P.   Lactoferrin
G.   Folate   Q.   Lactadherin
H.   Honey   R.   Iron
I.   Beikost   S.   Bifidus factors
J.   Puberty   T.   Alpha-lactalbumin

ESSAY QUESTIONS

PAGE(S)

547   01.   Discuss the importance of omega-3 fatty acids in the development of infants.

547   02.   Why do some infant formulas now contain omega-3 fatty acids?

548   03.   Describe substances present in breast milk that affect immunologic function of the infant.

550,551   04.   Discuss the special nutritional needs of the preterm infant and ways to meet these needs.

550,551   05.   Why is preterm breast milk suitable to meet the special needs of the preterm infant?

551-553   06.   Discuss guidelines for introducing first foods to an infant.

551-553   07.   Explain the appropriate procedure for introducing new foods to children.

553   08.   What practices by caretakers encourage the development of good eating habits during early childhood?

556-559   09.   Give examples of how hunger and nutrient deficiencies affect behavior in children.

558-559   10.   Describe the physical and mental effects of lead exposure on children.

559-560   11.   What is the relationship of nutrition to hyperactivity in children?

561,562   12.   Discuss the effects of food allergies and food intolerances on nutritional status.

562-566   13.   Discuss the effects of obesity in childhood. What steps can be taken to prevent and to treat this condition in the child?

572,573   14.   Describe common eating patterns of teenagers and suggest appropriate changes to foster better eating habits.

572   15.   What accounts for the increased need for iron in male and female adolescents?

573-575   16.   List 6 nutrition problems associated with drug abuse and tobacco use in adolescents.

581-583   17.   Describe relationships among obesity, hypertension, and blood cholesterol in children and adolescents.

581   18.   Describe the role of genetics in the risk for type 2 diabetes and heart disease in children.

CHAPTER 17
LIFE CYCLE NUTRITION: ADULTHOOD AND THE LATER YEARS

AN. PAGE(S)

c   587(K)   01.   What fraction of the U.S. population is at least 65 years old?
    a.   1/100
    b.   1/30
    c.   1/8
    d.   1/3

d   588(K)   02.   How long in years is the potential human life span?
    a.   80
    b.   95
    c.   105
    d.   130

d   588(K)   03.   Approximately how many years is the human life span?
    a.   75
    b.   100
    c.   115
    d.   130

b   588(K)   04.   What is the life expectancy of males and females in the United States?
    a.   62-67 years
    b.   68-80 years
    c.   81-84 years
    d.   85-89 years

b   589(A)   05.   What would be the physiological age of a 75-year old woman whose physical health is equivalent to that of her 50-year old daughter?
    a.   25 years
    b.   50 years
    c.   70 years
    d.   125 years

d   587(K)   06.   What is the fastest-growing age group in the United States?
    a.   21-30 years
    b.   35-50 years
    c.   Over 65 years
    d.   Over 85 years

b   589(A)   07.   Approximately what percentage of a person's life expectancy is under control of her genes?
    a.   0
    b.   25
    c.   50
    d.   75

d   589(A)   08.   Approximately what percentage of a person's life expectancy is dependent upon his personal behavior?
    a.   0
    b.   25
    c.   50
    d.   75

a   591(K)   09.   Which of the following is a proposed mechanism for energy restriction and improvement of longevity in animals?
a.   Reduction in oxidative stress
b.   Increase in the metabolic rate
c.   Enhancement of lipid oxidation
d.   Acceleration of growth and development

c   590,591(K) 10.   Which of the following is a finding from studies of diet restriction in rats?
a.   Restriction of specific nutrients exerted antiaging effects.
b.   Energy-restricted diets led to life extension in 90% of the rats.
c.   Energy-restricted diets led to lowering of the metabolic rate and body temperature.
d.   Restriction of food intake only after rats reached maturity, but not before, resulted in extension of life span.

c   588,589(K) 11.   Studies of adults show that longevity is related, in part, to all of the following **except**
a.   weight control.
b.   regularity of meals.
c.   short periods of sleep.
d.   no or moderate alcohol intake.

a   590,591(K) 12.   Which of the following is a feature of energy intake and longevity?
a.   Improvements in longevity depend on reducing energy intake but not on body fat content.
b.   Restriction of energy intake in genetically obese animals does not seem to improve longevity.
c.   Biochemical markers for longevity in humans are improved only when energy intake is reduced by at least one-third.
d.   The activities of the genes of older mice on energy-restricted diets are similar to those of mice on standard diets.

a   592(K)   13.   All of the following are characteristics of body weight and older people **except**
a.   a higher body weight reduces the risk of sarcopenia.
b.   being overweight at age 75 does not reduce longevity.
c.   being moderately overweight may not carry any health risks.
d.   a low body weight may be more detrimental than a high one.

b   592(K)   14.   What is sarcopenia?
a.   Loss of central visual activity
b.   Loss of muscle mass and strength
c.   Aging induced chronic inflammation of the stomach
d.   Intestinal dysmotility from excessive use of laxatives

c   593(A)   15.   A person with dysphagia has
a.   no teeth.
b.   low immunity.
c.   difficulty in swallowing.
d.   diminished muscle mass.

a   593(A)   16.   A person who is edentulous has
                      a.   no teeth.
                      b.   low immunity.
                      c.   difficulty in swallowing.
                      d.   diminished muscle mass.

d   593(K)   17.   Which of the following is a characteristic of aging and the immune system?
                      a.   Immunity in older people does not seem to be affected by regular exercise.
                      b.   In the United States, infectious diseases are a minor cause of deaths in the elderly.
                      c.   Immune function does not decline with age in people who maintain good nutrition.
                      d.   Antibiotics are often ineffective in treating old people who have deficient immune systems.

d   593(K)   18.   Atrophic gastritis is typically characterized by all of the following signs **except**
                      a.   inflamed stomach mucosa.
                      b.   lack of hydrochloric acid.
                      c.   abundant bacteria in the stomach.
                      d.   insufficient secretion of pepsinogen and gastrin.

a   594(K)   19.   Which of the following is a finding of studies of nutritional status and lifestyle?
                      a.   Men living alone eat less than men living with others.
                      b.   Women living alone eat less than women living with others.
                      c.   The level of education does not appear to be related to the incidence of malnutrition.
                      d.   Men and women living in federally funded housing have a very low risk for malnutrition.

b   594(K)   20.   Studies of the eating habits of older adults demonstrate all of the following **except**
                      a.   men living alone eat less than men living with others.
                      b.   women living alone eat less than women living with others.
                      c.   malnutrition was associated with a lower level of education.
                      d.   adults living alone often consume insufficient amounts of food.

a   594(K)   21.   Among the elderly, malnutrition is most common in those living
                      a.   in nursing homes.
                      b.   with their children.
                      c.   at home with others.
                      d.   at home by themselves.

a   595(A)   22.   A person with a pressure ulcer has damage to her
                      a.   skin.
                      b.   colon.
                      c.   mouth.
                      d.   stomach.

c   595(A)   23.   Approximately what percentage decline in basal metabolism is seen in an 80-year-old person compared with a 40-year-old?
                      a.   1-2
                      b.   2-4
                      c.   4-8
                      d.   8-16

c   595(A)   24.   Approximately what percentage decline in total energy expenditure is seen in a 70-year-old versus a 30-year-old?
a.   2
b.   10
c.   20
d.   30

d   595(K)   25.   What is the highest age group recognized in the Dietary Reference Intakes?
a.   40 years and over
b.   50 years and over
c.   65 years and over
d.   71 years and older

a   595(A)   26.   Which of the following describes the nutrient needs of older people?
a.   They vary according to individual histories.
b.   They remain the same as in young adult life.
c.   They increase; therefore, supplementation is required.
d.   They decrease for vitamins and minerals due to changes in body composition.

a   595(A)   27.   Which of the following is a feature of elderly people and water metabolism?
a.   They do not feel thirsty or recognize dryness of the mouth.
b.   They have a higher total body water content compared with younger adults.
c.   They show increased frequency of urination which results in higher requirements.
d.   They frequently show symptoms of overhydration such as mental lapses and disorientation.

b   595(K)   28.   What is the minimum number of glasses of water per day recommended for older adults?
a.   4
b.   6
c.   8
d.   10

c   592(K)   29.   The prevalence of overweight diminishes with aging, starting after age
a.   45.
b.   55.
c.   65.
d.   75.

b   596(K)   30.   Vitamin B12 deficiency in the elderly is least likely to occur from
a.   intestinal bacterial overgrowth.
b.   insufficient intake of vitamin B12.
c.   reduced output of intrinsic factor.
d.   reduced output of hydrochloric acid.

d   596(K)   31.   All of the following are characteristics of vitamin B12 nutrition in older people **except**

          a.   the RDA is the same as for younger adults.

          b.   older adults are advised to obtain most of their vitamin B12 from fortified foods and supplements.

          c.   up to 30% of those over 50 years of age are at risk of vitamin B12 deficiency due to atrophic gastritis.

          d.   the DRI Committee recommends that older people increase intake of meats to provide adequate vitamin B12.

c   597(K)   32.   Which of the following statements describes one aspect of mineral nutrition of older adults?

          a.   Zinc intake is adequate for about 95% of this group.

          b.   Calcium intakes of females are near the RDA for this group.

          c.   Iron-deficiency anemia in this population group is less common than in younger adults.

          d.   Calcium allowances for this group have recently been increased by the Committee on Dietary Allowances.

d   597(A)   33.   A condition that increases the likelihood of iron deficiency in older people is

          a.   lack of intrinsic factor.

          b.   loss of iron due to more frequent running activity.

          c.   blood loss from yearly physical testing procedures.

          d.   poor iron absorption due to reduced stomach acid secretion and/or use of antacids.

a   597(K)   34.   Which of the following is a feature of vitamin D nutrition in the elderly?

          a.   Aging reduces the kidneys' ability to convert vitamin D to its active form.

          b.   Most elderly are able to maintain near RDA levels of intake of the vitamin.

          c.   The RDA for vitamin D in the elderly is lower due to less excretion by the kidneys.

          d.   Most elderly rely primarily on self-synthesis of the vitamin due to their greater time spent outdoors.

b   596,597(K)   35.   Which of the following is a recent finding of vitamin D nutrition in the elderly?

          a.   Self-synthesis capacity is high.

          b.   The skin's capacity to synthesize the vitamin is reduced.

          c.   The presence of atrophic gastritis reduces bioavailability of the vitamin.

          d.   Symptoms of deficiency include dermatitis and diminished taste acidity.

c   598(K)   36.   What are the thickenings that occur to the lenses of the eye, thereby affecting vision, especially in the elderly?

          a.   Retinitis

          b.   Keratoids

          c.   Cataracts

          d.   Rhodolipids

d   598(K)   37.   What nutrients appear to be protective of cataract formation?

          a.   Iron and calcium

          b.   Chromium and zinc

          c.   Vitamin B12 and folate

          d.   Vitamin C and vitamin E

b   598(K)   38.   What organ is affected by macular degeneration?
a.   Bone
b.   Eyes
c.   Liver
d.   Kidneys

b   599(A)   39.   Which of the following foods seems to benefit rheumatoid arthritis in some people?
a.   Milk
b.   Olive oil
c.   Iodized salt
d.   Refined cereals

d   599(K)   40.   Which of the following types of diets has been shown to prevent or reduce arthritis inflammation?
a.   High in simple sugars, low in canned fruit
b.   High in animal protein, low in canned fruit
c.   Low in polyunsaturated fat, high in oleic acid
d.   Low in saturated fat, high in omega-3 fatty acids

c   599(K)   41.   All of the following are features of arthritis **except**
a.   the immune system is directly involved in rheumatoid arthritis.
b.   weight loss improves the pain in the hands from osteoarthritis.
c.   weight-bearing exercises often aggravate the pain from osteoarthritis.
d.   supplements of glucosamine and chondroitin seem to reduce the pain of arthritis.

c   600(A)   42.   Approximately what fraction of U.S. adults over age 85 have Alzheimer's disease?
a.   1/10
b.   1/4
c.   1/3
d.   1/2

d   600(K)   43.   Factors known to be related to the appearance of Alzheimer's disease include all of the following **except**
a.   an increase in free radicals.
b.   an increase in beta-amyloid.
c.   a decrease in acetylcholine synthesis.
d.   a decrease in homocysteine synthesis.

c   600(K)   44.   What percentage of U.S. adults are affected by Alzheimer's disease by age 65?
a.   0.5
b.   1
c.   10
d.   20

d   600(K)   45.   Which of the following is a characteristic of Alzheimer's disease?
a.   It affects 60% of those over 80 years of age.
b.   It is responsive to dietary choline supplementation.
c.   It is associated with stability of brain nerve cell number.
d.   It is associated with clumps of beta-amyloid protein in the brain.

a   602(K)   46.   What is a congregate meal?
    a.   A meal provided for the elderly in a place such as a community center
    b.   A meal prepared for the elderly that meets one-third of the Dietary Recommended Intakes
    c.   A meal prepared for disadvantaged people of all ages to encourage communal gathering of different population groups
    d.   A meal provided through the Nutrition Screening Initiative for the elderly and served primarily to church congregations

b   602(K)   47.   Goals of the federal Elderly Nutrition Program include the provision of all of the following **except**
    a.   transportation services.
    b.   high-cost nutritious meals.
    c.   opportunity for social interaction.
    d.   counseling and referral to other social services.

b   608(A)   48.   What are the known consequences of taking a single two-tablet dose of aspirin?
    a.   It inhibits monoamine oxidase activity.
    b.   It doubles the bleeding time of wounds.
    c.   It increases production of prostagladins that enhance fever.
    d.   It is excreted very rapidly in people taking vitamin C supplements.

c   609(K)   49.   What two nutrients are commonly lost from the body as a consequence of chronic intake of mineral oil?
    a.   Niacin and folate
    b.   Iodine and vitamin B_{12}
    c.   Calcium and vitamin D
    d.   Vitamin C and vitamin B_6

a   609(K)   50.   What two nutrients are known to interfere significantly with the utilization of the antibiotic tetracycline?
    a.   Iron and calcium
    b.   Zinc and chromium
    c.   Vitamin B_{12} and folate
    d.   Vitamin C and vitamin E

c   609(K)   51.   Characteristics associated with the use of nicotine gum as an antismoking aid include all of the following **except**
    a.   side effects include nausea and hiccups.
    b.   the nicotine is absorbed primarily from the mouth.
    c.   alkaline foods interfere with absorption of the nicotine.
    d.   its effectiveness is reduced if food is consumed within 15 minutes of chewing.

a   609,610(K) 52.   Aspirin is best known to alter the requirements or utilization of
    a.   iron and folate.
    b.   zinc and chromium.
    c.   biotin and cobalamin.
    d.   calcium and phosphorus.

c   610(K)   53.   What nutrient, when taken in large doses, is known to reduce excretion of aspirin, thereby retaining more of the medication in the bloodstream?
a.   Iron
b.   Calcium
c.   Vitamin C
d.   Omega-3 fats

b   610,611(A)   54.   Which of the following foods in particular must be restricted in the diet of a person taking a monoamine oxidase inhibitor drug?
a.   Soybeans
b.   Aged cheeses
c.   Acid-forming foods
d.   Cruciferous vegetables

d   610(K)   55.   Which of the following drugs has a chemical structure similar to folate?
a.   Tyramine
b.   Coumadin
c.   Tamoxifen
d.   Methotrexate

MATCHING (Answers can be used only once.)

C   587   01.   Number of people per 100 of the U.S. population who are at least 65 years old
E   590   02.   Dietary restriction of this extends lifespan
K   592   03.   Loss of muscle mass
D   593   04.   Percentage of people over age 60 with atrophic gastritis
L   593   05.   Term that describes a person without teeth
I   593   06.   Term that describes difficulty in swallowing
A   595   07.   Water intake recommendation for adults, in ounces per kg body weight
Q   596   08.   A condition characterized, in part, by inflamed stomach and abundant bacteria
R   596   09.   Lack of this substance is a symptom of atrophic gastritis
M   596   10.   Stomach bacterial utilization of this nutrient increases risk for deficiency
J   596   11.   Low intake of milk by elderly people contributes to deficiency of this nutrient
G   598   12.   Thickening of the eye lenses that occurs with aging
S   599   13.   Nutrient that may reduce inflammation of rheumatoid arthritic joints
T   599   14.   Type of arthritis involving defective immune system
P   599   15.   Type of arthritis resulting in deterioration of joint cartilage
B   600   16.   Percentage of U.S. adults age 65 years or **less** with Alzheimer's disease
O   600   17.   Substance that is essential to memory process
H   600   18.   Substance found in brains of people with Alzheimer's disease that triggers free-radical formation
N   609   19.   Intake of this substance along with milk reduces calcium absorption
F   610   20.   Chronic intake of this substance increases the need for folate

A.   1   K.   Sarcopenia
B.   10   L.   Edentulous
C.   13   M.   Vitamin B$_{12}$
D.   30   N.   Tetracycline
E.   Energy   O.   Acetylcholine
F.   Aspirin   P.   Osteoarthritis
G.   Cataracts   Q.   Atrophic gastritis
H.   Aluminum   R.   Hydrochloric acid
I.   Dysphagia   S.   Omega-3 fatty acids
J.   Vitamin D   T.   Rheumatoid arthritis

ESSAY QUESTIONS

PAGE(S)

589-592	01.	Discuss the roles of fitness and stress in the aging process and longevity.
589,590	02.	Describe the effects of physical inactivity in the elderly.
589	03.	List 6 major lifestyle behaviors thought to promote long-term health.
590,591	04.	Describe the effects of energy restriction on longevity of animals and people.
591-594	05.	Give several reasons for the decline in nutritional status consequent to aging.
591-594	06.	Discuss how psychological, social, and economic factors affect nutritional status of the elderly.
595-597	07.	List nutrients of special consideration for older adults and present reasons for their concern.
596,597	08.	List the factors that increase the risk for vitamin B_{12} and iron deficiency in older adults.
598	09.	Discuss the role of nutrition in prevention/treatment of cataracts and macular degeneration.
599	10.	Explain the relationship between diet and arthritis treatment.
600	11.	Discuss the relationship between nutrition and Alzheimer's disease.
599,600	12.	Describe the physiologic and biochemical changes that occur in the brain of the person with Alzheimer's disease.
603	13	List strategies for improving the food buying habits of the elderly.
609,610	14.	Give three examples each of how drugs can alter nutrient absorption and how foods can alter drug absorption.
608-610	15.	Discuss the adverse side effects of frequent use of aspirin.
610,611	16.	Explain the relationship of tyramine and monoamine oxidase (MAO) activity. What foods are prohibited for people taking MAO inhibitors?

CHAPTER 18
DIET AND HEALTH

AN. PAGE(S)

a   614(K)   01.   The immune system treats foreign substances such as bacteria and toxins as
- a.   antigens.
- b.   antibodies.
- c.   synergisms.
- d.   immunoglobulins.

b   614(K)   02.   The most important organs of the immune system include all of the following **except**
- a.   spleen.
- b.   muscle.
- c.   lymph nodes.
- d.   thymus gland.

c   614(K)   03.   What percentage of cells of the body are white blood cells?
- a.   0.01
- b.   0.1
- c.   1
- d.   10

b   614,615(K)   04.   Immunoglobulins are produced primarily by
- a.   T-cells.
- b.   B-cells.
- c.   antigens.
- d.   phagocytes.

b   614,615(K)   05.   Functions of the T-cells include all of the following **except**
- a.   recognition of antigens.
- b.   production of antibodies.
- c.   release of killer chemicals.
- d.   suppression of the immune response when approximate.

a   614,615(K)   06.   Common cell types that make up the immune system include all of the following **except**
- a.   P-cells.
- b.   B-cells.
- c.   T-cells.
- d.   phagocytes.

b   615(A)   07.   The process by which immune cells engulf and then destroy bacteria is known as
- a.   bactocydosis.
- b.   phagocytosis.
- c.   cytotoxicosis.
- d.   immunoglobinemia.

a   616(K)   08.   Presently, HIV is known to be transmitted by direct contact with contaminated body fluids from all of the following sources **except**
- a.   saliva.
- b.   blood.
- c.   semen.
- d.   vaginal secretions.

c   616(K)   09.   Initial confirmation of HIV infection after exposure to the virus takes about
  a.   1-3 days.
  b.   1-2 weeks.
  c.   1-3 months.
  d.   6-12 months.

d   617(K)   10.   About 50% of people with HIV infection will progress to AIDS within
  a.   1 year.
  b.   2 years.
  c.   5 years.
  d.   10 years.

b   616,617(K)   11.   What term identifies the involuntary loss of more than 10% of body weight?
  a.   CD4+ depletion
  b.   Wasting syndrome
  c.   Opportunistic malignancy
  d.   Cognitive dietary restraint

c   616(A)   12.   What term describes an infection that becomes life-threatening in a person with a depressed immune system but not in an individual with a normal immune system?
  a.   Wasting infection
  b.   Acquired infection
  c.   Opportunistic infection
  d.   Lymphocyte depleting infection

b   616,617(K)   13.   What type of lymphocytes are most affected by infection with HIV?
  a.   B
  b.   CD4+
  c.   Monocytes
  d.   Phagocytes

d   617(A)   14.   The progression of HIV in a person is best monitored by measuring the
  a.   severity of diarrhea.
  b.   changes in body weight.
  c.   appearance of skin cancer.
  d.   levels of blood CD4+ cells.

a   617(A)   15.   What is the most common micronutrient deficiency in people with HIV infection?
  a.   Zinc
  b.   Selenium
  c.   Vitamin E
  d.   Vitamin A

d   617,618(A)   16.   All of the following are characteristics of nutrition in people with HIV infection **except**
  a.   the FDA warns these individuals to avoid sushi.
  b.   common bacteria on foods become life-threatening to these individuals.
  c.   appropriate nutrient intake can prevent and reverse malnutrition.
  d.   the DRI Committee and the American Medical Association have devised specific dietary strategies for treatment.

c   618(K)   17.   The diseases most common today include all of the following **except**
     a.   cancer.
     b.   diabetes.
     c.   tuberculosis.
     d.   diseases of the heart and blood vessels.

b   618(K)   18.   Of the ten leading causes of illness and death, how many are associated directly with nutrition?
     a.   1
     b.   4
     c.   7
     d.   10

d   618(K)   19.   Which of the following leading causes of death in the United States does **not** bear a relationship to diet?
     a.   Cancer
     b.   Heart disease
     c.   Diabetes mellitus
     d.   Pneumonia and influenza

d   618(K)   20.   Which of the following risk factors for disease may be modified by diet?
     a.   Age
     b.   Gender
     c.   Heredity
     d.   Low HDL level

c   619(K)   21.   Being obese is known to increase the probabilities of contracting all of the following diseases **except**
     a.   cancer.
     b.   diabetes.
     c.   kwashiorkor.
     d.   hypertension.

c   619,620(K)   22.   All of the following disorders are influenced strongly by genetics **except**
     a.   diabetes.
     b.   hypertension.
     c.   diverticulosis.
     d.   atherosclerosis.

a   620(K)   23.   What is the term given to mounds of lipid material mixed with smooth muscle cells and calcium that develop in the artery walls?
     a.   Plaques
     b.   Angina streaks
     c.   Arterial thickening
     d.   Pre-thromboemboli

a   620(A)   24.   By what age do most people first have well-developed arterial plaque?
     a.   30
     b.   40
     c.   50
     d.   60

b   620,621(A)   25.   The obstruction of a blood vessel by a clot that broke away from arterial plaque is termed
     a.   an anginism.
     b.   an embolism.
     c.   circulatory hypoxia.
     d.   a de-plaquing event.

b   620,621(K)   26.   A significant reduction in blood flow to the brain is termed
     a.   angina.
     b.   a stroke.
     c.   a vascular event.
     d.   metabolic syndrome.

c   621(A)   27.   A person's level of C-reactive protein appears to be a strong predictor for
     a.   cancer.
     b.   diabetes.
     c.   a heart attack.
     d.   HIV progression.

d   624; 621(K)   28.   Which of the following may be classified as an emerging risk factor for coronary heart disease?
     a.   BMI of more than 30
     b.   High LDL-cholesterol levels
     c.   Low HDL-cholesterol levels
     d.   High C-reactive protein levels

c   621(K)   29.   Tiny, disc-shaped bodies in the blood that are important in clot formation are called
     a.   plaques.
     b.   T-cells.
     c.   platelets.
     d.   thrombocytes.

d   622(K)   30.   What disease accounts for the majority of deaths of U.S. women?
     a.   Diabetes
     b.   Lung cancer
     c.   Breast cancer
     d.   Coronary heart disease

b   622-624(K)   31.   Which of the following is **not** considered a diet-related risk factor for coronary heart disease?
     a.   Obesity
     b.   High sugar intake
     c.   Glucose intolerance
     d.   High blood cholesterol

a   622(K)   32.   Which of the following describes a known association with coronary heart disease (CHD)?
     a.   In men, CHD begins 10-15 years earlier than in women.
     b.   Women who take estrogen to reduce risk for osteoporosis are at significantly higher risk for CHD.
     c.   Men with blood cholesterol levels in the borderline-high range account for up to 10% of all deaths from CHD.
     d.   Women younger than 45 years of age tend to have higher LDL cholesterol than do men of that age, but this difference disappears after menopause.

b   622(K)   33.   What is prehypertension?

       a.   A predictor of stroke risk
       b.   Slightly high blood pressure
       c.   A precursor for Syndrome X
       d.   A component of the metabolic syndrome

d   622(K)   34.   Which of the following blood pressure readings first signifies a diagnosis of hypertension?

       a.   110 over 50
       b.   120 over 70
       c.   130 over 80
       d.   140 over 90

b   622,623(A)   35.   What blood cholesterol carrier is of greatest concern in atherosclerosis?

       a.   HDL
       b.   LDL
       c.   HDK
       d.   VLDK

d   623(K)   36.   All of the following are features of low-density lipoproteins and coronary heart disease **except**

       a.   LDL is more atherogenic than is HDL.
       b.   most blood cholesterol is in the form of LDL cholesterol.
       c.   LDL-lowering treatments are designed to stabilize arterial plaques.
       d.   excess LDL cholesterol in the blood is removed by high-density lipoproteins.

d   623,624(K)   37.   All of the following are associations between smoking and coronary heart disease **except**

       a.   smoking damages platelets.
       b.   smoking increases blood pressure.
       c.   smoking as a risk factor for CHD is the same for women and men.
       d.   cessation of smoking begins to lower the risk of CHD after 18 months.

b   624(A)   38.   A person who produces a normal amount of insulin but whose cells show suboptimal response is said to be

       a.   polydipsic.
       b.   insulin resistant.
       c.   hyperglucagonemic.
       d.   pancreatic beta-cell deficient.

a   624(A)   39.   Which of the following is **not** one of the factors that would lead a person with high blood pressure to develop the metabolic syndrome?

       a.   Diuretic use
       b.   Insulin resistance
       c.   Abdominal obesity
       d.   High blood triglycerides

d   624(K)   40.   Direct contributors to the metabolic syndrome include all of the following **except**

       a.   obesity.
       b.   hypertension.
       c.   insulin resistance.
       d.   high sodium intake.

c   625-629(K)   41.   Risk factors for coronary heart disease that can be minimized by behavioral change include all of the following **except**
   a.   stress.
   b.   smoking.
   c.   heredity.
   d.   hypertension.

c   624-629(A)   42.   Anyone who is medically advised to lower blood cholesterol should
   a.   eat fish oil capsules.
   b.   take lecithin supplements.
   c.   achieve desirable body weight.
   d.   lower the intake of insoluble fiber.

d   626,627(A)   43.   Among the following, which should be the first action taken to lower blood cholesterol?
   a.   Begin drug treatment.
   b.   Consume a high protein diet.
   c.   Consume large amounts of fish and fish oils.
   d.   Achieve and maintain appropriate body weight.

d   627(A)   44.   To lower a high blood cholesterol level, all of the following are recommended **except**
   a.   consume 2 servings/week of fish.
   b.   consume 300 mg or less of cholesterol per day.
   c.   lower the saturated fat intake to $\leq$ 10% total energy.
   d.   decrease the carbohydrate intake to 50% of total energy.

a   627(K)   45.   How are phytosterols thought to lower blood cholesterol?
   a.   They reduce cholesterol absorption.
   b.   They trap more cholesterol in the GI tract.
   c.   They interfere with liver cholesterol synthesis.
   d.   They enhance cholesterol degradation in the peripheral tissues.

b   628(A)   46.   The substitution of soy protein for animal protein leads to a reduction in the blood levels of all of the following **except**
   a.   LDL.
   b.   HDL.
   c.   cholesterol.
   d.   triglycerides.

d   628(A)   47.   About how many servings/day of soy protein is needed to provide a significant benefit to heart health?
   a.   1
   b.   2
   c.   3
   d.   4

b   628(K)   48.   Moderate daily alcohol consumption is defined as
   a.   1 drink for both women and men.
   b.   1 drink for women and 2 for men.
   c.   2 drinks for both women and men.
   d.   2 drinks for women and 4 for men.

a   628(K)   49.   Which of the following is a known relationship between alcohol intake and risk factors for cardiovascular disease?

     a.   Moderate alcohol intake raises HDL cholesterol and inhibits formation of blood clots.

     b.   The benefits of light alcohol intake on CVD risk are greatest in people of ages 25-44 years.

     c.   Gin and vodka contain antiplaque compounds such as phenols and other phytochemicals.

     d.   The beneficial effects of alcohol in lowering blood pressure appear stronger for men than women.

a   628(K)   50.   What type of exercise is considered best to strengthen the heart and blood vessels?

     a.   Aerobic exercise

     b.   Anaerobic exercise

     c.   Heavy weight training

     d.   Short duration exercise

c   628,629(K)   51.   Improvement in cardiovascular health by regular aerobic exercise results from all of the following **except**

     a.   lowering blood pressure.

     b.   redistributing body water.

     c.   increasing fat tissue while decreasing lean tissue.

     d.   increasing the volume of oxygen delivered by the heart.

b   629(K)   52.   Which of the following illustrates an association between physical activity, dieting, and HDL?

     a.   In men, weight loss due solely to dieting appears to have no effect on HDL levels.

     b.   In women, weight loss due solely to dieting appears to lower HDL concentrations.

     c.   In men, regular weight training (anaerobic activity) is known to lower HDL concentrations.

     d.   In women, dieting combined with moderate aerobic activity appears to significantly lower HDL levels.

c   629(K)   53.   How many million people in the United States are believed to have hypertension?

     a.   10

     b.   30

     c.   60

     d.   100

a   629(A)   54.   What is the best predictor for risk of a stroke?

     a.   Blood pressure

     b.   LDL-cholesterol

     c.   HDL-cholesterol

     d.   Trans-fatty acid intake

c   630(K)   55.   At what age do most people with hypertension first develop the disorder?

     a.   35

     b.   50

     c.   60

     d.   70

d 630(A) 56. How does obesity increase the risk for development of hypertension?
a. The excess fat pads surrounding the kidneys impair blood flow to these organs and lead to higher output of renin.
b. Sodium intake in the obese significantly exceeds the recommended intake, thereby predisposing them to higher blood pressure.
c. Higher activities of lipoprotein lipase in the obese trigger the angiotensin cascade leading to increased peripheral resistance to blood flow.
d. Obesity frequently is associated with high blood insulin levels which signal the kidneys to retain sodium, which increases blood pressure.

c 630(K) 57. The ballooning out of an artery wall at a point where it has been weakened by deterioration is called a(an)
a. aorta.
b. plaque.
c. aneurysm.
d. diverticula.

c 630(K) 58. Risk factors that predict the development of hypertension include all of the following **except**
a. age.
b. race.
c. salt intake.
d. family background.

b 630(K) 59. Risk factors for sodium or salt sensitivity include all of the following **except**
a. being black.
b. being white.
c. being over 50 years of age.
d. having a parent with hypertension.

a 630(K) 60. Which of the following statements describes a relationship between salt intake and high blood pressure?
a. A high salt intake is not a risk factor for the development of high blood pressure.
b. Ninety-five percent of people under 50 years of age with high blood pressure respond favorably to low salt intake.
c. Most people are genetically sensitive to sodium and can develop high blood pressure from excess salt intake.
d. Ninety-five percent of people with high blood pressure who restrict salt intake show a significant decrease in blood pressure.

b 631(K) 61. Which of the following describes a relationship between sodium/salt and high blood pressure?
a. People with chronic kidney disease are less likely to be salt-sensitive.
b. Body weight loss is at least as effective as sodium restriction in lowering blood pressure.
c. People over 30 years of age with hypertension are most likely to be salt-sensitive.
d. Lowering sodium intakes reduces blood pressure only in certain ethnic groups.

d   631(A)   62.   Which of the following is **not** among the recommendations by health professionals to treat hypertension?
  a.   Increase fiber intake
  b.   Eat foods high in potassium
  c.   If overweight, reduce weight
  d.   Decrease intake of dairy products to avoid sodium

c   631(K)   63.   The DASH diet was developed to lower the risk for
  a.   cancer.
  b.   diabetes.
  c.   hypertension.
  d.   metabolic syndrome.

a   631(A)   64.   Diuretics act to lower blood pressure by
  a.   increasing fluid loss.
  b.   decreasing potassium loss.
  c.   reducing arterial plague formation.
  d.   increasing retention of calcium and potassium.

c   631(A)   65.   People who use diuretics are most at risk of developing imbalances of
  a.   sodium.
  b.   calcium.
  c.   potassium.
  d.   phosphate.

a   632(K)   66.   What percentage of people with diabetes have type 1?
  a.   5-10
  b.   10-20
  c.   20-35
  d.   45-55

c   632(K)   67.   What is believed to be the primary cause of type 1 diabetes?
  a.   Defect in insulin sensitivity
  b.   Excessive body weight gain
  c.   Defect of the immune system
  d.   Excessive intake of simple carbohydrates

a   632(K)   68.   Insulin stimulates the actions of all the following metabolic activities **except**
  a.   fat release.
  b.   glucose uptake.
  c.   protein synthesis.
  d.   glycogen synthesis.

c   632,633(K) 69.   All of the following are characteristics of diabetes mellitus **except**
  a.   type 1 diabetes can occur at any age.
  b.   type 2 diabetes develops primarily when people reach adulthood.
  c.   the two major forms are variations of the insulin-dependent type.
  d.   the most common form is characterized by resistance to insulin by body cells.

b   632,633(K)   70.   In which of the following conditions would the pancreas be unable to synthesize insulin?
a.   Hyperglycemia
b.   Type 1 diabetes mellitus
c.   Type 2 diabetes mellitus
d.   Adult-onset diabetes mellitus

d   633(K)   71.   Which of the following conditions is characterized by insulin resistance of fat cells?
a.   Hypoglycemia
b.   Atherosclerosis
c.   Type 1 diabetes mellitus
d.   Type 2 diabetes mellitus

a   633(K)   72.   Insulin resistance is defined as
a.   reduced sensitivity of cells to blood insulin.
b.   impaired secretion of insulin by the pancreas.
c.   increased destruction of insulin-producing cells.
d.   refusal of people with type 1 diabetes to self-inject insulin.

c   633(A)   73.   Type 2 diabetes usually develops after people reach the age of
a.   21.
b.   30.
c.   40.
d.   55.

c   633(A)   74.   Almost every person with type 2 diabetes has
a.   sarcopenia.
b.   osteoporosis.
c.   excess body fat.
d.   insulin dependency.

c   633,634(K)   75.   Diabetes is known to lead to all of the following **except**
a.   impaired vision.
b.   impaired circulation.
c.   increased resistance to infections.
d.   increased loss of water via the urine.

d   633-635(K)   76.   A person with diabetes is most likely to develop
a.   AIDS.
b.   cancer.
c.   diverticulosis.
d.   strokes and heart attacks.

c   633,634(K)   77.   Which of the following is **not** a common, long-term consequence of diabetes?
a.   Blindness
b.   Kidney failure
c.   Decrease in infections
d.   Increase in heart attacks

b 633,634(A) 78. What is the primary reason for increased urine output in uncontrolled diabetes?
   a. Insufficient levels of circulating insulin permit the kidney to lose excess water.
   b. High levels of blood glucose spill into the urine drawing water with it by osmosis.
   c. Excess circulating insulin affects the output of antidiuretic hormone which allows greater losses of water.
   d. Large amounts of body fat and glycogen are broken down resulting in increased release of cellular water.

d 633,634(K) 79. All of the following are among the symptoms of diabetes **except**
   a. polyuria.
   b. polydipsia.
   c. polyphagia.
   d. polysaccharidosis.

a 633,634(A) 80. The frequent urination experienced by a diabetic is known as
   a. polyuria.
   b. polyphagia.
   c. polyuresis.
   d. pseudodiuresis.

c 634(A) 81. The excessive thirst experienced by a diabetic is known as
   a. hydration.
   b. polyuresis.
   c. polydipsia.
   d. hyperhydration.

b 634(K) 82. Gangrene is a common complication in primarily people with
   a. cancer.
   b. diabetes.
   c. pancreatitis.
   d. HIV infection.

d 635(A) 83. The role of diet for people with diabetes includes all of the following **except**
   a. diets should provide a consistent carbohydrate intake spaced throughout the day.
   b. diets of up to 35% fat energy improve both blood glucose and lipid metabolism.
   c. the dietary amount of carbohydrate is more important than the source of carbohydrate.
   d. diets high in polyunsaturated fatty acids may reduce the susceptibility of blood lipoproteins to oxidation.

a 636(K) 84. The chief cause of death in people between the ages of 45 and 64 is
   a. cancer.
   b. diabetes.
   c. heart attack.
   d. kidney failure.

a   636(K)   85.   A cancer that originates from bone is a
                         a.   sarcoma.
                         b.   carcinoma.
                         c.   osteocarcinoma.
                         d.   hematopoietic neoplasm.

a   638(K)   86.   Which of the following describes the actions of a carcinogen?
                         a.   Cancer-initiating substance
                         b.   Cancer-inhibitory substance
                         c.   Cancer treatment substance
                         d.   Cancer antipromoter substance

a   638,639(K)   87.   Factors that favor the development of cancer once the initiating event has taken
                         place are called
                         a.   promoters.
                         b.   carcinogens.
                         c.   antipromoters.
                         d.   post-initiators.

a   636;638,639(K) 88. What is the term given to the factors that enhance the **development** of cancer after
                         it has been initiated?
                         a.   Promoters
                         b.   Post-initiators
                         c.   Tumor formatives
                         d.   Tumor directives

b   638(K)   89.   Which of the following statements represents current thought in the development
                         of cancer?
                         a.   Fat in the diet appears to be protective against many types of cancer.
                         b.   Food additives play only a small role, if any, in the causation of cancer.
                         c.   Food contaminants play only a small role, if any, in the causation of cancer.
                         d.   Protein in the diet from animal sources appears to be protective of many
                               types of cancer.

c   639(K)   90.   All of the following are characteristics of diet and cancer **except**
                         a.   diets high in energy are thought to promote cancer.
                         b.   within a given population, cancer rates and fat intake are not related.
                         c.   *trans*-fatty acid intake seems to protect against colon cancer in women
                               but not men.
                         d.   risk for prostate cancer seems to correlate with fat intake from meats but
                               not vegetables.

b   640(A)   91.   Which of the following is known to speed up the passage of bile through the large
                         intestines, thereby decreasing exposure time to microorganisms?
                         a.   Milk
                         b.   Fiber
                         c.   Omega-3 fats
                         d.   Refined starches

a   640(K)   92.   Which of the following dietary components is thought to have an inverse correlation to colon cancer?
- a.   Fiber
- b.   Unsaturated fats
- c.   Inositol and biotin
- d.   Protein from animal sources

a   640(K)   93.   Antioxidant substances that are believed to help protect against cancer include all of the following **except**
- a.   EDTA.
- b.   vitamin E.
- c.   vitamin C.
- d.   beta-carotene.

b   640(K)   94.   Which of the following is **not** among the recommendations issued by health professionals to reduce cancer risks?
- a.   Moderate or stop intake of alcohol.
- b.   Increase intake of foods high in iron.
- c.   Limit intake of red meats.
- d.   Eat at least 5 servings a day of vegetables and fruits.

a   642(K)   95.   Which of the following defines the association between nutrition and chronic disease?
- a.   Diet can influence the time of onset of some chronic diseases.
- b.   Diet is the primary factor affecting the development of chronic diseases.
- c.   Dietary influence in the development of chronic diseases is direct, straightforward, and well understood.
- d.   Dietary advice for combating heart disease and cancer prevents their development if instituted early in life.

c   647,648(K)   96.   Which of the following is currently accepted as a medical treatment in the United States?
- a.   Biofield therapeutics
- b.   Orthomolecular therapy
- c.   Cancer radiation therapy
- d.   Microwave resonance therapy

d   647(K)   97.   Conventional medicine and alternative medical therapies are commonly linked together into a practice called
- a.   interactive therapy.
- b.   yin and yang medicine.
- c.   herbal-assisted healing.
- d.   complementary medicine.

c   648(K)   98.   What is ayurveda?
- a.   A system that combines biofeedback with hypnosis
- b.   An oriental plant found to suppress colon and breast tumor growth in animals and people
- c.   A Hindu system for enhancing the body's ability to prevent illness and to heal itself
- d.   A variation of standard acupuncture technique that applies electromagnetic impulses to the needles

b   648(K)   99.   Chelation therapy is purported to work by ridding the body of
                         a.   tumor cells.
                         b.   toxic metals.
                         c.   organic toxins.
                         d.   excess fat-soluble vitamins.

b   648(K)   100.   Macrobiotic diets refer to diets that
                         a.   are tailored to very large individuals.
                         b.   are restricted to a few grains and vegetables.
                         c.   recommend specific ratios of the macronutrients.
                         d.   encompass a very broad range of vegetables and fruits.

b   650(K)   101.   Approximately what percentage of modern medicines are derived, in part, from
                         wild plants?
                         a.   5
                         b.   15
                         c.   35
                         d.   50

b   650,651(K)   102.   What is the name of the substance first extracted from the bark of old Pacific yew
                         trees (and now synthesized in the laboratory) and found effective in treating
                         cancer?
                         a.   Ephedra
                         b.   Paclitaxal
                         c.   Kombucha
                         d.   Germanium

MATCHING (Answers can be used only once.)

T	618	01.	The primary cause of death of Americans
N	616	02.	Specific type of immune cells most affected in people with AIDS
O	620	03.	Disease characterized by the accumulation of lipids on the inner arterial walls
P	620	04.	A mound of lipid material embedded in arterial walls
F	621	05.	Small, cell-like bodies required for formation of a blood clot
E	620	06.	A blood clot that has broken loose and circulates in the bloodstream
I	620	07.	A blood clot that is attached to arterial plaque
C	620	08.	Consequence of a clot that stops blood flow to the brain
S	615	09.	Immune cells that practice phagocytosis
J	630	10.	The bursting of an artery from constant elevated blood pressure
L	636	11.	A substance or event that gives rise to a cancer
M	636	12.	A cancer that arises from the intestinal mucosa
D	636	13.	A cancer that arises from muscle
K	636	14.	Growth of tissue forming an abnormal mass with no function
G	636	15.	Substance that favors development of a cancer after the cellular DNA has been altered
Q	632	16.	This type of diabetes is usually controlled by insulin injections
R	633	17.	This type of diabetes is usually controlled **without** insulin injections
H	634	18.	Term that describes the death of tissue due to deficient blood supply, common in severe diabetic cases
A	615	19.	Immune cells that produce antibodies
B	615	20.	Immune cells that attack antigens

A.	B-cells	K.	Neoplasm
B.	T-cells	L.	Initiator
C.	Stroke	M.	Carcinoma
D.	Sarcoma	N.	CD4+
E.	Embolus	O.	Atherosclerosis
F.	Platelets	P.	Plaque
G.	Promoter	Q.	Type 1 diabetes
H.	Gangrene	R.	Type 2 diabetes
I.	Thrombus	S.	Macrophages
J.	Aneurysm	T.	Heart disease

ESSAY QUESTIONS

PAGE(S)

614,615	01.	Describe the actions of phagocytes and lymphocytes against foreign substances.
614,615	02.	List ways that malnutrition affects immunity.
615	03.	Explain the meaning and significance of the "downward spiral" of malnutrition and disease.
616,617	04.	a. How does AIDS develop? b. Describe the wasting syndrome of HIV
617,618	05.	Discuss the benefits of nutrition support for people with HIV infection.
620-643	06.	Discuss the role of nutrition in the development and treatment of three common degenerative diseases.

620,621	07.	Explain the processes in the development of atherosclerosis.
623,624	08.	Describe the effects of smoking on cardiovascular health.
622,623	09.	Discuss the major risk factors for coronary heart disease.
623	10.	Discuss the importance of LDL cholesterol as an independent risk factor for coronary heart disease.
624	11.	Explain the meaning and significance of the metabolic syndrome.
624-629	12.	Outline the recommendations for reducing the risk of coronary heart disease.
626,627	13.	Discuss implementation of the 4 main goals to both prevent and treat coronary heart disease.
627,628	14.	Discuss the benefits of consuming phytosterol-enriched foods on coronary heart disease.
627-629	15.	Discuss strategies for favorably altering the lipoprotein profiles in men and women.
628;631	16.	Discuss the influence of moderate alcohol intake on cardiovascular disease risk.
629-631	17.	How does hypertension develop? Why does obesity aggravate the hypertensive state?
630,631	18.	Describe the major recommendations for reducing risk for hypertension.
632-636	19.	Compare and contrast the two major types of diabetes and their recommended dietary management.
635,636	20.	Describe the recommendation for fat intake in people with diabetes.
635,636	21.	Describe the dilemma faced by people with diabetes when they change the ratios of dietary carbohydrate to fat.
637-639	22.	Outline the steps involved in the development of cancer.
640	23.	List the major recommendations for reducing the risks of cancer.
647,648	24.	List five general areas of alternative medicine and give two specific examples of each.
647	25.	List three defining characteristics of alternative therapies.
648,649	26.	Explain, through the use of examples, the risk versus benefit relationship of therapeutic intervention.
650-653	27.	Give examples of the reported adverse effects of herbal therapy.

CHAPTER 19
CONSUMER CONCERNS ABOUT FOODS AND WATER

AN. PAGE(S)

b   657(A)   01.   The potential of a substance to harm someone is known as a
a.   hazard.
b.   toxicity.
c.   risk level.
d.   safety level.

a   657(A)   02.   What term describes the possibility of harm from normal use of a substance?
a.   Hazard
b.   Toxicity
c.   Bioinsecurity
d.   Food insecurity

c   658(K)   03.   Which of the following appears first on the Food and Drug Administration's priority concerns for food safety?
a.   Food additives
b.   Pesticide residues
c.   Foodborne illnesses
d.   Environmental contaminants

b   658(K)   04.   Which of the following is **not** among the major food safety concerns of the FDA?
a.   Pesticide residues
b.   Proper food disposal
c.   Environmental contaminants
d.   Nutritional adequacy of foods

c   658(K)   05.   According to the Centers for Disease Control, how many people in the United States experience foodborne illness every year?
a.   0.5 million
b.   12 million
c.   76 million
d.   150 million

c   658(K)   06.   What branch of the Department of Health and Human Services is responsible for **monitoring** foodborne illness?
a.   EPA
b.   FAO
c.   CDC
d.   WHO

a   658(K)   07.   What is the international agency that has adopted standards to regulate the use of pesticides?
a.   WHO
b.   FDA
c.   CDC
d.   USDA

b   658(K)   08.   What is the leading cause of food contamination in the United States?
- a.   Naturally occurring toxicants
- b.   Food poisoning from microbes
- c.   Pesticide residues from farmers
- d.   Food additives from the food industry

d   659(A)   09.   Which of the following is an example of food intoxication?
- a.   Addition of alkaline and acidic agents to foods
- b.   Illness produced by acute overconsumption of high-fat foods
- c.   Addition of alcohol-containing beverages in the cooking of foods
- d.   Illness produced from ingestion of food contaminated with natural toxins

b   659(K)   10.   Which of the following is one of the most common pathogenic microorganisms in U.S. foods?
- a.   *Escherichia coli*
- b.   *Campylobacter jejuni*
- c.   *Staphylococcus aureas*
- d.   *Clostridium perfringens*

a   660(K)   11.   Which of the following is the major food source for transmission of *Campylobacter jejuni*?
- a.   Raw poultry
- b.   Uncooked seafood
- c.   Contaminated water
- d.   Imported soft cheeses

d   659(K)   12.   *Clostridium botulinum* poisoning is a hazard associated with
- a.   nitrosamines.
- b.   rotting vegetables.
- c.   undercooked poultry.
- d.   improperly canned vegetables.

b   659(K)   13.   Which of the following is a characteristic of botulism illness?
- a.   It is rarely fatal and victims usually recover completely.
- b.   It is caused by a toxic compound rather than by invasion of pathogenic bacteria.
- c.   It is caused by ingestion of food contaminated with a combination of aflatoxin and mold.
- d.   It most often occurs from eating foods that were stored under aerobic conditions of high pH.

b   659(K)   14.   Which of the following is a characteristic of botulism?
- a.   A chief symptom is diarrhea.
- b.   A full recovery may take years.
- c.   It is caused by the organism *Staphylococcus aureus*.
- d.   It is a toxicant produced in foods stored under aerobic conditions.

a   659(K)   15.   A child is brought into the emergency room with breathing difficulties. He also has difficulty swallowing and speaking. The mother mentions that he ate some home-canned beans yesterday. You suspect microbiological food poisoning. The most likely toxin is
a.   botulinum.
b.   giardiasis toxin.
c.   campylobacteria toxin.
d.   salmonella toxin.

c   665(K)   16.   Which of the following has caused botulism poisoning in infants?
a.   Milk
b.   Eggs
c.   Honey
d.   Cheese

d   659(K)   17.   What organism produces the most common food toxin?
a.   *E. coli*
b.   *Giardia lamblia*
c.   *Clostridium botulinum*
d.   *Staphylococcus aureus*

d   659(A)   18.   What fraction of reported foodborne illnesses can be attributed to the food industry?
a.   1/10
b.   1/3
c.   1/2
d.   4/5

c   659(A)   19.   The industrial application of heat to inactivate most but not all bacteria in a food is commonly known as
a.   sanitization.
b.   sterilization.
c.   pasteurization.
d.   depathogenation.

d   659(K)   20.   The most common symptoms of foodborne infection include all of the following **except**
a.   fever.
b.   cramps.
c.   diarrhea.
d.   double vision.

d   660(K)   21.   Which of the following foods are associated with illness from *Salmonella*?
a.   Raw vegetables
b.   Pickled vegetables
c.   Home-canned vegetables
d.   Raw meats, poultry, and eggs

b 660(A) 22. A patient with a high temperature complains of headache, stomach ache, fever, and vomiting. Upon questioning, he admits to eating several raw eggs the day before. The most likely organism causing these symptoms is
  a. *E. coli.*
  b. *Salmonella.*
  c. *Perfringens.*
  d. *Campylobacter jejuni.*

a 661,662(A) 23. All of the following are rules to help prevent illness from *Salmonella* **except**
  a. use hands to mix foods.
  b. thaw meats in the refrigerator.
  c. use a meat thermometer to avoid undercooking.
  d. use hot, soapy water to wash hands, utensils, and countertops.

d. 661(A) 24. Of the millions of imported shipments of raw foods arriving in U.S. ports each year, approximately what percentage is **not** inspected by the FDA?
  a. Less than 5
  b. Less than 20
  c. 50
  d. 98

c 661(K) 25. What system was developed by government regulatory agencies and the food industry to help identify and/or control food contamination and foodborne disease?
  a. The Two-Forty-One-Forty rule
  b. Safe Handling Certification Program
  c. Hazard Analysis Critical Control Points
  d. North American Residue Monitoring Program

d 661(A) 26. Which of the following would most likely result from placing cooked hamburger patties on the same plate that held the uncooked patties?
  a. Flavor declination
  b. Meat juice retention
  c. Fat drippings exudation
  d. Microbial cross-contamination

c 663(A) 27. To minimize the possibility of foodborne illness, hamburger should be cooked to an internal temperature of at least
  a. 125° F.
  b. 140° F.
  c. 160° F.
  d. 195° F.

a 662(A) 28. Why is ground meat more susceptible to microbial contamination than unground meat?
  a. It has more surface area.
  b. It is usually undercooked.
  c. It has a higher fat content.
  d. It is not inspected as often.

b 662(K)   29.   Which of the following is a characteristic of meat contamination?
- a.   A USDA seal of inspection insures the absence of most harmful bacteria.
- b.   Consumers are not able to detect the presence of harmful bacteria by odor or taste.
- c.   The presence of naturally occurring antibodies in meats slows the growth of harmful organisms.
- d.   Ground meat is very resistant to contamination because of the high heat released by the grinding machines.

d 663(A)   30.   The seal "Graded by USDA" that appears on packaged meat and poultry means that the product is
- a.   uncooked.
- b.   not hazardous.
- c.   free of bacteria.
- d.   assessed for tenderness.

b 662(K)   31.   Which of the following foods is best known to transmit hepatitis?
- a.   Poultry
- b.   Seafood
- c.   Legumes
- d.   Raw vegetables

c 663(A)   32.   What unintended benefit is derived from the freezing of fish by the food industry?
- a.   It tenderizes the product.
- b.   It inactivates botulinum toxin.
- c.   It kills mature parasitic worms.
- d.   It destroys the toxin from hepatitis A and B.

a 665(A)   33.   A patient reports that since returning from overseas travel to a developing country, she has been experiencing stomach cramps and diarrhea. Which of the following food-borne organisms is most likely responsible for these symptoms?
- a.   *E. coli*
- b.   *Clostridium botulinum*
- c.   *Clostridium perfringens*
- d.   *Listeria monocytogenes*

b 665(K)   34.   Among the following organisms, which is primarily responsible for causing "traveler's" diarrhea?
- a.   *Vibrio*
- b.   *Escherichia coli*
- c.   *Clostridium botulinum*
- d.   *Staphylococcus aureus*

a 665(K)   35.   What are the chances of contracting diarrhea from travel to other countries?
- a.   1 in 2
- b.   1 in 10
- c.   1 in 100
- d.   1 in 1000

d   666(A)   36.   Which of the following is inappropriate advice on sanitation for someone traveling to another country?
                         a.   Drink all beverages without ice.
                         b.   Boil the local water before use to kill microbes.
                         c.   Drink carbonated beverages because carbonation inhibits growth of bacteria.
                         d.   Eat vegetables raw with the peel to decrease risk from wash-water contamination.

b   665(K)   37.   Which of the following methods of thawing meats or poultry increases health risk?
                         a.   In the refrigerator
                         b.   At room temperature
                         c.   In a microwave oven
                         d.   Under cool running water

a   665(A)   38.   Which of the following is the most appropriate method to thaw turkey?
                         a.   In the refrigerator
                         b.   At room temperature
                         c.   On top of a warm oven
                         d.   Under very low heat in the oven

c   664,665(A) 39.   Which of the following practices is safest for minimizing microbial contamination of prepared foods?
                         a.   Store food in a controlled atmosphere of chlorine bleach vapors.
                         b.   Restrict the food's exposure at room temperature to a maximum of 4-6 hours.
                         c.   Restrict the food's exposure at between 40° F and 140° F to a maximum of 2 hours.
                         d.   Store food under air-tight conditions at a temperature of 32° F for a maximum of 1 month.

a   664(K)   40.   All of the following are characteristics of oysters in the diet **except**
                         a.   they are the primary factor in traveler's diarrhea.
                         b.   eating them raw is a risk factor for some bacterial infections.
                         c.   some oyster-borne microbes are destroyed when the consumer drinks alcohol.
                         d.   many oyster-borne bacteria, but not viruses, are destroyed by some hot sauces.

c   665(A)   41.   If you suspect that you are suffering from a foodborne illness, appropriate actions to take include all of the following **except**
                         a.   refrain from eating or drinking any more of the tainted product.
                         b.   drink clear liquids to help combat diarrhea and vomiting, and call a physician.
                         c.   find a portion of the remaining suspected food and taste it to detect any off flavors.
                         d.   find the remainder of the suspected food and store it in the refrigerator for possible inspection by health authorities.

a   666(K)   42.   Which of the following is an example of a food preservation technique?
                         a.   Irradiation is used to sterilize spices.
                         b.   Sulfites act to retard growth of pathogenic organisms.
                         c.   Carotenoids are used to retard formation of nitrosamines.
                         d.   Nitrites may form unique radiolytic particles when the food is overheated.

a   666(A)   43   What is the chief reason for not using irradiation for preserving dairy products?
- a. It imparts off flavors.
- b. It coalesces the fat particles.
- c. It is inefficient at killing microorganisms.
- d. It results in high amounts of food radioactive particles.

d   666(K)   44.   Which of the following is a feature of irradiated foods?
- a. The World Health Organization has not approved of food irradiation.
- b. Irradiation of foods such as strawberries and mangoes hastens their ripening.
- c. The labels of all foods must indicate treatment by irradiation except for meats.
- d. The irradiation label is not required on commercially prepared foods that contain irradiated ingredients.

c   666(K)   45.   A common term to describe the process of irradiation is
- a. UHT treatment.
- b. radura treatment.
- c. cold pasteurization.
- d. pulsed electron beam.

d   667(K)   46.   What nutrients in foods are most vulnerable to losses during food handling and preparation?
- a. Trace elements
- b. Fat-soluble vitamins
- c. Polyunsaturated fats
- d. Water-soluble vitamins

a   668(K)   47.   Which of the following are examples of heavy metals?
- a. Mercury and lead
- b. Iron and chromium
- c. Carbon and nitrogen
- d. Molybdenum and fluoride

b   668(A)   48.   Which of the following is an example of heavy metal exposure from foods?
- a. Cooking foods for prolonged periods in iron utensils.
- b. Ingestion of food containing high amounts of mercury.
- c. Ingestion of food supplements containing high levels of calcium and sodium salts.
- d. Cooking foods over superheated charcoal containing high levels of copper and iron.

a   670(K)   49.   Which of the following is a characteristic of heavy metals in the U.S. food supply?
- a. Virtually all fish contain mercury.
- b. Mercury contamination of fish is most severe in tuna.
- c. Toxicity is most severe in the elderly population group.
- d. Contamination is usually higher in farm-raised fish than in ocean fish.

a   668(K)   50.   The increase in the concentration of contaminants in the tissues of animals high on the food chain is termed
    a.   bioaccumulation.
    b.   hyperconcentration.
    c.   evolutionary containment.
    d.   functional high level accumulation.

c   668,669(K)   51.   Which of the following is a feature of an organic halogen?
    a.   Heavy metal
    b.   Safe additive
    c.   Toxic chemical
    d.   Component of most proteins

d   668,669(K)   52.   What was the toxic substance that accidentally found its way into the food chain in the early 1970s and to which almost all of Michigan's residents became exposed?
    a.   Lead acetate
    b.   Methylmercury
    c.   *Listeria monocytogenes*
    d.   Polybrominated biphenyl

d   671(A)   53.   What is the principal factor related to solanine concentration in potatoes?
    a.   Contamination
    b.   Irradiation malfunction
    c.   Soil heavy metal content
    d.   Improper storage conditions

a   671(K)   54.   Which of the following is a characteristic of solanine?
    a.   It is not destroyed by cooking.
    b.   It enhances absorption of lead.
    c.   It antagonizes the thyroid gland.
    d.   It is destroyed when potatoes start to sprout.

a   671(K)   55.   Which of the following is a feature of naturally occurring food toxicants?
    a.   Lima beans contain deadly cyanide compounds.
    b.   The toxic solanine in potatoes is inactivated by cooking.
    c.   The toxic laetrile in certain fruit seeds is a moderately effective cancer cure.
    d.   Mustard greens and radishes contain compounds that are known to worsen a cholesterol problem.

a   671(K)   56.   Many countries restrict the varieties of commercially-grown lima beans due to the seed's content of
    a.   cyanide.
    b.   solanine.
    c.   goitrogens.
    d.   hallucinogens.

b   672(K)   57.   What term is used to describe the highest level of a pesticide that is allowed in a food when the pesticide is used according to label directions?
    a.   Toxicity level
    b.   Tolerance level
    c.   Risk concentration
    d.   Optimum concentration

a   672(K)   58.   What organization is responsible for setting tolerance guidelines for the use of a pesticide on food?
                      a.   EPA
                      b.   FDA
                      c.   WHO
                      d.   DDT

b   672(K)   59.   What organization is responsible for **enforcing** the tolerances that are set for a pesticide on food?
                      a.   EPA
                      b.   FDA
                      c.   WHO
                      d.   DDT

d   672,673(K) 60.   Which of the following describes the role of the FDA in the monitoring of pesticides?
                      a.   It samples all food shipments for all pesticides.
                      b.   It samples all food shipments for some pesticides.
                      c.   It samples some food shipments for all pesticides.
                      d.   It samples some food shipments for some pesticides.

c   672(K)   61.   What is meant when the FDA invokes a certification requirement?
                      a.   The food or supplies must show proof that the foods were produced and processed in the United States.
                      b.   A new food is being introduced on the U.S. market and the processing method must first be approved by the FDA.
                      c.   The food manufacturer must have its own products tested to guarantee that certain chemicals do not exceed legal limits.
                      d.   The FDA laboratories have tested a new food product and approved all remaining pesticide residue as falling within agency guidelines.

a   673(K)   62.   What is the name of the program that reports on the dietary intakes of pesticides from our food supply?
                      a.   Total Diet Study
                      b.   Toxicant Monitoring Program
                      c.   Food Safety and Health Program
                      d.   Diet and Market Analysis Report

d   674(K)   63.   All of the following practices are known to minimize exposure to food pesticide residues **except**
                      a.   throwing away the outer leaves of leafy vegetables.
                      b.   using a knife to peel citrus fruits rather than biting into the peel.
                      c.   throwing away the fats and oils in broths and pan drippings from cooked meats.
                      d.   washing waxed fruits and vegetables in water to remove the wax-impregnated pesticides.

a   673(A)   64.   Of the amount of pesticides considered acceptable (safe) for human consumption, approximately what percent is actually ingested by people in the United States?
                      a.   1
                      b.   10
                      c.   50
                      d.   100

b   675(A)   65.   Most food additives are classified as
                         a.   emulsifiers.
                         b.   preservatives.
                         c.   color enhancers.
                         d.   bleaching agents.

a   675,676(K) 66.   What organization regulates and monitors the use of chemical additives?
                         a.   FDA
                         b.   HRS
                         c.   WHO
                         d.   USDA

b   675(K)   67.   What list is composed of substances widely used for many years without apparent
                         ill effects?
                         a.   FDA
                         b.   GRAS
                         c.   Delaney
                         d.   Additive Safety

a   675(A)   68.   Caffeine is permitted as a food additive because it is part of the
                         a.   GRAS list.
                         b.   Delaney Clause.
                         c.   WHO Mandate of 1985.
                         d.   USDA Bulletin of 1962.

b   675,676(K) 69.   Which of the following dictates that an additive must not have been found to be a
                         carcinogen in any test on animals or human beings?
                         a.   Additive Rules
                         b.   Delaney Clause
                         c.   FDA GRAS List
                         d.   Contaminant Law

b   676(K)   70.   What is the origin of the quotation "No additive shall be deemed to be safe if it is
                         found to induce cancer when ingested by man or animal?"
                         a.   GRAS list
                         b.   Delaney Clause
                         c.   WHO Mandate of 1985
                         d.   USDA Bulletin of 1962

d   676(K)   71.   What is the term that describes the allowance of most additives in foods at levels
                         100 times below those at which the risks of adverse effects are known to be zero?
                         a.   Toxicity range
                         b.   Zone of hazard
                         c.   Acceptable area
                         d.   Margin of safety

a   676(A)   72.   Which of the following substances in the diet would typically have the lowest
                         margin of safety?
                         a.   Table salt
                         b.   Pesticides
                         c.   Preservatives
                         d.   Color additives

c   676(K)   73.   What level of cancer risk to human beings from a food additive is accepted by the FDA?
   a.   0
   b.   1 in 1,000
   c.   1 in 1,000,000
   d.   1 in 100,000,000

d   676(K)   74.   What defines the FDA's *de minimus* rule?
   a.   A requirement that the least toxic food additive be used on foods
   b.   The minimum amount of a food particle that can be detected
   c.   The minimum amount of nitrite that can be added to foods to prevent spoilage over a certain time frame
   d.   The amount of a food additive that causes no more than a one-in-a-million risk of cancer to human beings

c   675,676(K) 75.   What category is assigned to additives put in foods after a rational decision-making process?
   a.   Indirect
   b.   Incidental
   c.   Intentional
   d.   Contaminants

d   676(A)   76.   What is the classification given to a substance put into food to give a certain color?
   a.   Indirect additive
   b.   Incidental additive
   c.   Peripheral additive
   d.   Intentional additive

b   677(K)   77.   All of the following are among the characteristics of antimicrobial food additives **except**
   a.   nitrates also preserve the color of hot dogs.
   b.   ordinary baking powder is one of the most common.
   c.   sodium propionate is used in cheeses and margarine.
   d.   nitrites can be converted to cancer-causing substances in the stomach.

b   677(A)   78.   Sugar and salt are used as antimicrobial agents in foods because they prevent microbial use of the food's
   a.   fat.
   b.   water.
   c.   protein.
   d.   carbohydrate.

a   677(K)   79.   Of the following, which is used most widely as an antimicrobial agent?
   a.   Sugar
   b.   Saccharin
   c.   Sodium nitrite
   d.   Sodium propionate

c   677,678(K) 80.   All of the following are among antioxidant agents used by food processors **except**
   a.   BHA.
   b.   BHT.
   c.   solanine.
   d.   vitamin E.

c   677,678(A)   81.   Which of the following properties are shared by vitamins C and E, BHA and BHT, and sulfites?
a.   Flavor enhancers
b.   Antimicrobial agents
c.   Antioxidant activities
d.   Incidental food additives

d   678(k)   82.   Which of the following is a feature of the substance BHT?
a.   It is a food antimicrobial.
b.   It is a common food colorant.
c.   It contributes significantly to the total additive intake from the diet.
d.   It decreases cancer formation when given in large amounts to animals exposed to carcinogens.

a   677(A)   83.   When a slice of fresh apple turns a brown color it is most likely the result of
a.   oxidation.
b.   dehydration.
c.   microbial contamination.
d.   ethylene oxide treatment in the ripening process.

b   677(K)   84.   Which of the following substances added to foods inhibits formation of botulinum toxin?
a.   BHA
b.   Nitrites
c.   Table salt
d.   Sodium ascorbate

a   677(A)   85.   Which of the following activities would result in the **least** exposure to nitrites?
a.   Eating bacon
b.   Drinking beer
c.   Driving a new car
d.   Smoking cigarettes

d   677(A)   86.   Which of the following activities would result in the **highest** exposure to nitrites?
a.   Eating bacon
b.   Drinking beer
c.   Driving a new car
d.   Smoking cigarettes

b   677(K)   87.   Which of the following is **not** among the features of nitrites?
a.   Preserves color
b.   Imparts off-flavors
c.   Present in natural foods
d.   Protects against bacterial growth

a   677(K)   88.   Which of the following is **not** one of the features of sulfites?
a.   Improves flavor
b.   Prevents oxidation
c.   Destroys appreciable amounts of thiamin
d.   Causes adverse reactions in some people with asthma

b 677(K) 89. What vitamin undergoes the most destruction in foods preserved with sulfites?
   a. Folate
   b. Thiamin
   c. Vitamin D
   d. Ascorbic acid

a 677(K) 90. Which of the following is a feature of sulfite food additives?
   a. They are frequently used in wines.
   b. They inhibit growth of most microbes.
   c. They interact with folate to inhibit its absorption.
   d. They are one of the few substances to have virtually no side effects.

a 677(K) 91. What is the only food intended to be consumed raw in which the FDA allows the use of sulfite additives?
   a. Grapes
   b. Lettuce
   c. Carrots
   d. Strawberries

a 677(K) 92. Why are sulfites a prohibited additive for refined grain products in the United States?
   a. They destroy thiamin.
   b. They impart off colors.
   c. They impart off flavors.
   d. They shorten the shelf-life.

b 678(K) 93. Common natural food color additives include all of the following **except**
   a. caramel.
   b. alginates.
   c. grape skins.
   d. dehydrated beets.

a 678(A) 94. Which of the following is the most common use for adding carotenoids to foods?
   a. To color the food
   b. To extend shelflife
   c. To inhibit microbial growth
   d. To inhibit nitrosamine formation

c 678(K) 95. Common food emulsifying agents include all of the following **except**
   a. lecithin.
   b. alginates.
   c. caramel.
   d. monoglycerides.

a 678(K) 96. What is the largest single group of food additives?
   a. Flavoring agents
   b. Artificial sweeteners
   c. Antimicrobial agents
   d. Artificial coloring agents

d   678(K)   97.   Which of the following is a flavor-enhancing food additive?
a.   BHT
b.   Beta-carotene
c.   Sodium propionate
d.   Monosodium glutamate

b   678(K)   98.   All of the following are features of monosodium glutamate in foods **except**
a.   it is a GRAS ingredient.
b.   it is not allowed in infant foods.
c.   it enhances the tastes of sweet, salty, bitter, and sour.
d.   it induces adverse reactions primarily in people with hypertension.

b   678(A)   99.   Which of the following conditions is known to make people more sensitive to experiencing the MSG symptom complex?
a.   Obesity
b.   Asthma
c.   Diabetes
d.   Hypertension

c   678(K)   100.   What additive common to Asian foods is thought to be associated with acute, temporary intolerance reactions?
a.   Nitrites
b.   Carotenoids
c.   Monosodium glutamate
d.   Polybrominated biphenyl

d   679(K)   101.   Which of the following is an example of an indirect food additive?
a.   Nitrites
b.   Vitamin E
c.   Irradiation
d.   Tin from the can

b   679(A)   102.   What classification is given to a substance that leaches from the inside lining of a can to the fruit resulting in an off-flavor?
a.   Direct additive
b.   Indirect additive
c.   Migratory contamination
d.   Peripheral contamination

d   679(K)   103.   Why should consumers use only specialized glass or ceramic containers rather than common packaging materials to heat foods in microwave ovens?
a.   Several types of common packaging materials may catch on fire.
b.   Many common packaging materials contain traces of PCBs which are released into the food.
c.   Many substances in common packaging materials interact with flavor components in food and impart off-flavors.
d.   There are substances in common packaging materials that can migrate into the food and present a health hazard.

c   679(K)   104.   Which of the following toxic substances are formed from production of paper products used in food packaging?
    a.   PBBs
    b.   URPs
    c.   Dioxins
    d.   BHT and BHA

a   679(K)   105.   Which of the following is a food contaminant formed during chlorine treatment of wood used in the manufacture of paper?
    a.   Dioxin
    b.   Alginate
    c.   Acrylamide
    d.   Hydrochloride

c   679(K)   106.   What is the standard chemical used to remove caffeine from coffee beans?
    a.   Nitric acid
    b.   Sodium propionate
    c.   Methylene chloride
    d.   Polybrominated biphenyl

b   679(A)   107.   What carcinogen is known to be produced when high carbohydrate foods are cooked at high temperature?
    a.   Dioxins
    b.   Acrylamides
    c.   Carrageenan
    d.   Nitrosamines

b   679(A)   108.   Which of the following foods represents a common source of acrylamide intake in the United States?
    a.   Raw fruits
    b.   French fries
    c.   Raw vegetables
    d.   Grilled seafood

a   680(A)   109.   Which of the following is a characteristic of antibiotic use in animals raised for human consumption?
    a.   Antibiotics are used in animal feed to enhance growth.
    b.   Antibiotic use in dairy cows often gives the milk off-flavors.
    c.   The antibiotic levels are essentially zero by the time the food reaches consumers.
    d.   Although some antibiotics may be present in the food, the level is too low to induce adverse side effects even in sensitive people.

a   680(K)   110.   Which of the following is a feature of hormones used in food production?
    a.   Bovine growth hormone is used to stimulate growth of calves in the United States.
    b.   The cost of using hormones usually results in higher-priced but better quality products.
    c.   Bovine growth hormone given to cattle does not show residues in the meat or milk.
    d.   They are naturally occurring substances and therefore require only minimal regulation by the FDA and USDA.

c   680(K)   111.   Which of the following is a feature of bovine growth hormone use in the United States?
  a.   It decreases udder infections in cows.
  b.   None can be detected in meat or milk of cows receiving it.
  c.   If consumed from foods, it is denatured by enzymes in the GI tract.
  d.   If consumed from foods, it could potentially stimulate receptors for human growth hormone.

b   681(K)   112.   Which of the following is a feature affecting the public water supply?
  a.   Surface water is derived primarily from underground aquifers.
  b.   Contaminants break down more slowly in groundwater than in surface water.
  c.   Groundwater sources are most susceptible to contamination by runoff of pesticides and wastes from highways.
  d.   Contaminants such as gasoline from leaking underground storage tanks are likely to primarily affect the quality of surface water.

a   681(K)   113.   What is meant by potable water?
  a.   Water fit for drinking
  b.   Water that must be boiled before drinking
  c.   Water that must be chlorinated before drinking
  d.   Water suitable only for use on lawns and gardens

c   681(K)   114.   What substance is commonly added to public water supplies to disinfect the water?
  a.   Ozone
  b.   Flouride
  c.   Chlorine
  d.   Penicillin

a   682(K)   115.   What is the chief purpose of using ozone as a commercial water treatment?
  a.   It acts as a disinfectant.
  b.   It complexes with heavy metals.
  c.   It stabilizes the carbon filtration process.
  d.   It promotes chlorine dissipation and thus enhances taste.

a   682(K)   116.   Which of the following is a characteristic of home water treatments?
  a.   Activated carbon filters do not remove microorganisms.
  b.   Boiling the water is effective at removing all organic chemicals as well as killing microorganisms.
  c.   Most home filtration systems are highly efficient at removing virtually all types of contaminants.
  d.   Most home filtration systems combine the processes of heavy metal removal, killing of microorganisms, softening of the water, and addition of enhancers.

a   682(K)   117.   Which of the following is a feature of bottled waters that are sold to consumers?
  a.   Bottled water is classified as a food and is regulated by the FDA.
  b.   Cost and stability are the two main reasons for choosing to use bottled water.
  c.   Bottled water is classified as an indirect additive to the diet and is regulated by the EPA.
  d.   Government regulations mandate that labels on bottled water reveal sources and heavy metal content.

b   682(K)   118.   What is the most common source of bottled water?
          a.   Glacier run-off
          b.   Springs and wells
          c.   Rivers in the wilderness
          d.   Municipal water supplies

a   682(A)   119.   Water that has the odor of "rotten eggs" is most likely contaminated with
          a.   sulfur.
          b.   dioxins.
          c.   Giardia.
          d.   Cryptosporidium.

c   683(A)   120.   If a person's home water supply becomes contaminated with pathogenic organisms, what product is recommended to make the water safe to drink?
          a.   Rubbing alcohol
          b.   Antibiotic creams
          c.   Plain laundry bleach
          d.   Household ammonia

MATCHING (Answers can be used only once.)

K   657   01.   Term that designates the ability of a substance to harm living organisms if enough is consumed

I   657   02.   Term designating that a substance is possibly toxic under normal use conditions

M   664   03.   Typical foodborne infection that results from eating undercooked or raw shellfish

P   668   04.   The act of concentrating contaminants within the flesh of animals high on the food chain

N   671   05.   Toxic compound common in cabbage, turnips, and radishes

L   671   06.   Poisonous narcotic-like substance present in potato sprouts

R   672   07.   Term that describes the maximum amount of a pesticide residue permitted on a food when the chemical is used according to directions

G   672   08.   Term that judges that the risks for consumption of pesticides on foods are acceptable

F   675   09.   Acronym for a list of food additives long-believed to be safe

Q   676   10.   Zone between the normal concentration used and that in which a hazard exists

J   677   11.   Substance added to cured meats to preserve color

O   677   12.   Carcinogenic substances formed within the stomach

T   676   13.   Class of substances that are purposely added to foods

D   678   14.   Organization that is responsible for certifying food colors

H   677   15.   A food additive known to destroy thiamin

B   678   16.   A preservative commonly used in snack foods to slow the development of off-flavors, odors, and color changes

E   678   17.   Artificial flavoring agent

A   680   18.   Hormone that promotes growth and milk production in cows

S   679   19.   Substance used to remove caffeine from coffee

C   682   20.   Organization that is responsible for ensuring that public water systems meet minimum health standards

A.	BGH	F.	GRAS	K.	Toxicity	P.	Bioaccumulation
B.	BHT	G.	Safe	L.	Solanine	Q.	Margin of Safety
C.	EPA	H.	Sulfite	M.	Hepatitis	R.	Tolerance Level
D.	FDA	I.	Hazard	N.	Goitrogen	S.	Methylene chloride
E.	MSG	J.	Nitrite	O.	Nitrosamines	T.	Intentional additives

ESSAY QUESTIONS

PAGE(S)

657,658   01. Compare and contrast the terms food hazard with substance toxicity.

659   02. Describe 2 well-publicized outbreaks of foodborne infection that happened in the 1990s.

659,660   03. List three major pathogenic microbes that are transmitted by foods; describe their food sources, symptoms of sickness, and methods of prevention.

661-665   04. What precautions should consumers take when selecting and consuming seafood?

661,662   05. What steps can consumers take to ensure food safety in the kitchen?

665,666   06. Explain the precautions that should be taken to minimize the risk of traveler's diarrhea.

666,667   07. What is irradiation? Explain the pros and cons of irradiation as a food-processing method.

667,668   08. What steps can consumers take to minimize nutrient losses during food preparation?

670,671   09. Give several examples of naturally occurring toxicants in foods and appropriate methods to minimize exposure to them.

673   10. Describe the use of alternatives to conventional chemical application for the control of agricultural pests.

675,676   11. What is the meaning and significance of the Delaney Clause? Why does the food industry consider it to be disadvantageous to consumers?

674   12. What are the USDA criteria for organically grown crops?

673,674   13. Discuss the concerns of the public regarding the use of pesticides. Describe methods to minimize intake of pesticide residues on foods.

677   14. What are sulfites? Explain current FDA regulations regarding their use.

677,678   15. List the major antioxidant additives in the food supply and their side effects in human beings.

679,680   16. Give examples of different types of indirect food additives and explain how they become part of the food supply.

679   17. Discuss the formation and significance of acrylamide and dioxins in food.

681   18. Explain the differences between groundwater and surface water as sources of drinking water.

681-683   19. Discuss the origin of common drinking water contaminants such as heavy metals, microbials, and organic toxicants.

683   20 If the safety of a person's water supply is compromised, what steps can the consumer take to disinfect the contaminated water?

CHAPTER 20
HUNGER AND THE GLOBAL ENVIRONMENT

AN. PAGE(S)

a   694(K)   01.   Which of the following is a major reason for hunger in the United States?
       a.   Poverty
       b.   High cost of food
       c.   Excessive food waste
       d.   Lack of nutrition education

c   695(K)   02.   What fraction of the U.S. population receives food assistance?
       a.   1/25
       b.   1/15
       c.   1/6
       d.   1/3

c   696(A)   03.   What is the average monthly benefit for a recipient of the Food Stamp Program?
       a. $10
       b. $35
       c. $80
       d. $200

d   696(K)   04.   Approximately how many people, in millions, are served by the U.S. Food Stamp Program?
       a.   1
       b.   5
       c.   9
       d.   20

d   696(K)   05.   What is the largest federal food assistance program in the United States?
       a.   WIC
       b.   EAT
       c.   Meals on Wheels
       d.   Food Stamp Program

a   696(A)   06.   Food stamps may be used to purchase all of the following **except**
       a.   soap.
       b.   seeds.
       c.   cereal.
       d.   cola beverages.

b   696(K)   07.   What is the acronym for the food assistance program designed to help nutritionally at-risk children, infants, and pregnant women?
       a.   FAP
       b.   WIC
       c.   EAT
       d.   MOW

a   696(K)   08.   What is the name of the largest U.S. national food recovery program?
       a.   Second Harvest
       b.   Goodwill Food Assistance
       c.   Salvation Army Ready-to-Eat Meals
       d.   Food Salvage and Rescue Organization

b   697(A)   09.   A period of extreme food shortage resulting in widespread starvation and death is known as
a.   plague.
b.   famine.
c.   food poverty.
d.   food insecurity.

b   697(K)   10.   The worst famine in the 20th century occurred in
a.   India.
b.   China.
c.   Africa.
d.   Ireland.

c   698(K)   11.   The number of malnourished people in the world is estimated at
a.   100 million.
b.   500 million.
c.   800 million.
d.   1,500 million.

d   699(K)   12.   Approximately what number of children worldwide die each year of malnutrition?
a.   50,000
b.   500,000
c.   1 million
d.   6 million

a   699(A)   13.   Due to technological advances in agriculture, a loaf of bread that cost $1.00 40 years ago would now be priced at about
a.   50¢.
b. $1.00.
c. $1.35.
d. $3.50.

b   699(K)   14.   What is meant by carrying capacity of the earth?
a.   The number of tons of edible food that can be produced by all of the earth's cultivable land
b.   The maximum number of living organisms that can be supported in an environment over time
c.   The amount of oxygen consumed by all living organisms in relation to the amount of oxygen produced by all living plants
d.   The total weight of all living organisms in relation to the weight of all non-living material including the earth's water mass

b   699(K)   15.   Diseases of poverty are known to include all of the following **except**
a.   cholera.
b.   diabetes.
c.   dysentery.
d.   tuberculosis.

a   699(K)   16.   What is administered by health care workers to help treat the diarrhea and dehydration common to children suffering from diseases of poverty?
a.   Oral rehydration therapy
b.   Ozone purified waste water
c.   Protein-energy repletion formula
d.   Charcoal-filtered water and corn starch

d   699-701(K)   17.   Which of the following is **not** one of the three major factors affecting world
population growth?
    a.   Birth rates
    b.   Death rates
    c.   Standard of living
    d.   Scientific knowledge

d   699(K)   18.   What is the approximate yearly increase in the world's population?
    a.   0.5 million
    b.   12 million
    c.   50 million
    d.   70 million

b   702(K)   19.   What is the yearly percentage increase of the world's population?
    a.   0.5
    b.   1
    c.   4
    d.   10

c   700,701(K) 20.   All of the following are major factors affecting population growth **except**
    a.   birth rates.
    b.   death rates.
    c.   ozone depletion.
    d.   standards of living.

b   700,701(K) 21.   What is the chief reason why people living in poverty and hunger bear numerous
children?
    a.   Birth control expenses are prohibitive.
    b.   Only a small percentage of the children may survive to adulthood.
    c.   The low educational level of adults limits their understanding of family
planning.
    d.   The parents seek greater fulfillment through having more children since
there are few other interests in their lives.

b   701(K)   22.   Which of the following describes a known long-term relationship among poverty,
hunger, and population growth?
    a.   As economic status improves, population growth rises.
    b.   As economic status improves, population growth diminishes.
    c.   Lack of natural resources rather than poverty is the most important
contributor to overpopulation.
    d.   Over the last decade the increase in the world's food output is greater than
the increase in the world's population.

c   702(K)   23.   All of the following are examples of fossil fuels **except**
    a.   oil.
    b.   coal.
    c.   solar.
    d.   natural gas.

a   702(K)   24.   Worldwide food production is limited by all of the following **except**
    a.   shrinking of desert areas.
    b.   thinning of the ozone layer.
    c.   higher levels of carbon dioxide in the atmosphere.
    d.   increasing salt concentration of food-producing land.

d   702(K)   25.   Which of the following is a characteristic of farm irrigation?
            a.   It makes the soil more porous.
            b.   It helps preserve the water supply.
            c.   It contributes to soil preservation.
            d.   It increases the salt content in the soil.

d   703(A)   26.   What term applies to the practice of replacing cut trees with an equal number of new ones?
            a.   Forest preservation
            b.   Forest equalization
            c.   Equilibrium harvesting
            d.   Sustainable management

d   710(K)   27.   Which of the following is a feature of U.S. agribusiness practices?
            a.   They promote protection of soil and water.
            b.   They frequently lead to higher crop prices.
             c.   They are designed to benefit mostly small family farms.
            d.   They are used to support application of pesticides and fertilizers.

c   708;710(K) 28.   What is the term given to agricultural practices that are designed to minimize use of energy and chemicals?
            a.   Integrated production
             b.   Progressive agriculture
             c.   Sustainable agriculture
             d.   Resource management production

c   710(K)   29.   The use of computer technologies in agriculture is termed
            a.   green electrons.
            b.   high tech agriculture.
            c.   precision agriculture.
            d.   programmed agriculture.

a   710(A)   30.   Precision agriculture requires the use of
            a.   computers.
            b.   organic fertilizer.
            c.   natural pesticides.
            d.   nonpoint water sources.

b   712(A)   31.   In the practice of agriculture, approximately what percentage more energy is required to produce most animal foods in comparison to grains?
            a.   100
            b.   200
            c.   450
            d.   1000

MATCHING (Answers can be used only once.)

I	682	01.	Number, in millions, of malnourished people worldwide
A	685	02.	Percent yearly increase in the world's population
S	694	03.	Intermittent hunger caused by lack of money
T	696	04.	Name of the largest national food recovery program
R	696	05.	USDA program aimed at preventing or remediating domestic malnutrition and hunger for the poor
L	697	06.	Extreme scarcity of food
F	698	07.	Number of children, in millions, under age 5 with vitamin A deficiency
E	698	08.	Percent of the world's population with iron deficiency anemia
B	700	09.	Number, in billions, of people in the world
K	702	10.	Damages radiation-sensitive crops
J	702	11.	Coal belongs to this type of fuel
P	702	12.	Solar energy belongs to this type of fuel
G	702	13.	Approximate number of cultivated crops in the world today
Q	703	14.	Term that describes the replacement of trees at a rate equal to the harvesting of trees
D	709	15.	Percentage of yearly world energy use that is consumed by the food industry
N	709	16.	This source of water for crops increases the salinity of the soil
O	709	17.	Type of water pollution caused by runoff
H	709	18.	Average number of gallons of water needed daily to provide edible food for each person in the United States
C	709	19.	Number of pounds of grain needed to produce one pound of animal weight gain
M	709	20.	Produced in large quantities by cows

A.	1	K.	Ozone depletion
B.	6	L.	Famine
C.	8	M.	Methane
D.	20	N.	Irrigation
E.	30	O.	Nonpoint
F.	80	P.	Alternative
G.	150	Q.	Sustainable
H.	350	R.	Food Stamp
I.	800	S.	Food insecurity
J.	Fossil	T.	Second Harvest

ESSAY QUESTIONS

PAGE(S)

694,695	01.	List and discuss the causes of hunger in the United States.
694	02.	How is food insecurity identified in U.S. households?
695,696	03.	Describe government programs that aid the hungry in the United States.
696,697;699-701	04.	Discuss how overpopulation is related to the world hunger problem.
701-705	05.	Describe four ways in which major improvements could be made in worldwide environmental problems.
701	06.	Discuss 5 environmental problems that limit food production.

708-712	07.	Give five examples each of energy practices used in low input and high input agriculture.
708-710	08.	Discuss the adverse environmental effects of high input agricultural practices.
708-712	09.	Compare and contrast major aspects of high input and low input agricultural practices.
710,711	10.	Give five examples each of cultivation practices used in sustainable and nonsustainable agriculture.
710,711	11.	What is meant by precision agriculture and how is it used to sustain agricultural output?
712	12.	Compare and contrast the requirements for production of animal foods versus plant foods.

Lesson 1: Nutrition Basics

Answer	Objective	Q#	
c	13/V1	01.	During the 1940s, to help the nation improve their nutrient status, nutrition scientists developed the a. Food Guide Pyramid. b. Diet-Planning Principles. c. Recommended Dietary Allowances. d. concept of "vitamins."
c	13/V2	02.	The nutrient that provides us with fuel for the brain and nervous system is a. protein. b. fat. c. carbohydrate. d. vitamins.
b	13/V2	03.	Proteins are considered the a. main source of quick energy for the body. b. building blocks of life. c. activator of chemical reactions in the body. d. best source of concentrated energy.
c	13/V2	04.	The nutrient that forms the basis of many hormones and provides the most concentrated form of energy is a. carbohydrate. b. minerals. c. fat. d. protein.
a	13/V2	05.	Nearly every chemical reaction in the body occurs in an environment consisting of a. water. b. minerals. c. carbohydrate. d. fat.
b	13/V3	06.	What foods are found at the base of the Food Guide Pyramid? a. Fruits and vegetables b. Grains and cereals c. Dairy products d. Meat products
d	13/V3	07.	The top of the Pyramid consists of a. foods that supply many kcalories but few nutrients. b. high fat and high sugar foods. c. "junk" foods. d. all of the above.

---

d   13/V3   08.   Vegetarians can apply the Food Guide Pyramid by substituting
   a. legumes for protein.
   b. seeds/nuts for protein.
   c. peanut butter for protein.
   d. all of the above.

c   13/V3   09.   A serving of meat is
   a. what you typically get at a restaurant.
   b. what most people typically eat.
   c. 3-4 ounces.
   d. 6-8 ounces.

b   13/V4   10.   All of the following are health concerns of each Pathway subject who will be followed for one year EXCEPT
   a. weight control.
   b. cancer.
   c. diabetes.
   d. high blood cholesterol.

Objective	Q#	
13/V1	11.	What was developed by nutrition scientists in 1940 to help the nation prevent deficiencies?
13/V3	12.	According to the Food Guide Pyramid, what constitutes a serving of milk?
13/V3	13.	According to the Food Guide Pyramid, what constitutes a serving of fruit?
6/V4	14.	What are the three health concerns of the Pathway subjects being profiled for one year?

Answer

11.   Recommended Dietary Allowances (RDA)

12.   Milk = 1 cup

13.   1/2 cup sliced (or one medium whole fruit, such as an apple or banana)

14.   Type II diabetes (diabetes), high blood cholesterol (CVD, heart disease), and weight loss (weight control)

Lesson 2: The Digestive System

Answer	Objective	Q#	
c	7/V1	01.	What is the very first thing you should do if you suspect someone is choking on food? a. Perform the Heimlich maneuver. b. Strike the person sharply on the back. c. Ask the person to try to talk. d. Attempt to dislodge the food with your fingers.
b	7/V1	02.	The life-saving technique that utilizes an upper abdominal thrust to try to dislodge food from the airway of someone who is choking is known as a. CPR. b. Heimlich maneuver. c. Mouth-to-mouth resuscitation. d. All of the above.
c	7/V2	03.	Which of the following foods that delay gastric emptying may cause an increase in belching? a. Carbohydrate b. Protein c. Fat d. Calcium
b	7/V3	04.	The use of an antacid is indicated primarily for which of the following conditions? a. Excessive gas b. Acid indigestion c. Excessive belching d. Bloating
c	7/V3	05.	An effective way of treating heartburn or acid indigestion is to a. drink milk. b. hold your breath. c. take antacids. d. drink water.
c	7/V4	06.	Which of the following is most likely to result from insufficient intake of fiber? a. Diarrhea b. Bloating c. Constipation d. Pancreatitis

a	7/V4	07.	People are said to be constipated when they experience	

a. painful or difficult bowel movements.
b. more than a day or two without a bowel movement.
c. soft or watery bowel movements with little notice.
d. none of the above.

b	7/V5	08.	Peptic ulcers can be caused by	

a. acidic foods.
b. bacteria.
c. spicy foods.
d. smoking.

Objective	Q#	
7/V1	09.	The most obvious sign of choking is that the person cannot
7/V2	10.	The function of belching is to rid the small intestine or stomach of
7/V2	11.	Flatus (gas from the lower abdomen) is produced by fermentation of undigested food products caused by
7/V3	12.	The greatest danger from vomiting is
7/V3	13.	The relaxation of the gastroesophageal sphincter which produces a burning sensation in the esophagus is called

Answer

09.   speak (make a sound, cough).

10.   carbon dioxide (gas).

11.   bacteria (GI tract or colon).

12.   dehydration.

13.   acid indigestion (heartburn).

Lesson 3: Carbohydrates: Simple and Complex

Answer	Objective	Q#	
c	1/V1	01.	Athletes or active individuals who require large amounts of energy should consume a diet high in a. protein. b. fat. c. carbohydrate. d. water.
c	1/V1	02.	Tennis players require immediate bursts of energy which come from a. amino acids. b. fatty acids. c. glycogen. d. glycerol.
b	8/V2	03.	The hormone that is secreted when blood glucose is high is a. glucagon. b. insulin. c. thyroxin. d. epinephrine.
a	9/V3	04.	Which of the following statements is the most accurate regarding studies documenting hyperactivity and sugar intake in children? a. There is very little evidence to support the statement that sugar causes hyperactivity. b. There is considerable evidence that sugar and hyperactivity are positively linked. c. There is substantial scientific proof that sugar causes hyperactivity. d. None of the above.
d	9/V3	05.	Parents should limit a child's intake of sugar because a. it causes hyperactivity. b. it takes the place of healthier foods. c. it may adversely affect the child's growth. d. b and c.

Lesson 3: Carbohydrates: Simple and Complex

Objective	Q#
1/V1	06.	High carbohydrate diets have been shown to increase an athlete's
8/V2	07.	Hypoglycemia refers to a low level of

Answer

06.	endurance. (stamina, energy, aerobic capacity)
07.	blood glucose (blood sugar).

Answer	Objective	Q#	
d	8/V1	01.	When whole wheat is refined, the part(s) of the grain that is(are) removed is(are) the a. bran. b. germ. c. endosperm. d. a and b.
c	8/V1	02.	When we eat refined white bread, the part of the wheat grain that we are eating is the a. bran. b. germ. c. endosperm. d. all of the above.
c	4/V2	03.	Which of the following conditions/diseases does fiber NOT protect against? a. Obesity b. Cancer c. Cataracts d. Hypertension
c	4/V2	04.	When people go on a high-fiber diet, by what percent can they lower blood cholesterol? a. 5-10% b. 15-20% c. 20-30% d. More than 50%
d	4/V2	05.	High-fiber foods are helpful for people who wish to lose weight because they a. take longer to eat. b. are more filling. c. provide few calories. d. all of the above.
d	4/V3	06.	High levels of dietary fiber intake may protect us against a. colon cancer. b. rectal cancer. c. breast cancer. d. all of the above.

d   4/V4   07. People with inflammatory bowel diseases could possibly benefit from higher fiber diets because fiber
   a. can preserve the mucosa of the colon.
   b. can improve peristaltic action of the GI tract.
   c. will cause more frequent and regular bowel movements.
   d. a and b.

a   4/V4   08. In patients with inflammatory bowel disease or Crohn's disease, high-fiber intakes may benefit them by
   a. normalizing the intestinal contents throughout the colon.
   b. causing them to have lower blood pressure which accompanies Crohn's disease.
   c. preventing weight gain that accompanies inflammatory bowel disease.
   d. all of the above.

b   5/V6   09. The newest dietary recommendation regarding fiber for people with type II diabetes is that fiber intake
   a. should be lower than for the general population to prevent constipation.
   b. should be increased by eating more whole fruits, whole grains, and legumes.
   c. is not necessary to address, whereas sugar intake is important to address.
   d. none of the above.

a   5/V6   10. In order to increase fiber intake, people with type II diabetes would be encouraged to eat all of the following foods EXCEPT
   a. orange juice.
   b. whole oranges.
   c. potatoes.
   d. broccoli.

Lesson 4: Carbohydrates: Fiber

Objective	Q#	
8/V1	11.	How much fiber per serving is found in whole wheat kernels and in refined wheat flour, respectively?
4/V2	12.	List three of the "famous five" conditions that fiber is known to protect against.
4/V2	13.	When people go on high-fiber diets and reduce their blood cholesterol by as little as 10%, they can reduce their risk for heart attack by
4/V3	14.	Against what type of cancer might high intakes of dietary fiber offer protection?
5/V5	15.	When people increase their dietary fiber intake, they must also increase their intake of
5/V5	16.	Cite one symptom associated with overdosing on dietary fiber.

Answer

11. 9 grams and 1 gram

12. Answers must include three of the following:
*Heart disease   *Cancer
*Obesity   *Diabetes
*High blood pressure

13. 20%.

14. Answer may include any of the following:

* Colon   * Rectal
* Breast

15. water (fluids).

16. Answer may be any of the following:

* Abdominal bloating   * Gas
* Diarrhea ("runs")   * Constipation

Answer	Objective	Q#	
b	8/V1	01.	The best energy source for strenuous, aerobic type activities, such as hiking, is

    a. phospholipids.
    b. triglycerides.
    c. carbohydrates.
    d. sterols.

| d | 8/V1 | 02. | Foods that are good choices for an activity such as hiking include |

    a. high fat foods.
    b. peanut butter.
    c. salami.
    d. all of the above.

| d | 8/V1 | 03. | Foods such as peanuts, GORP, cheese, and salami are good choices for hiking because they |

    a. provide concentrated energy.
    b. are easily packed.
    c. are high-fat foods.
    d. all of the above.

| d | 8/V2 | 04. | Lipoproteins |

    a. transport lipids through a watery medium, the blood.
    b. are protein-based vehicles for the transport of lipids.
    c. are composed of lipids and proteins.
    d. all of the above.

| a | 8/V2 | 05. | Lipids need a transport carrier |

    a. to move them through the bloodstream.
    b. in case they are not absorbed in the stomach.
    c. because lipids are water soluble.
    d. none of the above.

| d | 10/V3 | 06. | Blood cholesterol is impacted by |

    a. lifestyle.
    b. nutrition.
    c. heredity.
    d. all of the above.

| b | 10/V3 | 07. | Cholesterol is necessary for the production of many other compounds in the body but can become harmful when blood levels |

    a. exceed 135 mg/dl.
    b. exceed the body's ability to use it.
    c. can only be controlled through medications.
    d. a and b.

d   10/V3   08.   What changes in lifestyle could bring about reductions in blood cholesterol?
- a. Regular aerobic-type exercise
- b. Restricting total fat
- c. Restricting saturated fat
- d. All of the above

a   11/V4   09.   Fat substitutes were developed to
- a. help control kcalories in foods.
- b. help people reduce body fat.
- c. make foods taste better.
- d. all of the above.

b   12/V4   10.   A fat substitute that has recently been approved by the FDA is
- a. Simplesse.
- b. Olestra.
- c. Fatestra.
- d. Simpola.

a   11/V4   11.   Simplesse is a fat substitute made of
- a. protein particles.
- b. whipped egg whites.
- c. blended sugars.
- d. sugar with a fatty acid.

d   11/V5   12.   Blood triglyceride levels can be reduced by reducing which of the following foods?
- a. Alcohol
- b. Sweets
- c. Complex carbohydrates
- d. a and b

a   11/V5   13.   The recommendation for blood cholesterol is
- a. less than 200 mg/dl.
- b. 210-150 mg/dl.
- c. under 100 mg/dl.
- d. 250-285 mg/dl.

d   11/V5   14.   Someone with high blood cholesterol would be advised to frequently monitor and reduce
- a. dietary cholesterol intake.
- b. total fat intake.
- c. saturated fat intake.
- d. all of the above.

Answer	Objective	Q#	
c	3/V1	01.	The American Heart Association recommends the percentage of total calories that come from fat should not exceed a. 10%. b. 20%. c. 30%. d. 40%.
b	3/V1	02.	From an optimum health perspective, the best type of fat is a. polyunsaturated fat. b. monounsaturated fat. c. saturated fat. d. none of the above.
b	3/V1	03.	What is the recommended intake for saturated fat? a. 10% or more b. No more than 10% c. 12% - 14% d. Less than 30%
d	8/V2	04.	A person can reduce fat in a diet that has beef as its base by a. selecting leaner cuts of meat. b. choosing chicken or fish occasionally. c. becoming a vegan-vegetarian. d. a and b.
a	8/V2	05.	Meat-eaters can reduce fat in their diets by a. baking, broiling, or braising meats. b. frying or sauteing meats in olive oil. c. using regular hamburger for meat loaf. d. selecting regular hamburger instead of sirloin steaks.
d	8/V2	06.	Some people who eat high-meat diets may have a greater risk for a. cardiovascular disease. b. colon cancer. c. obesity. d. all of the above.
d	8/V2	07.	If a person is performing physical labor at a very high level of intensity and/or for very long periods of time, the person could a. increase total kcalories. b. consume more fat than the average person. c. expend more calories than the average person. d. all of the above.

d   8/V3   08.   The foundation of a Mediterranean diet consists of
   a.   olive oil as the primary fat.
   b.   fruits and vegetables as the base.
   c.   lots of grains and breads.
   d.   all of the above.

b   8/V3   09.   Most people who consume a Mediterranean diet typically
   a.   suffer from obesity.
   b.   do not suffer from cardiovascular disease.
   c.   show signs of type II diabetes.
   d.   do not develop lung cancer.

c   8/V3   10.   Problems such as cardiovascular disease, diabetes, obesity, and some cancers seem to occur less often in populations who consume a typical
   a.   American diet.
   b.   American Indian diet.
   c.   Mediterranean diet.
   d.   none of the above.

a   8/V3   11.   Olive oil and seafood have been shown to
   a.   decrease risk for cardiovascular disease.
   b.   increase risk for obesity.
   c.   increase risk for type II diabetes.
   d.   decrease risk for skin cancer.

a   9/V4   12.   If you wanted to reduce the fat and kcalories in a 10 oz. portion of prime rib, you could
   a.   eat 5 oz. and save the rest for the next day.
   b.   cut away all visible fat but still eat the 10 oz.
   c.   refuse to eat any of the meat.
   d.   either a or b.

d   9/V4   13.   If you wanted to reduce the fat and kcalories in mashed potatoes prepared with milk and butter, you could
   a.   use instant mashed potatoes.
   b.   mash the potatoes with water and use butter flavoring instead.
   c.   use skim milk and low-fat margarine instead.
   d.   b and c.

a   9/V4   14.   Over a period of time, if one were to consistently reduce fat in the diet, one could
   a.   lose body fat.
   b.   gain lean muscle.
   c.   increase aerobic capacity.
   d.   none of the above.

d   4/V5   15. People who have type II diabetes can reduce fat intake by
   a. eating more fruits and vegetables.
   b. drinking skim milk.
   c. eating smaller portions of meat.
   d. all of the above.

a   4/V5   16. Reducing fat intake for a person with type II diabetes can be accomplished by
   a. increasing fruits and vegetables.
   b. increasing meat portions.
   c. decreasing breads and grains.
   d. a and c.

Lesson 7 : Protein: Form and Function

Answer	Objective	Q#	

d 6/V1 01. Which of the following statements is accurate regarding protein?
    a. "Protein builds muscle bulk and strength."
    b. "Protein supplements provide an important energy boost."
    c. "People in North America don't suffer from protein deficiencies."
    d. None of the above.

d 6/V1 02. Protein is needed for normal development of cells and muscle mass but excessive amounts of protein
    a. are even better and will bring faster results.
    b. will not significantly increase the building of body tissue.
    c. won't add significant strength to the body.
    d. b and c.

b 6/V1 03. In order to gain muscle size and strength, it is necessary to
    a. increase protein intake well above the RDA.
    b. train intensely with adequate rest periods in between.
    c. train every day at the highest intensity possible.
    d. all of the above.

d 9/V2 04. High intakes of animal protein sources are associated with serious health risks such as
    a. increased cardiovascular disease.
    b. colon cancer.
    c. breast cancer.
    d. all of the above.

c 9/V2 05. Cardiovascular disease, colon cancer, and breast cancer risks have been shown to increase with diets high in
    a. all protein.
    b. plant protein.
    c. animal protein.
    d. all of the above.

d 8/V3 06. Kwashiorkor, a condition frequently found in the Republic of Guinea, is characterized by
    a. a diet lacking in a direct source of protein such as meat.
    b. a starch-based diet.
    c. a diet consisting of water and oil with lots of rice.
    d. all of the above.

d 8/V3 07. Marasmus can be characterized as a condition in which
    a. overeating results in bloating and edema.
    b. the person is starving from total malnutrition.
    c. the immune system is impaired, allowing for microbe attack.
    d. b and c.

d   8/V3   08.   In the U.S., protein-energy malnutrition can be seen most often in which of the following populations?
  a. Cancer patients
  b. AIDS patients
  c. Inner city children
  d. All of the above

c   8/V4   09.   What percent of protein is provided by the School Lunch Program funded by the federal government?
  a. 10%
  b. 30%
  c. 50%
  d. 100%

d   8/V4   10.   The primary component(s) of the School Lunch Program that help prevent protein-energy malnutrition in U.S. school children is(are)
  a. meat or meat alternates.
  b. milk.
  c. pasta and breads.
  d. a and b.

d   9/V5   11.   For someone who has high blood cholesterol, protein foods should
  a. come from plant sources rather than animal sources.
  b. represent the bulk of the diet.
  c. not be a concern if they are eating from the Food Guide Pyramid.
  d. a and c.

b   9/V5   12.   The best examples of protein sources for people with high blood cholesterol are
  a. meat and fish.
  b. beans and rice.
  c. milk and dairy products.
  d. any of the above.

Lesson 8: The Protein Continuum

Answer	Objective	Q#	
a	5/V1	01.	Protein intakes may increase as a result of illness as well as

    a. when women are lactating.
    b. during moderate anaerobic activity.
    c. during times of optimal health.
    d. any of the above.

| d | 5/V1 | 02. | What is the typical protein intake for adults living in the U.S.? |

    a. 100% of the RDA for protein
    b. Between 80-120 grams/day
    c. Two to three times the RDA for protein
    d. b and c

| d | 7/V2 | 03. | People who consume a diet in which meat is the primary source of protein are |

    a. at less risk for cancer than vegetarians.
    b. thought to be at greater risk for cancer than vegetarians.
    c. more likely to develop heart disease than vegetarians.
    d. b and c.

| c | 7/V2 | 04. | What vitamin does meat provide that is NOT in plant-based diets? |

    a. vitamin A.
    b. vitamin D.
    c. vitamin B_{12}.
    d. riboflavin.

| d | 7/V2 | 05. | Reasons why people choose to become vegetarians include |

    a. ethical issues surrounding animal rights.
    b. personal health reasons.
    c. weight loss.
    d. any of the above.

| c | 7/V2 | 06. | People who are semi-vegetarians eat |

    a. meat or animal products every other day.
    b. animal foods most of the time except on religious holidays.
    c. meat, milk, or eggs only periodically.
    d. any of the above.

| d | 6/V3 | 07. | How can people reduce the amount of animal protein they eat daily? |

    a. Eat meat less often and in smaller portions.
    b. Choose meat alternates as protein sources.
    c. Select plant-based protein sources occasionally.
    d. Any of the above.

a   6/V3   08. For people who wish to lose weight, most experts might advise them to

  a. consider eating more vegetarian protein sources.

  b. stay at the top of the Food Guide Pyramid for food choices.

  c. focus on the middle of the Food Guide Pyramid for choices.

  d. eat only plant-based proteins, completely eliminating meat.

Answer	Objective	Q#	
d	1/V1	01.	A power plant and the body's metabolism are similar in that both a. generate energy. b. store unused energy. c. release energy when needed. d. all of the above.
c	13/V3	02.	If you take in a large number of calories but exercise vigorously and regularly, you will probably a. gain weight. b. lose weight. c. maintain weight. d. none of the above.
d	13/V3	03.	Every time you put on an extra pound of body fat, you can a. increase blood pressure. b. decrease blood pressure. c. become more susceptible to some cancers. d. a and c.
d	11/V4	04.	During a prolonged fast, the brain a. adapts to using 20-30 mg of glucose per minute. b. relies mostly on ketone bodies. c. is less reliant on glucose to function. d. all of the above.
d	14/V5	05.	Chronic alcohol use affects metabolism and the energy pathway by a. disrupting liver function. b. damaging the liver. c. leading to malnutrition. d. all of the above.

Lesson 9: Metabolism

Objective	Q#	
10/V2	06.	The nutrient that is the most calorie dense on a weight-to-weight basis is
13/V3	07.	For a person with diabetes, the metabolic rate can be increased through
11/V4	08.	Long-term fasting can cause the heart muscle to
	09.	How does alcohol intake impact the body's use of B vitamins?

Q#	Answer
06.	fat (fatty acids, triglycerides).
07.	exercise (physical activity).
08.	diminish in size (atrophy, get smaller, shrink).
09.	Prevents absorption (depletes vitamins)

Lesson 10: Weight Control: Energy Regulation

Answer	Objective	Q#	

d   3/V1   01.   Factors that affect food intake include
- a.   genetics.
- b.   hunger and appetite.
- c.   age.
- d.   all of the above.

a   3/V1   02.   When people eat dessert even if they are stuffed from a meal, they are responding to a cue to eat known as
- a.   sensory specific satiety.
- b.   gluttony syndrome.
- c.   over-indulgence syndrome.
- d.   appestatic satiety.

b   3/V1   03.   Internal cues regarding eating should tell people to
- a.   eat when they are full, stop when they are satisfied.
- b.   eat when they are hungry, stop when they are satisfied.
- c.   continue eating beyond satiety, ignoring feelings.
- d.   all of the above.

c   11/V2   04.   What population has been the primary target of body image idealization especially in the U.S. culture?
- a.   Males
- b.   Adolescents
- c.   Females
- d.   Children

a   11/V2   05.   Glamorizing thinness through the media has been historically aimed at what population?
- a.   Upper middle class white females
- b.   Lower socioeconomic groups
- c.   Higher socioeconomic white males
- d.   Middle class non-Caucasian adolescents

a   11/V2   06.   Even though men are not exempt from the pressure brought on by the media to be thin, it appears that men as opposed to women
- a.   derive a sense of self-esteem not based on size or shape.
- b.   realize the difference between media hype and truth.
- c.   are able to identify better ways to lose weight.
- d.   all of the above.

c   7/V3   07.   Body weight that is associated with the lowest mortality or minimum death is referred to by experts as
- a.   ideal weight.
- b.   mortal weight.
- c.   desirable weight.
- d.   average weight.

d   7/V3   08.   Desirable weight might be defined as that weight which
- a.   is not associated with hypertension, diabetes, or heart disease.
- b.   is associated with the lowest mortality (death) rate.
- c.   can be maintained for more than 5 years.
- d.   a and b.

c   7/V3   09.   Which of the following statements might be good advice from someone who has gone through many weight changes over a lifetime?
- a.   "Keep trying to change your body image - it can only get better."
- b.   "Look to fashion models as your role model - they are where it's at."
- c.   "Make peace with your body - every body type is beautiful."
- d.   "Don't worry about your health as long as you look good in clothes."

c   10/V4   10.   In studies performed on women who were able to maintain their lost weight, findings showed that
- a.   they attended regular support groups.
- b.   they kept regular track of food intake.
- c.   all of them exercised regularly.
- d.   all of the above.

d   10/V4   11.   The biggest factor associated with weight loss in people who managed to lose weight and keep it off was
- a.   keeping food diaries.
- b.   going to support groups.
- c.   visiting with a dietitian.
- d.   exercising on a regular basis.

a   5/V5   12.   A factor in weight gain or inability to lose weight might be
- a.   a slower metabolic rate than normal for height and weight.
- b.   an increased thermogenic rate compared with normal for height.
- c.   the inability to increase dynamic effect of food.
- d.   any of the above.

a   5/V5   13.   If people are trying to lose weight and are 20% below their predicted metabolic rate, they will
- a.   have a harder time burning kcalories and not lose much weight.
- b.   be tired most of the time and gain weight quickly.
- c.   expect to lose weight quickly on 1500 kcal/day.
- d.   a and b.

Lesson 11: Weight Control: Health Effects

Answer	Objective	Q#	
c	8/V1	01.	Compared to average weight for women in the U.S., fashion models are a. 10% below the average. b. 18% below the average. c. 23% below the average. d. 35% below the average.
b	8/V1	02.	When comparing fashion models to the average woman in the U.S., models have body weights that are a. considered the ideal by the medical profession. b. unrealistic and unattainable for most women. c. attainable for most women if they work hard to lose weight. d. usually too high for the average height of models.
d	4/V2	03.	Which of the following factors do experts consider a criterion for successful weight loss? a. If blood pressure went down b. If diabetes improved c. If some, but not necessarily all, weight was lost d. Any of the above
c	4/V2	04.	If people need to lose 50 pounds of weight and only achieve a 25 pound weight loss, the criteria established by the medical profession would consider those people to be a. underachievers. b. failures. c. successful. d. hopeless.
b	9/V3	05.	Total body fat or scale weight does not provide as clear an index of risk for disease as can be provided by a. body mass index. b. waist-to-hip ratio. c. lower body fat index. d. none of the above.
a	9/V3	06.	People with high waist-to-hip ratios have a higher risk for heart disease and are characterized by shape as a. "apples." b. "slugs." c. "pears." d. "sloths."

d   3/V4   07.   As a way to lose weight, "yo-yo" diets may produce quick weight loss
   a.   with a subsequent higher regain of weight.
   b.   but no permanent weight lost.
   c.   and may result in a slower metabolic rate.
   d.   all of the above.

c   3/V4   08.   A cycle of quick weight loss and weight regain which may cause the body's metabolism to slow down is known as
   a.   "cyclic regaining."
   b.   "dieting madness."
   c.   "yo-yo dieting."
   d.   "on-off cycling."

c   2/V5   09.   For people who are considered morbidly obese by medical standards, an extreme procedure in which the stomach size is restricted surgically is known as
   a.   esophageal stapling.
   b.   gastric liposuction.
   c.   gastric bypass.
   d.   divisional resection.

a   2/V5   10.   An extreme surgical procedure, such as a gastric bypass, produces dramatic weight loss in morbidly obese people by
   a.   restricting the size of the stomach so it holds less food.
   b.   stimulating the hypothalamus to not respond to excess food.
   c.   shortening the GI tract so that food is not absorbed.
   d.   reducing the length of the colon so food passes quickly.

b   7/V6   11.   Of the most common eating disorders, the one which is most medically dangerous is
   a.   bulimia nervosa.
   b.   anorexia nervosa.
   c.   obesity nervosa.
   d.   purging nervosa.

b   7/V6   12.   One of the criteria for diagnosing anorexia is
   a.   refusal to eat complex carbohydrates.
   b.   being 85% or less of normal body weight for age.
   c.   people see themselves as physically fit.
   d.   all of the above.

d   7/V6   13.   A distinguishing characteristic of people with bulimia is they
   a.   eat high-protein foods without realizing it.
   b.   are preoccupied with body weight and shape.
   c.   believe that weight and shape are central to self-concept.
   d.   b and c.

c   7/V6   14.   All of the following are acceptable treatments for bulimia EXCEPT
     a.   helping the person normalize eating patterns.
     b.   focusing on the person's social world.
     c.   treating all people with bulimia in a hospital setting.
     d.   changing the attitudes regarding weight and shape.

d   4/V7   15.   For a number of decades, experts have been saying that the best weight loss program involves
     a.   regular exercise.
     b.   eating healthful diets.
     c.   keeping tract of kcalories in vs. kcalories out.
     d.   all of the above.

c   4/V7   16.   The best advice regarding weight gain and pregnancy is
     a.   lose weight as fast as possible after pregnancy.
     b.   don't gain any weight during pregnancy.
     c.   lose weight slowly to keep it off permanently.
     d.   eat a lot, exercise a lot, then lose a lot.

b   4/V7   17.   If a woman gains as much as 45 pounds during pregnancy, the best advice regarding weight loss after pregnancy is
     a.   lose weight quickly for permanent weight loss.
     b.   lose weight slowly for permanent weight loss.
     c.   exercise more often than before pregnancy.
     d.   b and c.

Lesson 12: Vitamins: Water-Soluble

Answer	Objective	Q#
b	2/V1	01.
d	5/V2	02.
d	7/V3	03.
b	7/V3	04.
d	7/V3	05.
d	7/V3	06.

01. In which of the following ways do B vitamins interact with energy-yielding foods?
   a. They provide an essential source of additional energy.
   b. They are not a source of energy, but they are needed to convert the foods we eat into energy.
   c. B vitamins only interact with fatty acids to produce energy.
   d. B vitamins only interact with carbohydrates to produce energy.

02. Researchers state that the immune system is positively affected by
   a. fat-soluble vitamins.
   b. niacin.
   c. thiamin.
   d. vitamin C.

03. One way to manage fruits and vegetables on long voyages at sea is to
   a. store them in a freezer.
   b. replenish them in port.
   c. use canned products.
   d. all of the above.

04. As far as cooking vegetables is concerned, the key in preventing vitamin losses is to
   a. cook until soft to the touch.
   b. not overcook—keep slightly crisp.
   c. use a lot of water when cooking.
   d. drink the water in which the vegetables were cooked.

05. Much of the vitamin content in vegetables will be destroyed if they are cooked
   a. at high temperatures.
   b. for extended periods.
   c. submerged in water.
   d. all of the above.

06. Preferred ways to cook vegetables include
   a. steamed with a little water.
   b. boiled.
   c. microwaved.
   d. a and c.

Lesson 12: Vitamins: Water-Soluble

Objective	Q#	
2/V1	07.	What group of nutrients help to extract the energy from food during metabolism?
5/V2	08.	When studying allergies and aging, what water-soluble vitamin has been shown to have a positive effect?

Q#	Answer
07.	B vitamins (coenzymes)
08.	Vitamin C

Answer	Objective	Q#	
a	2/V1	01.	If taken in excess, vitamin A can produce adverse effects, such as

    a.   intracranial pressure in the brain resulting in headaches.
    b.   blurred vision resulting in headaches.
    c.   bone mineralization resulting in rickets.
    d.   all of the above.

| a | 2/V1 | 02. | Intracranial pressure resulting in headaches is a side effect of taking excessive amounts of vitamin |

    a.   A.
    b.   D.
    c.   E.
    d.   K.

| c | 3/V2 | 03. | Examples of the adverse effects of oxidation reactions include |

    a.   headaches brought on by vitamin A toxicity.
    b.   bubbles forming when soap mixes with greasy dishes.
    c.   butter or oil turning rancid or having off-flavors.
    d.   all of the above.

| a | 3/V2 | 04. | Rust forming on a metal surface or butter turning rancid are examples of |

    a.   an oxidation reaction which produces undesirable results.
    b.   a mineral interacting with a hard surface.
    c.   iron particles interacting with water molecules.
    d.   b and c.

| b | 3/V3 | 05. | Which vitamin can protect lipids, especially vitamin A and polyunsaturated fatty acids, against the effects of free radical attack? |

    a.   Vitamin C
    b.   Vitamin E
    c.   Vitamin D
    d.   Vitamin K

| a | 3/V3 | 06. | Several conditions and/or chronic diseases might be prevented in the future through the use of |

    a.   antioxidant supplementation with vitamins C and E.
    b.   medications that have yet to be discovered.
    c.   new exercise equipment that is currently being developed.
    d.   all of the above.

| b | 3/V3 | 07. | Young patients who have heart disease might be advised to take |

    a.   vitamin A supplements.
    b.   vitamin E supplements.
    c.   vitamin D supplements.
    d.   multiple vitamins.

a 4/V4 08. People who participate in vigorous aerobic-type exercise could possibly benefit from vitamin C and E supplementation to prevent against
   a. tissue damage due to free radical production.
   b. muscle aches and pains associated with vigorous exercise.
   c. heart problems associated with aerobic-type exercises.
   d. the onset of heart disease which occurs when people train for marathons.

b 4/V4 09. Vitamin E supplements are often taken by runners to help prevent damage to lungs caused by
   a. heavy exercise during cold weather.
   b. exercising when air pollution is high.
   c. exercising indoors.
   d. any of the above.

d 4/V4 10. According to research, the body system, especially in the elderly, that shows improvement when given antioxidant supplements is the
   a. nervous system.
   b. respiratory system.
   c. digestive system.
   d. immune system.

Objective Q#

2/V1 11. Excessive intakes of vitamin A have been shown to produce intracranial pressure resulting in

3/V2 12. When rust forms on an iron railing or cooking oil smells rancid, the undesirable effect is caused by a process known as

3/V3 13. When oxygen breaks down fatty acids used by the cells to produce energy for the body, potentially damaging intermediates may be produced from a process known as

4/V4 14. What body system appears to improve when elderly people take vitamin E and other antioxidants?

Q# Answer   Q# Answer

11. headaches.   14. The immune system (immunity, immune response)

12. oxidation (free radical production).

13. lipid peroxidation.

Lesson 14: Major Minerals and Water

Answer	Objective	Q#	
c	8/V1	01.	What percent of water loss from the body could result in a life-threatening situation? a. 1% b. 5% c. 10% d. 3%
d	8/V1	02.	The very first reliable sign of dehydration is a. thirst. b. chills. c. cramps. d. fatigue.
d	8/V1	03.	Some of the physical symptoms reflecting dehydration in a child might include a. deep, dark circles under the eyes. b. increased heart rate for age. c. dry, tacky mucous membranes in the mouth. d. all of the above.
d	8/V1	04.	Advice to parents of a child who is dehydrated would include a. offering the child a teaspoon of clear liquids every 5-10 minutes. b. ignoring the situation until the child asks for something to drink. c. encouraging the child to drink liquids frequently, especially if they have been vomiting. d. a and c.
c	7/V2	05.	Regarding sodium intake, an average adult only needs a. 5 grams/day or 1 teaspoon. b. 5000 milligrams/day or 1 teaspoon. c. 500 milligrams/day or 1/10 of a teaspoon. d. a and b.
c	9/V3	06.	The population most affected by bone loss resulting in osteoporosis is a. males over the age of 65. b. female athletes who compete in marathons. c. women over the age of 50. d. all of the above in equal proportions.
a	9/V3	07.	The most common cause(s) of osteoporosis is(are) a. lack of estrogen in postmenopausal women. b. increased bone formation in the elderly. c. lack of weight-bearing exercise during the growing years. d. all of the above.

a   9/V3   08.   What type of exercise can improve the outcome of osteoporosis?
   a. Weight-bearing exercises, such as walking
   b. Swimming laps or water aerobics
   c. Meditation exercises
   d. All of the above

d   9/V3   09.   Dietary interventions to improve osteoporosis include
   a. increased calcium intakes.
   b. avoidance of meat and poultry.
   c. decreased salt intakes.
   d. all of the above.

c   9/V3   10.   The only oral medication known to stimulate bone formation and growth in patients with osteoporosis is
   a. hypoglycemic medication.
   b. oral insulin.
   c. calcium citrate with slow release fluoride.
   d. calcium gluconate with phosphorus.

d   9/V3   11.   Osteoporosis can be prevented by practicing the following advice:
   a. stop smoking.
   b. begin early administration of estrogen.
   c. take optimal amounts of calcium.
   d. all of the above.

c   9/V3   12.   Very often the first symptom that a person has osteoporosis is
   a. a feeling of tenderness in the hips.
   b. lower back problems.
   c. a broken hip or wrist.
   d. numbness of the toes.

a   6/V4   13.   An effect of increased water intake on the body of a person who is accustomed to greater quantities of salt is
   a. reduced edema or swelling of ankles.
   b. more bloating.
   c. more energy.
   d. all of the above.

Objective	Q#	
8/V1	14.	If athletes exercise for an hour, they could lose water equal to how many pounds of body weight?
8/V1	15.	Fatigue is the first reliable sign that a person is
8/V1	16.	Deep, dark circles under the eyes; lethargy; increased heart rate for age; and a dry mouth are all signs of

9/V3	17.	A slow and steady loss of bone calcium resulting in fracturing or splintering of bones is a characteristic of
9/V3	18.	Of the 25 million people with osteoporosis, what segment of the population is most affected and at what age?
9/V3	19.	The best exercise for someone with osteoporosis is
6/V4	20.	People could reduce the edema that accompanies high salt intakes by increasing their intake of
9/V3	21.	Discuss osteoporosis including a definition; how it develops; how age, sex, hormones, and genetics affect it; how activity affects it; and what dietary interventions can help prevent or treat osteoporosis.

Q#	Answer	Q#	Answer
14.	2-4 pounds	18.	Women over 50
15.	dehydrated.	19.	weight bearing (walking, weight training).
16.	dehydration.	20.	water.
17.	osteoporosis.		

Q#	Answer Explanation:
21.	Answers could include the following information:

Definition: osteoporosis is a condition whereby bone density is lost, thus creating fractures.

* Development and dietary influences:
* Strongest predictor of bone density is age, followed by sex.
* Skeletal growth and density occurs during the first two and a half decades of life.
* Calcium absorption declines after about age 65.
* Vitamin D is less active after age 65, therefore less calcium absorption.
* Women suffer from osteoporosis more than men before age 75, then it equals in frequency.
* Estrogen as well as testosterone play a part in the development of osteoporosis, but estrogen seems to be more protective in women up to menopause.
* Asian and Caucasian women have more osteoporosis than other ethnic groups.
* Weight bearing activities are protective against osteoporosis.
* High protein intakes seem to promote calcium excretion, thereby decreasing bone density.
* Dietary calcium and/or calcium supplements are necessary to maintain bone density as well as possibly fluoride supplements.

Answer	Objective	Q#	
d	4/V1	01.	The population(s) at greatest risk for iron deficiency is(are)

01. The population(s) at greatest risk for iron deficiency is(are)
    a. low-income, pregnant women.
    b. low-income children.
    c. adult males.
    d. a and b.

d   4/V1   02.

02. Foods provided by the Women, Infants, and Children program that are high in iron include
    a. dried beans.
    b. peanuts.
    c. iron-fortified cereals.
    d. all of the above.

c   2/V2   03.

03. Nonheme iron absorption can be hindered by a naturally occurring substance called
    a. nonheme factor.
    b. the meat factor.
    c. phytate.
    d. MFP.

a   2/V2   04.

04. Phytates are naturally occurring substances in plant foods that interfere with iron absorption by
    a. binding to iron, thus making it unavailable for absorption.
    b. competing with binding sites in cells, thus preventing iron absorption.
    c. changing iron into its ferric state, thus making it unavailable for absorption.
    d. none of the above.

d   2/V2   05.

05. Iron supplementation is especially important for infants and children in low income families because
    a. their primary food is very often milk which is a poor source of iron.
    b. without adequate iron intake children will not grow and learn appropriately.
    c. supplementation will prevent iron deficiency anemia.
    d. all of the above.

d   1/V3   06.

06. Male and female adolescents have an increased need for iron because
    a. they have greater overall nutrient needs.
    b. of the onset of menstruation in females.
    c. of the increase in lean body mass in males.
    d. all of the above.

d	4/V3	07.	The factors that could cause adolescence iron deficiency include all of the following EXCEPT

a. the onset of menstruation in females.
b. the development of more muscle mass in males.
c. peer influences on food choices.
d. foods available in the school cafeteria.

b	4/V3	08.	Because adolescents are often influenced by their peers regarding food choices or are not especially concerned about nutrition, they are most vulnerable to

a. protein-energy malnutrition.
b. iron deficiency.
c. frequent infections.
d. all of the above.

d	4/V4	09.	Iron deficiency is not as likely in the elderly but can still occur due to

a. lower food intakes.
b. poor nutrition habits.
c. disease and/or side effects of medication.
d. any of the above.

b	4/V4	10.	Programs such as Meals on Wheels provide iron-rich foods in a single meal that equal

a. $^2/_3$ of the RDA for iron for adults.
b. $^1/_3$ of the RDA for iron for adults.
c. ¾ of the RDA for iron for adults.
d. 100% of the RDA for iron for adults.

c	4/V4	11.	The primary function of Meals on Wheels is to provide

a. one hot and one cold meal every day to eligible people.
b. a means of delivering iron supplements to homebound people.
c. one well-balanced meal per day with $^1/_3$ of the RDA for iron for homebound adults.
d. any of the above.

d	4/V4	12.	If a client is suspected of having an iron deficiency, Meals on Wheels dietitians would suggest

a. a multivitamin supplement to enhance overall nutrition.
b. iron supplements to increase stored iron.
c. vitamin C to enhance iron absorption.
d. a and c.

d   5/V5

13. The Finnish studies in 1992 by Solomon reinforced findings that stated that high iron intakes in the form of heme iron
    a. put men at greater risk for cancer of the colon.
    b. put premenopausal women at greater risk for breast cancer.
    c. put both men and premenopausal women at greater risk for heart disease.
    d. put men at greater risk for heart disease.

d   5/V5

14. By replacing meat sources of iron in the diet with plant sources of iron, someone with a high risk for heart disease would also
    a. be reducing the nonheme form of iron which is most easily absorbed, therefore decreasing risk for heart disease.
    b. be reducing the heme form of iron which is most easily absorbed, therefore decreasing risk for heart disease.
    c. be reducing saturated fat in the diet, therefore decreasing risk for heart disease.
    d. b and c.

Objective	Q#	
1/V1	15.	Because infants grow rapidly, the most important mineral for growth and development is
2/V2	16.	What is the name of the substance found in plant foods that can bind with iron or zinc and render them unavailable for absorption?
4/V4	17.	Cite one cause of iron deficiency in the elderly.
10/V4	18.	The primary cause of iron deficiency in the elderly is
5/V5	19.	Replacing meat sources of iron with plant sources could reduce the risk for heart disease while automatically reducing iron intake in the form of

Q#	Answer
15.	iron.
16.	Phytate (phytic acid)
17.	Answer may include any of the following: * denture problems * low food intake * not cooking for self * housebound * not able to shop * GI problems * disease * medications
18.	low food intake.
19.	heme iron.

Answer	Objective	Q#	
b	1/V1	01.	Research clearly shows that the risk of dying not only from heart disease but from all causes is greatest for

    a. elite athletes such as marathoners.
    b. sedentary people, a.k.a. "couch potatoes."
    c. occasional exercisers, a.k.a. "week-end warriors."
    d. moderately active people who exercise 3-4 days/week.

| a | 1/V1 | 02. | Research has shown that being sedentary |

    a. increases the risk of dying from all causes.
    b. is better than being sporadically active.
    c. is not harmful as long as the person makes wise nutrition choices.
    d. can actually help a person who has suffered from a heart attack.

| d | 1/V2 | 03. | Overexercising has its drawback for those who try to do too much because it |

    a. may increase the risk for type II diabetes in some people.
    b. can cause muscle injuries that only rest and time will heal.
    c. can frustrate people if they do not see real improvements in performance.
    d. may compromise the immune system and may ultimately lead to diseases such as cancer.

| c | 1/V2 | 04. | Individuals who run 60 or 70 miles/week, such as marathon runners, may actually |

    a. feel it is not enough to achieve their goals.
    b. be overexercising to the benefit of their health.
    c. suppress their immune function and cause disease.
    d. all of the above.

| d | 5/V3 | 05. | In addition to being able to exercise at work, an employee who has access to a Wellness program and fitness facility at the job site |

    a. is more likely to make positive changes in lifestyle.
    b. has less absenteeism from work.
    c. becomes more educated in health issues.
    d. all of the above.

| b | 8/V3 | 06. | Among the physiological benefits of regular exercise, which of the following can occur? |

    a. Regular exercise will inhibit the blood chemistry responsible for the "good" cholesterol.
    b. Regular exercise can be a way to improve mood and relieve depression.
    c. Regular exercise has been shown to increase the need for "energizers."
    d. Regular exercise decreases blood flow to the brain, therefore activating endorphins, natural tranquilizers.

d   8/V3   07. Some companies use a Wellness program or fitness facility as a vehicle to
   a. recruit employees.
   b. increase morale of employees.
   c. control employee exercise programs.
   d. a and b.

c   8/V4   08. The general recommendation to support activity is to eat a diet
   a. high in protein and low in fat.
   b. low in protein and high in carbohydrate.
   c. high in carbohydrate and low in fat.
   d. high in carbohydrate and high in protein.

c   8/V4   09. Regardless of the intensity of an exercise program, the best diet emphasizes
   a. protein.
   b. fat.
   c. carbohydrate.
   d. water.

a   8/V4,V5   10. The very best combination of diet and exercise for an individual who is interested in achieving the basic elements of health is
   a. lots of complex carbohydrates and regular exercise regardless of the intensity.
   b. exercise two times a week with occasional "junk" food treats.
   c. moderate amounts of meat and fried foods combined with weight training two times a week.
   d. regular consumption of sports drinks and vigorous exercise at least three times a week.

d   8/V5   11. Walking is considered the best form of exercise because it
   a. is not expensive.
   b. promotes cardiovascular endurance.
   c. is easy to perform.
   d. all of the above.

c   8/V5   12. The most important component(s) of exercise from a health and longevity standpoint is(are)
   a. the intensity and duration of the activity.
   b. the duration and frequency of the activity.
   c. the frequency and regularity of the activity.
   d. the warm-up and cool-down periods.

c   8/V6   13.   Before undertaking an exercise or nutrition program, what preliminary steps should be taken?

     a.   Choose an expensive activity; that way you know you've invested money in it and be more likely to stay with it.

     b.   Go to an exercise physiologist who can teach you how the body works.

     c.   Choose an enjoyable activity that you know you will stay with whether you're alone or in a group.

     d.   Get an exercise stress test from a sports medicine doctor who is also knowledgeable in nutrition.

a   8/V6   14.   A person with high blood cholesterol should consider participating in an aerobic exercise program such as walking or jogging because aerobic exercise

     a.   will raise HDL ("good") cholesterol after a period of training and decrease the risk for heart disease.

     b.   will cause a sudden increase in the heartrate to near maximal levels which lowers the "bad" cholesterol.

     c.   forces more LDL ("bad") cholesterol out of the body through waste elimination.

     d.   keeps the blood circulating faster, even at rest, therefore causes a decrease in total blood cholesterol.

Objective	Q#	
1/V1	15.	According to research, what population has an increased risk of dying of heart attack or any other cause?
5/V3	16.	What type of exercise has been shown to reduce depression due to a release of brain endorphins?

Q#	Answer
15.	Sedentary people
16.	Aerobic exercise

Lesson 17: Physical Activity: Beyond Fitness

Answer	Objective	Q#	
a	2/V1	01.	By eating a high carbohydrate diet the day before any athletic event,

    a. muscles will have adequate fuel, i.e., glycogen for the competition.
    b. athletes can eat more protein the day of the competition.
    c. less water will be needed the day of the competition since carbohydrates are high in water.
    d. all of the above.

| d | 7/V1 | 02. | Regardless of the physical pursuits of an athlete, the recommended diet should be a foundation of |

    a. protein.
    b. amino acids.
    c. water.
    d. complex carbohydrates.

| d | 7/V1 | 03. | On the day of a competition, athletes should eat |

    a. enough to feel "fed" but not "full."
    b. enough food to keep their blood sugar levels up.
    c. complex carbohydrates and plenty of fluids.
    d. all of the above.

| d | 7/V1 | 04. | If athletes are going to drink caffeinated beverages prior to competition, they |

    a. should first try it out in practice to make sure it doesn't produce adverse side effects.
    b. need to experiment during training to see if it helps make the exercise seem easier.
    c. should drink them at least four hours before the event.
    d. a and b.

| c | 7/V2 | 05. | What dietary components might athletes in wheelchairs need less of and more of, respectively, than other athletes? |

    a. Protein and carbohydrates
    b. Fat and protein
    c. kCalories and water
    d. Vitamins and minerals

| b | 9/V2 | 06. | Physical activity is very important for physically challenged people because |

    a. it keeps them from becoming bored.
    b. they can eat more and, by consuming more nutrients, become healthier.
    c. they are not as strong as people who are not physically challenged.
    d. all of the above.

d   9/V2   07.   Exercise and nutrition are important components of a sound program for physically challenged people because they
- a. are investments in good physical health.
- b. help support a positive mental health.
- c. help people face the challenges of life and achieve dreams.
- d. all of the above.

c   8/V3   08.   For most athletes who are well-nourished, nutrition supplements such as protein powders and vitamin pills
- a. dramatically improve performance.
- b. improve performance only moderately.
- c. do not significantly improve performance.
- d. seem to cause a decrease in performance.

d   8/V3   09.   There is evidence that athletes who have taken steroids for as few as five years have developed
- a. blood cysts in the liver.
- b. cancer of the liver.
- c. impotence in males.
- d. all of the above.

d   8/V3   10.   A proven ergogenic aid that helps endurance athletes achieve a boost in energy is
- a. water.
- b. coffee.
- c. chocolate.
- d. sports drinks.

d   9/V4   11.   It has been demonstrated that regular aerobic exercise will help
- a. improve energy levels.
- b. reduce stress.
- c. improve HDL levels.
- d. all of the above.

Objective	Q#	
2/V1	12.	The substance that is most depleted during repetitive type exercises is
7/V1	13.	The foundation of an athlete's diet should consist of
8/V3	14.	Epoetin, steroids, and blood doping, all of which have been touted to improve athletic performance, are examples of
9/V4	15.	Regular aerobic exercise has been shown to improve which components of a blood lipid profile?

Q#	Answer
12.	muscle glycogen
13.	complex carbohydrates
14.	ergogenic aids.
15.	HDL (or triglycerides)

Lesson 18: Life Cycle: Pregnancy

Answer	Objective	Q#	
d	5/V1	01.	Advice to pregnant women who want to exercise includes

    a. don't begin a new program.
    b. swim, but do not lift weights
    c. walk, but not too intensely.
    d. all of the above.

a   5/V1   02. Swimming is actually one of the best exercises for
    a. placental blood profusion.
    b. losing weight while pregnant.
    c. increasing abdominal strength.
    d. increasing stress to the fetus.

c   4/V2   03. What percent of weight gain during pregnancy is due to maternal fat weight?
    a. 15%
    b. 20%
    c. 30%
    d. 45%

b   4/V2   04. Dieting during pregnancy is
    a. recommended if the mother is overweight.
    b. not recommended at all.
    c. dependant upon the initial weight of the mother.
    d. directly correlated to high birthweight.

c   11/V3   05. The highest at-risk age for pregnancy is
    a. 6-years postmenarchy.
    b. 4-years postmenarchy.
    c. 2-years postmenarchy.
    d. none of the above.

a   11/V3   06. The risk associated with teenage pregnancy is a
    a. low-birthweight infant.
    b. high-birthweight infant.
    c. low incidence of miscarriage.
    d. high incidence of gestational diabetes.

d   11/V3   07. The recommendation for iron supplementation is
    a. greater for pregnant teens.
    b. about 30-60 milligrams/day.
    c. necessary to preserve iron stores.
    d. all of the above.

d   11/V3   08.   The recommendation for folic acid is
     a.   about 400 micrograms/day.
     b.   necessary to prevent neural tube defects.
     c.   lower than the RDA.
     d.   a and b.

c   11/V3   09.   Supplementation of folic acid is known to prevent
     a.   eclampsia in pregnant women.
     b.   gestational diabetes in pregnant women.
     c.   spina bifida and other neural tube defects.
     d.   pregnancy-induced hypertension.

d   13/V4   10.   Among the reasons young mothers lose sight of personal fitness or nutrition goals is
     a.   overwork and fatigue.
     b.   stresses of being a new mother.
     c.   post-partum depression.
     d.   all of the above.

b   13/V4   11.   A young mother can reach personal fitness and nutrition goals by
     a.   asking her doctor for a tranquilizer.
     b.   finding a comfortable way to work through changes.
     c.   spending more time working out at a gym.
     d.   eating foods that are low-fat.

Lesson 19: Life Cycle: Lactation and Infancy

Answer	Objective	Q#	

a 7/V1 01. Research has shown that breastfed infants probably need
  a. fewer kcalories than formula fed infants.
  b. more kcalories than formula fed infants.
  c. more iron than formula fed infants.
  d. less iron than formula fed infants.

a 7/V1 02. Compared to formula fed infants, breast fed infants seem to need
  a. less energy.
  b. more energy.
  c. more iron.
  d. less iron.

d 7/V2 03. Indications that an infant is getting enough food are
  a. six to eight wet diapers/day.
  b. one bowel movement/day.
  c. infant is alert and happy.
  d. any of the above.

a 7/V2 04. One of the ways you can tell if an infant is getting enough food is
  a. by the number of wet diapers/day.
  b. if the infant is gaining two lbs./week.
  c. if the infant sleeps through the night by three weeks of age.
  d. by the number of feedings/day.

a 5/V3 05. A woman who is not breastfeeding
  a. has the same nutrient requirements as non-lactating women.
  b. needs more nutrients than non-lactating women.
  c. has the same nutrient requirements as lactating women.
  d. has a greater need for water than lactating women.

b 7/V3 06. Compared to breast feeding women, formula feeding women
  a. have identical nutrient needs.
  b. have fewer nutrient needs.
  c. need more water.
  d. need less water.

b 7/V4 07. Nutrition scientists agree that cow's milk can be given to infants
  a. as soon as they can sit up.
  b. after the age of 12 months.
  c. who are eating solid foods.
  d. any of the above.

c 7/V4 08. The recommended age to introduce cow's milk to infants is
           a. four to six months.
           b. six to 12 months.
           c. after 12 months.
           d. after two years.

b 7/V4 09. Breastfed infants need an additional iron source
           a. after they've been weaned.
           b. at about six months.
           c. at three months.
           d. they don't - they get enough iron from breast milk.

c 7/V5 10. Some research shows that introducing fruits before vegetables
           a. will cause the infant to develop a sweet tooth.
           b. causes more allergic reactions.
           c. has little impact on future food preferences.
           d. causes excess weight gain in the infant.

a 7/V5 11. The recommended order of introducing fruits and vegetables to infants
           a. doesn't seem to matter.
           b. is fruits then vegetables.
           c. is vegetables then fruits.
           d. is to mix them together at the same meal.

c 10/V6 12. Stress in the mother who breastfeeds has been shown to
           a. inhibit the quality of milk produced.
           b. cause greater milk production.
           c. inhibit the let-down reflex.
           d. cause weight loss in the infant.

d 10/V6 13. The let-down reflex
           a. triggers the release of milk from the breasts.
           b. can be inhibited by physical or emotional stress.
           c. occurs after the baby is born and is temporary.
           d. a and b.

Lesson 19: Life Cycle: Lactation and Infancy

Objective   Q#

7/V2   14.   Cite one guideline to determine if an infant is getting enough food.

7/V4   15.   Cow's milk can be given after what age?

Q#   Answer

14.   May include any of the following:
             * 6-8 wet diapers/day
             * One bowel movement/day
             * Happy and alert baby
             * Appropriate weight gain

15.   12 months (one year)

Lesson 20: Life Cycle: Childhood and Adolescence

Answer	Objective	Q#	
b	4/V1	01.	The first concrete element associated with trust, safety, and security between an infant and the primary caregiver is

01. The first concrete element associated with trust, safety, and security between an infant and the primary caregiver is
   a. love.
   b. food.
   c. attention.
   d. all of the above.

b   4/V1

02. When food is overly important or not attended to properly in the family, experts have found that there
   a. are more eating disorders.
   b. are fewer incidences of binging and purging.
   c. is a greater chance for discipline problems.
   d. all of the above.

a   4/V1

03. With regard to food intake, if parents do not set limits for children, children will
   a. probably become obese by the time they are adolescents.
   b. not learn to set limits for themselves in other aspects of life as well.
   c. become too independent as adults.
   d. all of the above.

b   4/V1

04. Parents can teach children to become responsible with regard to food intake by
   a. modeling the behavior they want the children to learn.
   b. creating positive learning experiences around food.
   c. giving children a certain amount of authority with regard to food choices.
   d. all of the above.

d   5/V2

05. An example of a parent giving children appropriate authority with regard to food intake might be
   a. allowing a four-year-old to choose a snack from a banana or whole wheat bread.
   b. telling a 16-year-old to eat all his meal before having dessert.
   c. begging an 18-year-old to eat homemade bean soup for dinner.
   d. allowing a six-year-old to go grocery shopping alone.

a   5/V2

c   5/V3   06.   If parents habitually overeat past the point of satiety, children will learn to

     a.   disregard their parents' actions and learn to eat sensibly.

     b.   listen to their own bodies and respond appropriately to internal hunger cues.

     c.   disregard their own internal hunger and satiety cues and habitually overeat.

     d.   listen to their peers when it comes to eating appropriately.

a   5/V3   07.   Children will learn to disregard their own internal hunger and satiety cues if they

     a.   observe their parents habitually overeating.

     b.   watch too much television, especially food advertisements.

     c.   eat too many complex carbohydrates during the day.

     d.   drink too many soft drinks.

d   5/V4   08.   The weight loss program known as ShapeDown helps adolescents lose excess weight by

     a.   treating not only the body but also the mind.

     b.   utilizing an interdisciplinary team of professionals.

     c.   involving all family members in the program.

     d.   all of the above.

d   5/V4   09.   The most powerful factor(s) to impact adolescent weight loss include(s)

     a.   genetics.

     b.   the closeness of the family.

     c.   peers.

     d.   a and b.

a   9/V5   10.   Adolescent girls who believe they do not measure up to media portrayal of the perfect young body image

     a.   may develop eating disorders.

     b.   develop a stronger self-image and more confidence.

     c.   usually are more accepting of their bodies in spite of the magazines.

     d.   frequently commit suicide.

d   9/V5   11.   Teen magazines could have a positive influence on adolescent body-image and self-image if the magazines would

     a.   focus on things teens can do rather than on what teens look like.

     b.   show "real" teens of all ethnic backgrounds and shapes and not teen models.

     c.   not emphasize the "Barbie" doll look as the ideal for teens.

     d.   all of the above.

b   7/V6   12.   Experts agree that people with type II diabetes who ate foods high in fat or sugar as adolescents

     a.   developed the disease because of their eating habits.
     b.   developed the disease because of their genetic background.
     c.   developed the disease because they were obese to begin with.
     d.   all of the above.

a   7/V6   13.   Adolescents who snack on high-fat foods or sugary foods will develop type II diabetes as adults if they

     a.   are genetically predisposed.
     b.   do not change their eating habits.
     c.   gain too much weight.
     d.   all of the above.

Lesson 21: Life Cycle: Adulthood and Aging

Answer	Objective	Q#	

d   4/V1   01. Relative to muscle mass, which of the following nutrients should be decreased?
- a. Fat
- b. High kcalorie foods
- c. Total kcalories
- d. All of the above

d   8/V2   02 Scientists are trying to convince older people
- a. that it's not how long we live, but how successfully.
- b. to stop trying to grow old gracefully.
- c. that it's best to go out like a light bulb—bright and quick!
- d. a and c.

b   8/V2   03. If scientists had their way, when it was time to die, we all should
- a. spend our remaining years in bed!
- b. go quickly, like a light bulb!
- c. be glad that medical science prolonged our life even in the absence of quality.
- d. none of the above.

d   5/V3   04. Exercises that help prevent the age-related decrease in muscle mass
- a. are non-existent.
- b. should include light weight training.
- c. can be as simple as regular daily walking.
- d. b and c.

d   9/V4   05. Alcohol use is not recommended for the elderly because
- a. blood alcohol levels rise more quickly.
- b. they have less body water due to less muscle mass.
- c. they are more sensitive to alcohol's effects.
- d. all of the above.

d   9/V4   06. Alcohol can affect an older adult
- a. by increasing blood alcohol level quickly.
- b. because they are more sensitive to alcohol's effects.
- c. because they have less body water to dilute it.
- d. all of the above.

a   7/V5   07. Diabetes impacts aging in which of the following ways?
- a. If blood glucose level is not well controlled, a person could die earlier than expected.
- b. A person with diabetes usually won't live beyond age 65.
- c. Diabetes is associated with liver damage, therefore shorter life span.
- d. Diabetes can't impact longevity, especially if there is no heredity factor.

d   ·   7/V5   08.   A person who has lived with diabetes for 20 - 40 years
- a. is more likely to have complications associated with the disease.
- b. is not likely to suffer any more ill effects than a younger person with the disease.
- c. should pay especially close attention to the level of glycemic control.
- d. a and c.

Objective	Q#	
4/V1	09.	As you age there is less of a need for foods that are high in
5/V3	10.	As a person ages there is a relative loss of
5/V3	11.	The type of exercise recommended to prevent osteoporosis is

Objective	Answer
09.	kcalories (fat, energy).
10.	muscle mass (lean body mass, muscle strength).
11.	weight bearing (walking, jogging, weight lifting, dancing, etc.).

Lesson 22: Diet and Health: Cardiovascular Disease

Answer	Objective	Q#	
c	3/v1	01.	Worldwide, the number one risk associated with cardiac disease and stroke is a. obesity. b. alcohol. c. smoking. d. heredity.
d	3/V1	02.	High blood pressure (hypertension) is caused by a. obesity. b. smoking. c. lack of exercise. d. all of the above.
d	3/V1	03.	High blood pressure or hypertension causes physical damage to the blood vessel walls and results in a. the formation of plaque. b. heart disease. c. stroke. d. all of the above.
b	3/V1	04.	On the average and compared to men, women tend to get heart disease a. as frequently as men. b. about 10-15 years later than men. c. but have fewer complications than men. d. all of the above.
a	3/V1	05.	As researchers found out more about blood cholesterol, the recommended acceptable value for blood cholesterol has a. dropped from 260 mg/dl to less than 200 mg/dl in a decade. b. steadily increased up to 200 mg/dl in the past decade. c. remained the same for 25 years. d. only reflected LDL values.
b	3/V1	06.	Part of the protection against heart disease women enjoy seems to come from the fact that women a. are generally less stressed out than men. b. produce estrogen which is known to elevate HDL and protect them. c. have generally lower total cholesterol than men. d. a and b.

d   3/V1   07.   Populations that may be more susceptible to potential heart damage caused by elevated triglycerides include
  a. younger men.
  b. people with diabetes.
  c. people with cancer.
  d. a and b.

c   3/V1   08.   Studies have shown that even being ten pounds overweight will increase your risk for heart disease by as much as
  a. 15%.
  b. 25%.
  c. 50%.
  d. 75%.

a   4/V1   09.   In general, experts recommend that to prevent heart disease mortality and morbidity, people should exercise
  a. daily for 30-40 minutes at moderate pace.
  b. every other day for 50 minutes at moderate pace.
  c. twice a week for one hour at intense pace.
  d. any of the above, depending on your schedule.

b   4/V2   10.   When LDL level is elevated and HDL is lower than recommended, the first thing that should be examined is a person's
  a. alcohol intake.
  b. exercise program.
  c. genetic background.
  d. smoking habits.

a   4/V2   11.   In addition to regular exercise, equally important in the prevention of heart disease is
  a. reducing fat intake, especially saturated fat.
  b. increasing monounsaturated fat intake.
  c. eliminating cholesterol from the diet.
  d. reducing the servings of dairy in the diet.

d   4/V2   12.   For the majority of people with high blood cholesterol, it is generally due to
  a. genetics.
  b. poor diet.
  c. lack of exercise.
  d. b and c.

c   4/V2   13.   The amount of time it usually takes to see an increase in HDL levels as a result of regular aerobic exercise is approximately
                          a.   one month.
                          b.   three months.
                          c.   six months.
                          d.   one year.

d   4/ V2   14.   With regard to vitamin supplementation for reducing heart disease risk experts recommend
                          a.   that men do not take iron supplements.
                          b.   modest doses of antioxidants, if at all.
                          c.   obtaining vitamins from whole foods.
                          d.   all of the above.

d   4/V2   15.   To see a significant regression in coronary disease, many experts recommend
                          a.   a very low-fat diet of no more than 10% of total kcalories.
                          b.   more regular aerobic exercise.
                          c.   a vegetarian eating plan with no meat.
                          d.   all of the above.

a   4/V2   16.   The reason why many experts recommend vegetarian diets is because they
                          a.   have little, if any, dietary cholesterol.
                          b.   are proven to provide protection against all diseases.
                          c.   have been shown to significantly increase longevity in all populations.
                          d.   all of the above.

b   4/V2   17.   A strong recommendation for people who are going through lifestyle and nutrition changes to reduce heart disease is to
                          a.   grin and bear it.
                          b.   find a good, social support group.
                          c.   go for it - all or nothing!
                          d.   none of the above.

Lesson 23: Diet and Health: Cancer, Immunology, and AIDS

Answer	Objective	Q#	
c	3/V1	01.	The type of fat that is most frequently associated with the growth of breast cancer is a. monounsaturated fat. b. saturated fat. c. polyunsaturated fat. d. vegetable fat.
b	4/V1	02.	Experts suggest that the threshold of fat intake to prevent breast cancer is a. less than 30% of total kcalories. b. less than 20% of total kcalories. c. about 30% of total kcalories. d. about 45% of total kcalories.
a	4/V1	03.	The American Cancer Society offers six suggestions for reducing the risk for cancer, including a. maintaining desirable body weight. b. eating the same types of foods daily. c. maintaining fiber intake at 10-15 grams/day. d. eating salt-cured foods, such as bacon, no more than three times/week.
d	4/V1	04.	The American Cancer Society suggests that women and men maintain desirable weight based on the following criteria: a. women should weigh 100 pounds for five feet plus five pounds for each inch over five feet. b. both women and men should weigh 106 pounds for five feet plus six pounds for each inch over five feet. c. men should weigh 106 pounds for five feet plus six pounds for each inch over five feet. d. a and c.
a	4/V1	05.	The recommendation from the American Cancer Society regarding alcohol intake and cancer prevention is to a. drink alcohol in limited amounts, if at all. b. drink an established amount of alcohol daily. c. become a teetotaler. d. consume beer or wine instead of hard liquor.
b	4/V1	06.	The statement that best characterizes fiber with regard to its positive impact on the prevention of cancer is: a. eat soluble fiber, such as oat bran, to reduce cancer risk. b. eat insoluble fiber, such as wheat bran, to reduce cancer risk. c. eat at least 10 grams of fiber/day to reduce cancer risk. d. b and c.

b   4/V1   07.   In addition to the fiber found in cruciferous vegetables (cabbage and broccoli), other compounds that might have a positive effect on cancers are known as
a. oxygen-retarding agents.
b. phytochemicals.
c. vitamin precursors.
d. lipid oxidizers.

d   5/V2   08.   Among hospitalized patients, health professionals see a general pattern with regard to immune function in that
a. appetite decreases and patients become malnourished.
b. immune function improves because of overall good care.
c. lack of nutrients leads to faulty immune function.
d. a and c.

a   5/V2   09.   Because of the lack of appetite, hospitalized patients can
a. become malnourished resulting in poor immune function.
b. lose unwanted body fat and unwanted pounds.
c. become more susceptible to AIDS or cancer.
d. all of the above.

c   5/V2   10.   Elderly people are usually subjects in studies on the immune system because as they age their immune systems
a. become stronger, allowing us to study longevity.
b. are more likely to be resistant to unusual viruses.
c. become the models to see how nutrition impacts immunity.
d. have been exposed to more viruses and bacterial infections.

a   5/V2   11.   By studying the immune systems of elderly people, health professionals are learning
a. what nutrients appear promising in reducing risk of diseases such as cancer.
b. that nutrition does not help people grow old more successfully.
c. to turn back the hands of time by supplementing with specific nutrients.
d. all of the above.

b   5/V2   12.   All of the following are simple rules to follow to help people strengthen their immune systems EXCEPT
a. maintain body weight within 10% of the ideal for age and sex.
b. use supplemental fiber equal to ten grain products daily.
c. limit dietary fat intake to less than 30% of total kcalories.
d. eat five servings of fruits and vegetables daily.

d   5/V2   13. When recommending supplemental antioxidant vitamins/minerals for people with compromised immune systems, experts agree that
   a. people should take them in prescribed safe doses so no harm will be caused.
   b. they still do not know what the appropriate doses are for this population.
   c. people should not take greater than twice the RDA for antioxidants.
   d. all of the above.

d   6/V3   14. HIV can be defined as
   a. a virus.
   b. an infection that attacks the immune system.
   c. a disease that attacks the T-4 cells in the body.
   d. all of the above.

c   6/V3   15. When CD-4 cell count is less than 200 and people have one or more opportunistic infections, they are defined as having
   a. HIV.
   b. multiple sclerosis.
   c. AIDS.
   d. Kaposi's sarcoma.

d   6/V3   16. People with AIDS must have good nutritional support because
   a. malnutrition can negatively impact the immune system further.
   b. good nutrition can add years of life to the AIDS patient.
   c. they will not be able to fight opportunistic infections as well without good nutrition.
   d. all of the above.

d   6/V3   17. Nutritional strategies that are provided to AIDS patients include
   a. nutrition education and intervention to preserve immunity.
   b. discussions on safe food handling and preparation.
   c. use of non-traditional supplements that have shown to improve immunity.
   d. a and b.

c   6/V3   18. Non-traditional nutrition supplements such as blue-green algae or potassium drinks may
   a. help improve immune function in AIDS patients.
   b. bring about weight gain in the form of lean body mass.
   c. interfere with medications or cause toxicity.
   d. offer a safe alternative treatment for AIDS.

b   6/V3   19.   Compared to healthy people, AIDS patients require a higher intake of
   a. carbohydrate.
   b. protein.
   c. fat.
   d. vitamins.

d   6/V3   20.   The most commonly malabsorbed nutrient(s) in AIDS patients is(are)
   a. lactose or milk sugar.
   b. protein or amino acids.
   c. fatty acids.
   d. a and c.

a   6/V3   21.   Multivitamin and mineral supplements are recommended to AIDS patients because they
   a. do not absorb some nutrients.
   b. typically eat only one meal/day.
   c. eat so many sweets and fatty desserts.
   d. all of the above.

b   6/V3   22.   People who have AIDS have a recommended dietary intake based on the following nutrient breakdown:
   a. 50% carbohydrate, 30% protein, 20% fat.
   b. 40% carbohydrate, 40% protein, 20% fat.
   c. 50% carbohydrate, 50% protein, no fat.
   d. 60% carbohydrate, 35% protein, 5% fat.

d   6/V3   23.   Very high protein intakes are recommended to AIDS patients because they
   a. become anorexic and lose lean body mass.
   b. are in negative nitrogen balance due to wasting.
   c. cannot tolerate high carbohydrate foods as a rule.
   d. a and b.

c   6/V3   24.   To prevent against the effects of anorexia, AIDS patients are encouraged to
   a. eat frequent large meals throughout the day.
   b. take medications to prevent vomiting.
   c. consume an instant breakfast or milkshake between meals.
   d. all of the above.

Lesson 24: Diet and Health: Diabetes

Answer	Objective	Q#	

d   2/V1   01.   Insulin injections are required daily for people with type I diabetes because
    a.   their bodies do not produce insulin.
    b.   it prevents many metabolic problems from occurring.
    c.   insulin stimulates the cells to remove glucose from the blood.
    d.   all of the above.

a   3/V1   02.   Severe weight loss, ketone production, and coma are metabolic complications generally associated with
    a.   type I diabetes.
    b.   type II diabetes.
    c.   all diabetic conditions.
    d.   hypoglycemia.

c   2/V2   03.   Because onset is more gradual with type II diabetes, making diagnosis difficult, experts surmise that
    a.   more than one-fourth of all people with diabetes remain undiagnosed.
    b.   more than one-third of all people with diabetes remain undiagnosed.
    c.   more than one-half of all people with diabetes remain undiagnosed.
    d.   more than three-fourths of all people with diabetes remain undiagnosed.

d   2/V2   04.   The risk factors associated with the onset of type II diabetes include
    a.   having a genetic background of diabetes.
    b.   being a female.
    c.   being over age 40.
    d.   all of the above.

b   2/V2   05.   Of the following populations, the group at highest risk for type II diabetes is
    a.   males under 40 years.
    b.   females over 40 years.
    c.   children under 11 years.
    d.   adolescents between 14 and 18 years.

d   2/V3   06.   When children with type I diabetes are released from the hospital, the primary role of diabetes educators is to
    a.   teach parents/families how to give insulin injections.
    b.   give the children their insulin injections until they are old enough to give them to themselves.
    c.   teach parents how to perform blood glucose tests.
    d.   a and c.

a	3/V3	07.	For parents of very young children with type I diabetes, the primary responsibility of the parents is to a. learn to test for blood glucose levels. b. teach their child to give themselves insulin injections. c. keep children calm so they do not increase blood glucose. d. all of the above.
b	3/V3	08.	Children with insulin-dependent diabetes should be monitored by medical professionals frequently because a. children frequently forget to take insulin injections. b. diabetes can adversely affect heart, eyes, and kidneys. c. parents are not willing to take responsibility for their children. d. all of the above.
b	4/V3	09.	Sweets and desserts can be included in the diet of a child with type I diabetes as long as they are a. given in very small amounts only twice/week. b. incorporated into a diet rich in fiber and complex carbohydrates. c. balanced with increased amounts of protein-rich foods. d. all of the above.
a	5/V3	10.	Care must be taken with regard to exercise in children with type I diabetes because exercise a. can decrease the amount of insulin needed during the day. b. has been shown to increase the amount of insulin needed. c. is not beneficial to children with type I diabetes. d. a and c.
d	2/V4	11.	The onset of diabetes type II is associated with all of the following factors EXCEPT a. being female. b. being overweight. c. being over forty. d. being male.
b	3/V4	12.	Diabetes is the number one cause of which of the following conditions/diseases? a. Heart disease b. Blindness c. Amputation d. Kidney failure
c	3/V4	13.	What percent of non-accidental or non-traumatic amputations of the feet, toes, or legs is attributed to diabetes? a. 25% b. 50% c. 75% d. 100%

a   3/V4   14.   What percent of new cases of end stage renal failure leading to dialysis is a consequence of diabetes?
   a. About 40%
   b. About 20%
   c. About 10%
   d. None of the above

c   3/V4   15.   Of the people who die of cardiovascular disease, what percent will have diabetes as well?
   a. 50%
   b. 70%
   c. 85%
   d. 100%

c   5/V5   16.   Glucose uptake can be increased by 10-20% above normal if a person with diabetes
   a. takes oral agents in addition to insulin injections.
   b. eats only foods high in complex carbohydrates and animal protein.
   c. exercises on a regular basis.
   d. all of the above.

a   5/V5   17.   Exercise is encouraged early on in the treatment of diabetes because exercise can
   a. stimulate muscles to take up 10-20 times more glucose than nonexercising muscles.
   b. prevent the heart problems associated with diabetes.
   c. prevent amputations because exercising legs are stimulated to release stored glycogen.
   d. burn excess kcalories and reduce body fat associated with the onset of diabetes.

d   4/V6   18.   Some medical experts state that the effects of raw vegetable diets on type II diabetes will
   a. reduce the need for insulin because people will lose significant weight on these diets.
   b. not provide all the nutrients necessary for body maintenance.
   c. need to be studied more to understand its effects on type II diabetes.
   d. all of the above.

Lesson 25: Consumer Concerns and Food Safety

Answer	Objective	Q#	
a	7/V1	01.	What is the primary reason bottled water sales have increased dramatically over the past several years? a. People believe that tap water from the public water supply is unhealthy or unclean. b. Manufacturers of bottled water have made it inexpensive to buy when compared to tap water. c. Grocery stores have increased the shelf space, making bottled water more visible to consumers. d. All of the above.
d	7/V1	02.	As an indication of the popularity of bottled water, sales of bottled water have surpassed the sale of a. milk. b. soft drinks. c. beer and wine. d. b and c.
b	7/V1	03.	To determine the source of bottled water, it is always best to a. ask the store manager. b. read the label. c. assume it is from a spring. d. check with friends.
d	4/V2	04.	Some of the alternatives to pesticide use for organic farming include a. earthworm castings. b. bat guana. c. seedless cow manure. d. all of the above.
c	4/V2	05.	An example of an insect that can be used to repel or eat other insects that damage or destroy crops is the a. cockroach. b. June bug. c. lady bug. d. earthworm.
a	4/V2	06.	As a way of repelling certain pests from destroying preferred crops, plants in combination can be used such as a. tomato plants and basil. b. oregano and basil plants. c. basil and cabbage plants. d. cabbage and tomato plants.

b   5/V3   07.   Some people have been known to react to the food additive known as MSG by exhibiting symptoms, such as
a.   stomach ulcers.
b.   intense headaches and depression.
c.   muscle pain, especially in the calves.
d.   all of the above.

d   5/V3   08.   In order to avoid the adverse side-effects of MSG or other food additives, people should
a.   learn to read labels to find the offensive additive.
b.   eat more fresh fruit, vegetables, and whole grains.
c.   ask that the offensive food additive be left out of foods when eating out.
d.   all of the above.

b   2/V4   09.   Time and temperature are two components of safe food handling. The third basic component is
a.   speed.
b.   cleanliness.
c.   frequency.
d.   intensity.

b   2/V4   10.   When bacteria on meat is transferred to vegetables that were cut on the same board as the meat, the process is referred to as
a.   sanitation-inhibition.
b.   cross-contamination.
c.   error-in-preparation.
d.   food-irresponsibility.

a   2/V4   11.   When handling fruits, vegetables, and meats in the kitchen, the best advice is to
a.   avoid cross-contamination by sanitizing utensils.
b.   keep foods refrigerated until ready to eat, then serve immediately.
c.   avoid taking a bite of raw food unless it's stamped "Safe For Consumption."
d.   wash hands and face immediately after handling meats.

Objective	Q#	
7/V1	12.	Sales of soft drinks, beer, and wine have taken a back seat compared to sales of
7/V1	13.	How can a consumer determine what the source of a bottled water is?
4/V2	14.	Bat guana is an alternative in organic farming for the use of
	15.	Name one alternative to pesticide used in organic farming.
2/V4	16.	Transfer of bacteria from one food to another during preparation and handling is known as
2/V4	17.	One basic component of safe food handling is
2/V4	18.	According to the components of safe food handling, the temperature range at which cold food is safest is

Q#	Answer
12.	bottled water.
13.	Read the label.
14.	pesticides.
15.	Answer may be any of the following: * Earthworm castings * Bat guana * Seedless cow manure * Lady bugs * Compatible plants
16.	cross-contamination.
17.	Answer may be any one of the following: * time. * temperature. * sanitation (cleanliness).
18.	less than 40 degrees F.

Answer	Objective	Q#	
c	1/V1	01.	The reasons the Pathways subjects chose to participate in the Nutrition Pathways program included all of the following EXCEPT a. a family history of heart disease. b. a family history of diabetes. c. having colon cancer. d. being overweight.
d	1/V1	02.	Of the three subjects who participated in the Nutrition Pathways program, the subject(s) who had the most life threatening condition included the one(s) a. with type II diabetes. b. who was overweight. c. with high blood cholesterol. d. a and c.
d	1/V1	03.	The Pathways subject who had high blood cholesterol was motivated to participate because his father a. had a heart attack when he was 48 years old. b. passed away shortly before the beginning of the program. c. also had high blood cholesterol. d. all of the above.
b	1/V1	04.	The goal of the weight loss subject to lose 40 pounds in one year was completely a. realistic. b. unrealistic. c. achieved. d. b and c.
a	2/V2	05.	Among the reasons why people fail to change nutrition and lifestyle habits include a. setting goals too high. b. changing old habits too slowly. c. having "gotten off the path" then returned. d. all of the above.
d	2/V2	06.	One of the lessons the subject with type II diabetes learned from the program about food intake was that a. deprivation is one reason why people fail at weight loss. b. people can have desserts, but in moderation. c. people must change their attitudes regarding sweets as being off limits. d. all of the above.

| c | 3/V3 | 07. | Other factors that can "get in the way" of achieving goals regarding lifestyle and nutrition changes include |

07. Other factors that can "get in the way" of achieving goals regarding lifestyle and nutrition changes include
   a. sessions with a health professional.
   b. taking a course in nutrition.
   c. jobs and everyday stresses.
   d. all of the above.

c   3/V3   08. Of the challenges faced by the subject who wanted to lose weight, the most critical to her success was
   a. managing a child by herself.
   b. remodeling her home.
   c. exercising regularly.
   d. controlling two work-related projects.

c   3/V3   09. The greatest success for the subject who has type II diabetes was
   a. losing 50 pounds by the end of the year.
   b. jogging two miles in 20 minutes.
   c. going from two insulin injections per day to none.
   d. all of the above.

b   3/V3   10. One of the outcomes of the program for the subject with high blood cholesterol was that he
   a. was able to stay off of cholesterol-lowering medication.
   b. had to go back on cholesterol-lowering medication.
   c. showed significant reductions in HDL and increases in LDL.
   d. a and c.

d   4/V4   11. The philosophical thread that runs through Nutrition Pathways includes the statement(s)
   a. "food should be for pleasure as well as nourishment."
   b. "nutrition and lifestyle is a matter of the right balance."
   c. "exercise is a critical component of a healthy lifestyle."
   d. all of the above.

b   4/V4   12. The philosophical emphasis throughout Nutrition Pathways can be best summed up in which one of the following statements?
   a. "Change your life."
   b. "Balance your choices."
   c. "Deprivation breeds success."
   d. "Variety equals challenge."

Lesson 26: Applied Nutrition

Objective	Q#	
5/V5	13.	Describe the importance of exercise with respect to stress reduction and balance in people's lives and its impact on type II diabetes, high blood cholesterol, and overweight.
6/V6	14.	What advice would you give to someone who wanted or needed to change nutrition or lifestyle habits? Include comments on the following: the need for evaluation of current physical and/or nutrition status; steps necessary to improve nutrient status or physical status; ways to handle challenges that might interfere with healthful choices; and the importance of balance and moderation in choices.

Q#	Answer

13.   Answers should include the following points:

* Exercise is critical for stress reduction as well as the overall success of a sound nutrition program.
* Exercise provides more energy to tackle the day.
* Exercise doesn't have to be structured, but must be balanced with good nutrition for success.
* Type II diabetes will improve with regular exercise because it helps muscles utilize more blood glucose.
* Exercise may help people with type II diabetes reduce insulin injections or stop them all together.
* Exercise will help with weight loss better than dieting alone and will help maintain weight once it is lost.
* Exercise helps HDL cholesterol increase and can reduce LDL cholesterol if done regularly and aerobically.

14.   Answers will be highly individualized but should include some of the following points:

* If the person has a life-threatening condition or disease, they must be evaluated by health care professionals before making changes.
* Progress slowly for permanent, safe changes.
* Make changes broad lifestyle changes, not temporary ones that you will discard after achieving your goal.
* Do not expect perfection from yourself when making changes—backsliding is to be expected, but get back on track when you discover the slip.
* Do not deprive yourself of favorite foods—build them into your eating plan and use moderation.
* Exercise should become a regular, weekly part of your nutrition program for life—not just until you have reached a goal.
* Keep a positive outlook and attitude—it took years to get this way—it'll take a long time for permanent change.